Business
BASICS

QUANTITATIVE METHODS

First edition May 1995

ISBN 0 7517 2072 0

British Library Cataloguing-in-Publication Data

A catalogue record for this book
is available from the British Library

Published by

BPP Publishing Limited
Aldine House, Aldine Place
London W12 8AW

Printed in Great Britain by
Ashford Colour Press, Gosport, Hampshire

BPP Publishing

PREFACE

BUSINESS BASICS are targeted specifically at the needs of:

- students taking business studies degrees;
- students taking business-related modules of other degrees;
- students on courses at a comparable level;
- others requiring business information at this level.

This *Quantitative Methods* text has been written with two key goals in mind.

- To present a substantial and useful body of knowledge on quantitative methods at degree level. This is not just a set of revision notes - it explains the subject in detail and does not assume prior knowledge.

- To make learning and revision as easy as possible. Each chapter:

  o starts with an introductory signpost and clear objectives;
  o contains numerous exercises;
  o includes a chapter roundup summarising the points made; and
  o ends with a quick quiz.

The philosophy of the series is thus to combine techniques which actively promote learning with a no-nonsense, systematic approach to the necessary factual content of the course.

BPP Publishing have for many years been the leading providers of targeted texts for students of professional qualifications. We know that our customers need to study effectively in order to pass their exams, and that they cannot afford to waste time. They expect clear, concise and highly-focused study material. As university and college education becomes more market driven, students rightly demand the same high standards of efficiency in their learning material. The BUSINESS BASICS series meets those demands.

BPP Publishing
May 1995

You may order other titles in the series using the form on page 297. If you would like to send in your comments on this book, please turn to the review form on page 299.

This book can simply be read straight through from beginning to end, but you will get far more out of it if you keep a pen and paper to hand. The most effective form of learning is *active learning*, and we have therefore filled the text with exercises for you to try as you go along. We have also provided objectives, a chapter roundup and a quick quiz for each chapter. Here is a suggested approach to enable you to get the most out of this book.

(a) Select a chapter to study, and read the signpost and objectives in the box at the start of the chapter.

(b) Next read the chapter roundup at the end of the chapter (before the quick quiz and the solutions to exercises). Do not expect this brief summary to mean too much at this stage, but see whether you can relate some of the points made in it to some of the objectives.

(c) Next read the chapter itself. Do attempt each exercise as you come to it. You will derive the greatest benefit from the exercises if you write down your solutions before checking them against the solutions at the end of the chapter.

(d) As you read, make use of the 'notes' column to add your own comments, references to other material and so on. Do try to formulate your own views. In business, many things are matters of interpretation and there is often scope for alternative views. The more you engage in a dialogue with the book, the more you will get out of your study.

(e) When you reach the end of the chapter, read the chapter roundup again. Then go back to the objectives at the start of the chapter, and ask yourself whether you have achieved them.

(f) Finally, consolidate your knowledge by writing down your answers to the quick quiz. You can check your answers to the non-computational questions by going back to the text. The very act of going back and searching the text for relevant details will further improve your grasp of the subject. Answers to computational questions are given right at the end of the chapter, after the solutions to exercises.

Further reading

While we are confident that the BUSINESS BASICS books offer excellent range and depth of subject coverage, we are aware that you will be encouraged to follow up particular points in books other than your main textbook, in order to get alternative points of view and more detail on key topics. We recommend the following books as a starting point for your further reading on *Quantitative Methods*.

Bancroft and O'Sullivan, *Maths and Statistics for Accounting and Business Studies* 2nd edition 1988, McGraw-Hill

Curwin and Slater, *Quantitative Methods for Business Decisions*, 3rd edition 1991, Chapman & Hall

Francis, *Business Mathematics and Statistics*, 3rd edition 1993, DP Publications

Lucey, *Quantitative Techniques*, 4th edition 1992, DP Publications

Morris, *Quantitative Approaches in Business Studies*, 1983, Macdonald & Evans.

Rowe *Refresher in Basic Mathematics* 2nd edition

THE POISSON DISTRIBUTION

Entries in the table give the probabilities that an event will occur x times when the average number of occurences is *m*.

m

x	0.1	0.2	0.3	0.4	0.5	0.6	0.7	0.8	0.9	1.0
0	.9048	.8187	.7408	.6703	.6065	.5488	.4966	.4493	.4066	.3679
1	.0905	.1637	.2222	.2681	.3033	.3293	.3476	.3595	.3659	.3679
2	.0045	.0164	.0333	.0536	.0758	.0988	.1217	.1438	.1647	.1839
3	.0002	.0011	.0033	.0072	.0126	.0198	.0284	.0383	.0494	.0613
4	.0000	.0001	.0003	.0007	.0016	.0030	.0050	.0077	.0111	.0153
5	.0000	.0000	.0000	.0001	.0002	.0004	.0007	.0012	.0020	.0031
6	.0000	.0000	.0000	.0000	.0000	.0000	.0001	.0002	.0003	.0005
7	.0000	.0000	.0000	.0000	.0000	.0000	.0000	.0000	.0000	.0001

m

x	1.1	1.2	1.3	1.4	1.5	1.6	1.7	1.8	1.9	2.0
0	.3329	.3012	.2725	.2466	.2231	.2019	.1827	.1653	.1496	.1353
1	.3662	.3614	.3543	.3452	.3347	.3230	.3106	.2975	.2842	.2707
2	.2014	.2169	.2303	.2417	.2510	.2584	.2640	.2678	.2700	.2707
3	.0738	.0867	.0998	.1128	.1255	.1378	.1496	.1607	.1710	.1804
4	.0203	.0260	.0324	.0395	.0471	.0551	.0636	.0723	.0812	.0902
5	.0045	.0062	.0084	.0111	.0141	.0176	.0216	.0260	.0309	.0361
6	.0008	.0012	.0018	.0026	.0035	.0047	.0061	.0078	.0098	.0120
7	.0001	.0002	.0003	.0005	.0008	.0011	.0015	.0020	.0027	.0034
8	.0000	.0000	.0001	.0001	.0001	.0002	.0003	.0005	.0006	.0009
9	.0000	.0000	.0000	.0000	.0000	.0000	.0001	.0001	.0001	.0002

m

x	2.1	2.2	2.3	2.4	2.5	2.6	2.7	2.8	2.9	3.0
0	.1225	.1108	.1003	.0907	.0821	.0743	.0672	.0608	.0550	.0498
1	.2572	.2438	.2306	.2177	.2052	.1931	.1815	.1703	.1596	.1494
2	.2700	.2681	.2652	.2613	.2565	.2510	.2450	.2384	.2314	.2240
3	.1890	.1966	.2033	.2090	.2138	.2176	.2205	.2225	.2237	.2240
4	.0992	.1082	.1169	.1254	.1336	.1414	.1488	.1557	.1622	.1680
5	.0417	.0476	.0538	.0602	.0668	.0735	.0804	.0872	.0940	.1008
6	.0146	.0174	.0206	.0241	.0278	.0319	.0362	.0407	.0455	.0504
7	.0044	.0055	.0068	.0083	.0099	.0118	.0139	.0163	.0188	.0216
8	.0011	.0015	.0019	.0025	.0031	.0038	.0047	.0057	.0068	.0081
9	.0003	.0004	.0005	.0007	.0009	.0011	.0014	.0018	.0022	.0027
10	.0001	.0001	.0001	.0002	.0002	.0003	.0004	.0005	.0006	.0008
11	.0000	.0000	.0000	.0000	.0000	.0001	.0001	.0001	.0002	.0002
12	.0000	.0000	.0000	.0000	.0000	.0000	.0000	.0000	.0000	.0001

BPP Publishing

THE POISSON DISTRIBUTION (continued)

Entries in the table give the probabilities that an event will occur x times when the average number of occurences is m.

m

x	3.1	3.2	3.3	3.4	3.5	3.6	3.7	3.8	3.9	4.0
0	.0450	.0408	.0369	.0334	.0302	.0273	.0247	.0224	.0202	.0183
1	.1397	.1304	.1217	.1135	.1057	.0984	.0915	.0850	.0789	.0733
2	.2165	.2087	.2008	.1929	.1850	.1771	.1692	.1615	.1539	.1465
3	.2237	.2226	.2209	.2186	.2158	.2125	.2087	.2046	.2001	.1954
4	.1733	.1781	.1823	.1858	.1888	.1912	.1931	.1944	.1951	.1954
5	.1075	.1140	.1203	.1264	.1322	.1377	.1429	.1477	.1522	.1563
6	.0555	.0608	.0662	.0716	.0771	.0826	.0881	.0936	.0989	.1042
7	.0246	.0278	.0312	.0348	.0385	.0425	.0466	.0508	.0551	.0595
8	.0095	.0111	.0129	.0148	.0169	.0191	.0215	.0241	.0269	.0298
9	.0033	.0040	.0047	.0056	.0066	.0076	.0089	.0102	.0116	.0132
10	.0010	.0013	.0016	.0019	.0023	.0028	.0033	.0039	.0045	.0053
11	.0003	.0004	.0005	.0006	.0007	.0009	.0011	.0013	.0016	.0019
12	.0001	.0001	.0001	.0002	.0002	.0003	.0003	.0004	.0005	.0006
13	.0000	.0000	.0000	.0000	.0001	.0001	.0001	.0001	.0002	.0002
14	.0000	.0000	.0000	.0000	.0000	.0000	.0000	.0000	.0000	.0001

m

x	4.1	4.2	4.3	4.4	4.5	4.6	4.7	4.8	4.9	5.0
0	.0166	.0150	.0136	.0123	.0111	.0101	.0091	.0082	.0074	.0067
1	.0679	.0630	.0583	.0540	.0500	.0462	.0427	.0395	.0365	.0337
2	.1393	.1323	.1254	.1188	.1125	.1063	.1005	.0948	.0894	.0842
3	.1904	.1852	.1798	.1743	.1687	.1631	.1574	.1517	.1460	.1404
4	.1951	.1944	.1933	.1917	.1898	.1875	.1849	.1820	.1789	.1755
5	.1600	.1633	.1662	.1687	.1708	.1725	.1738	.1747	.1753	.1755
6	.1093	.1143	.1191	.1237	.1281	.1323	.1362	.1398	.1432	.1462
7	.0640	.0686	.0732	.0778	.0824	.0869	.0914	.0959	.1002	.1044
8	.0328	.0360	.0393	.0428	.0463	.0500	.0537	.0575	.0614	.0653
9	.0150	.0168	.0188	.0209	.0232	.0255	.0281	.0307	.0334	.0363
10	.0061	.0071	.0081	.0092	.0104	.0118	.0132	.0147	.0164	.0181
11	.0023	.0027	.0032	.0037	.0043	.0049	.0056	.0064	.0073	.0082
12	.0008	.0009	.0011	.0013	.0016	.0019	.0022	.0026	.0030	.0034
13	.0002	.0003	.0004	.0005	.0006	.0007	.0008	.0009	.0011	.0013
14	.0001	.0001	.0001	.0001	.0002	.0002	.0003	.0003	.0004	.0005
15	.0000	.0000	.0000	.0000	.0001	.0001	.0001	.0001	.0001	.0002

AREA UNDER THE NORMAL CURVE

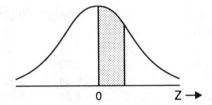

This table gives the area under the normal curve between the mean and the point Z standard deviations above the mean. The corresponding area for deviations below the mean can be found by symmetry.

$Z = \dfrac{(x - \mu)}{\sigma}$	0.00	0.01	0.02	0.03	0.04	0.05	0.06	0.07	0.08	0.09
0.0	.0000	.0040	.0080	.0120	.0160	.0199	.0239	.0279	.0319	.0359
0.1	.0398	.0438	.0478	.0517	.0557	.0596	.0636	.0675	.0714	.0753
0.2	.0793	.0832	.0871	.0910	.0948	.0987	.1026	.1064	.1103	.1141
0.3	.1179	.1217	.1255	.1293	.1331	.1368	.1406	.1443	.1480	.1517
0.4	.1554	.1591	.1628	.1664	.1700	.1736	.1772	.1808	.1844	.1879
0.5	.1915	.1950	.1985	.2019	.2054	.2088	.2123	.2157	.2190	.2224
0.6	.2257	.2291	.2324	.2357	.2389	.2422	.2454	.2486	.2517	.2549
0.7	.2580	.2611	.2642	.2673	.2704	.2734	.2764	.2794	.2823	.2852
0.8	.2881	.2910	.2939	.2967	.2995	.3023	.3051	.3078	.3106	.3133
0.9	.3159	.3186	.3212	.3238	.3264	.3289	.3315	.3340	.3365	.3389
1.0	.3413	.3438	.3461	.3485	.3508	.3531	.3554	.3577	.3599	.3621
1.1	.3643	.3665	.3686	.3708	.3729	.3749	.3770	.3790	.3810	.3830
1.2	.3849	.3869	.3888	.3907	.3925	.3944	.3962	.3980	.3997	.4015
1.3	.4032	.4049	.4066	.4082	.4099	.4115	.4131	.4147	.4162	.4177
1.4	.4192	.4207	.4222	.4236	.4251	.4265	.4279	.4292	.4306	.4319
1.5	.4332	.4345	.4357	.4370	.4382	.4394	.4406	.4418	.4429	.4441
1.6	.4452	.4463	.4474	.4484	.4495	.4505	.4515	.4525	.4535	.4545
1.7	.4554	.4564	.4573	.4582	.4591	.4599	.4608	.4616	.4625	.4633
1.8	.4641	.4649	.4656	.4664	.4671	.4678	.4686	.4693	.4699	.4706
1.9	.4713	.4719	.4726	.4732	.4738	.4744	.4750	.4756	.4761	.4767
2.0	.4772	.4778	.4783	.4788	.4793	.4798	.4803	.4808	.4812	.4817
2.1	.4821	.4826	.4830	.4834	.4838	.4842	.4846	.4850	.4854	.4857
2.2	.4861	.4864	.4868	.4871	.4875	.4878	.4881	.4884	.4887	.4890
2.3	.4893	.4896	.4898	.4901	.4904	.4906	.4909	.4911	.4913	.4916
2.4	.4918	.4920	.4922	.4925	.4927	.4929	.4931	.4932	.4934	.4936
2.5	.4938	.4940	.4941	.4943	.4945	.4946	.4948	.4949	.4951	.4952
2.6	.4953	.4955	.4956	.4957	.4959	.4960	.4961	.4962	.4963	.4964
2.7	.4965	.4966	.4967	.4968	.4969	.4970	.4971	.4972	.4973	.4974
2.8	.4974	.4975	.4976	.4977	.4977	.4978	.4979	.4979	.4980	.4981
2.9	.4981	.4982	.4982	.4983	.4984	.4984	.4985	.4985	.4986	.4986
3.0	.49865	.4987	.4987	.4988	.4988	.4989	.4989	.4989	.4990	.4990
3.1	.49903	.4991	.4991	.4991	.4992	.4992	.4992	.4992	.4993	.4993
3.2	.49931	.4993	.4994	.4994	.4994	.4994	.4994	.4995	.4995	.4995
3.3	.49952	.4995	.4995	.4996	.4996	.4996	.4996	.4996	.4996	.4997
3.4	.49966	.4997	.4997	.4997	.4997	.4997	.4997	.4997	.4997	.4998
3.5	.49977									

BPP Publishing

STUDENT'S T DISTRIBUTION

df	1 tail 2 tail	5% 10%	2.5% 5%	1% 2%	0.5% 1%	0.05% 0.1%
1		6.31	12.7	31.8	63.7	637
2		2.92	4.30	6.96	9.92	31.6
3		2.35	3.18	4.54	5.84	12.9
4		2.13	2.78	3.75	4.60	8.61
5		2.01	2.57	3.36	4.03	6.87
6		1.94	2.45	3.14	3.71	5.96
7		1.89	2.36	3.00	3.50	5.41
8		1.86	2.31	2.90	3.36	5.04
9		1.83	2.26	2.82	3.25	4.78
10		1.81	2.23	2.76	3.17	4.59
11		1.80	2.20	2.72	3.11	4.44
12		1.78	2.18	2.68	3.05	4.32
13		1.77	2.16	2.65	3.01	4.22
14		1.76	2.14	2.62	2.98	4.14
15		1.75	2.13	2.60	2.95	4.07
16		1.75	2.12	2.58	2.92	4.01
17		1.74	2.11	2.57	2.90	3.96
18		1.73	2.10	2.55	2.88	3.92
19		1.73	2.09	2.54	2.86	3.88
20		1.72	2.09	2.53	2.85	3.85
21		1.72	2.08	2.52	2.83	3.82
22		1.72	2.07	2.51	2.82	3.79
23		1.71	2.07	2.50	2.81	3.77
24		1.71	2.06	2.49	2.80	3.74
25		1.71	2.06	2.48	2.79	3.72
26		1.71	2.06	2.48	2.78	3.71
27		1.70	2.05	2.47	2.77	3.69
28		1.70	2.05	2.47	2.76	3.67
29		1.70	2.05	2.46	2.76	3.66
30		1.70	2.04	2.46	2.75	3.65
40		1.68	2.02	2.42	2.70	3.55
60		1.67	2.00	2.39	2.66	3.46
120		1.66	1.98	2.36	2.62	3.37
∞		1.65	1.96	2.33	2.58	3.29

THE CHI-SQUARED DISTRIBUTION (χ^2)

Percentage p

Degrees of freedom	99.5	99	97.5	95	90	10	5	2.5	1	0.5	0.1
1	0.0000	0.0002	0.0010	0.0039	0.016	2.71	3.84	5.02	6.63	7.88	10.8
2	0.010	0.020	0.051	0.103	0.211	4.61	5.99	7.38	9.21	10.6	13.8
3	0.072	0.115	0.216	0.352	0.584	6.25	7.81	9.35	11.3	12.8	16.3
4	0.207	0.297	0.484	0.711	1.06	7.78	9.49	11.1	13.3	14.9	18.5
5	0.412	0.554	0.831	1.15	1.61	9.24	11.1	12.8	15.1	16.7	20.5
6	0.676	0.872	1.24	1.64	2.20	10.6	12.6	14.4	16.8	18.5	22.5
7	0.989	1.24	1.69	2.17	2.83	12.0	14.1	16.0	18.5	20.3	24.3
8	1.34	1.65	2.18	2.73	3.49	13.4	15.5	17.5	20.1	22.0	26.1
9	1.73	2.09	2.70	3.33	4.17	14.7	16.9	19.0	21.7	23.6	27.9
10	2.16	2.56	3.25	3.94	4.87	16.0	18.3	20.5	23.2	25.2	29.6
11	2.60	3.05	3.82	4.57	5.58	17.3	19.7	21.9	24.7	26.8	31.3
12	3.07	3.57	4.40	5.23	6.30	18.5	21.0	23.3	26.2	28.3	32.9
13	3.57	4.11	5.01	5.89	7.04	19.8	22.4	24.7	27.7	29.8	34.5
14	4.07	4.66	5.63	6.57	7.79	21.1	23.7	26.1	29.1	31.3	36.1
15	4.60	5.23	6.26	7.26	8.55	22.3	25.0	27.5	30.6	32.8	37.7
16	5.14	5.81	6.91	7.96	9.31	23.5	26.3	28.8	32.0	34.3	39.3
17	5.70	6.41	7.56	8.67	10.1	24.8	27.6	30.2	33.4	35.7	40.8
18	6.26	7.01	8.23	9.39	10.9	26.0	28.9	31.5	34.8	37.2	42.3
19	6.84	7.63	8.91	10.1	11.7	27.2	30.1	32.9	36.2	38.6	43.8
20	7.43	8.26	9.59	10.9	12.4	28.4	31.4	34.2	37.6	40.0	45.3
21	8.03	8.90	10.3	11.6	13.2	29.6	32.7	35.5	38.9	41.4	46.8
22	8.64	9.54	11.0	12.3	14.0	30.8	33.9	36.8	40.3	42.8	48.3
23	9.26	10.2	11.7	13.1	14.8	32.0	35.2	38.1	41.6	44.2	49.7
24	9.89	10.9	12.4	13.8	15.7	33.2	36.4	39.4	43.0	45.6	51.2
25	10.5	11.5	13.1	14.6	16.5	34.4	37.7	40.6	44.3	46.9	52.6
26	11.2	12.2	13.8	15.4	17.3	35.6	38.9	41.9	45.6	48.3	54.1
27	11.8	12.9	14.6	16.2	18.1	36.7	40.1	43.2	47.0	49.6	55.5
28	12.5	13.6	15.3	16.9	18.9	37.9	41.3	44.5	48.3	51.0	56.9
29	13.1	14.3	16.0	17.7	19.8	39.1	42.6	45.7	49.6	52.3	58.3
30	13.8	15.0	16.8	18.5	20.6	40.3	43.8	47.0	50.9	53.7	59.7

BPP Publishing

PRESENT VALUE TABLE

This table shows the present value of £1 per annum, receivable or payable at the end of n years.

	Discount rates (r)											
Years (n)	1%	2%	3%	4%	5%	6%	7%	8%	9%	10%	11%	12%
1	0.99	0.98	0.97	0.96	0.95	0.94	0.93	0.93	0.92	0.91	0.90	0.89
2	0.98	0.96	0.94	0.92	0.91	0.89	0.87	0.86	0.84	0.83	0.81	0.80
3	0.97	0.94	0.92	0.89	0.86	0.84	0.82	0.79	0.77	0.75	0.73	0.71
4	0.96	0.92	0.89	0.85	0.82	0.79	0.76	0.74	0.71	0.68	0.66	0.64
5	0.95	0.91	0.86	0.82	0.78	0.75	0.71	0.68	0.65	0.62	0.59	0.57
6	0.94	0.89	0.84	0.79	0.75	0.70	0.67	0.63	0.60	0.56	0.53	0.51
7	0.93	0.87	0.81	0.76	0.71	0.67	0.62	0.58	0.55	0.51	0.48	0.45
8	0.92	0.85	0.79	0.73	0.68	0.63	0.58	0.54	0.50	0.47	0.43	0.40
9	0.91	0.84	0.77	0.70	0.64	0.59	0.54	0.50	0.46	0.42	0.39	0.36
10	0.91	0.82	0.74	0.68	0.61	0.56	0.51	0.46	0.42	0.39	0.35	0.32
11	0.90	0.80	0.72	0.65	0.58	0.53	0.48	0.43	0.39	0.35	0.32	0.29
12	0.89	0.79	0.70	0.62	0.56	0.50	0.44	0.40	0.36	0.32	0.29	0.26
13	0.88	0.77	0.68	0.60	0.53	0.47	0.41	0.37	0.33	0.29	0.26	0.23
14	0.87	0.76	0.66	0.58	0.51	0.44	0.39	0.34	0.30	0.26	0.23	0.20
15	0.86	0.74	0.64	0.56	0.48	0.42	0.36	0.32	0.27	0.24	0.21	0.18

	Discount rates (r)										
Years (n)	13%	14%	15%	16%	17%	18%	19%	20%	30%	40%	50%
1	0.88	0.88	0.87	0.86	0.85	0.85	0.84	0.83	0.77	0.71	0.67
2	0.78	0.77	0.76	0.74	0.73	0.72	0.71	0.69	0.59	0.51	0.44
3	0.69	0.67	0.66	0.64	0.62	0.61	0.59	0.58	0.46	0.36	0.30
4	0.61	0.59	0.57	0.55	0.53	0.52	0.50	0.48	0.35	0.26	0.20
5	0.54	0.52	0.50	0.48	0.46	0.44	0.42	0.40	0.27	0.19	0.13
6	0.48	0.46	0.43	0.41	0.39	0.37	0.35	0.33	0.21	0.13	0.09
7	0.43	0.40	0.38	0.35	0.33	0.31	0.30	0.28	0.16	0.09	0.06
8	0.38	0.35	0.33	0.31	0.28	0.27	0.25	0.23	0.12	0.07	0.04
9	0.33	0.31	0.28	0.26	0.24	0.23	0.21	0.19	0.09	0.05	0.03
10	0.29	0.27	0.25	0.23	0.21	0.19	0.18	0.16	0.07	0.03	0.02
11	0.26	0.24	0.21	0.20	0.18	0.16	0.15	0.13	0.06	0.02	0.01
12	0.23	0.21	0.19	0.17	0.15	0.14	0.12	0.11	0.04	0.02	0.008
13	0.20	0.18	0.16	0.15	0.13	0.12	0.10	0.09	0.03	0.013	0.005
14	0.18	0.16	0.14	0.13	0.11	0.10	0.09	0.08	0.03	0.009	0.003
15	0.16	0.14	0.12	0.11	0.09	0.08	0.07	0.06	0.02	0.006	0.002

CUMULATIVE PRESENT VALUE TABLE

This table shows the cumulative present value of £1 per annum, receivable or payable at the end of each year for n years.

Years	Discount rates (r)											
(n)	1%	2%	3%	4%	5%	6%	7%	8%	9%	10%	11%	12%
1	0.99	0.98	0.97	0.96	0.95	0.94	0.93	0.93	0.92	0.91	0.90	0.89
2	1.97	1.94	1.91	1.89	1.86	1.83	1.81	1.78	1.76	1.74	1.71	1.69
3	2.94	2.88	2.83	2.78	2.72	2.67	2.62	2.58	2.53	2.49	2.44	2.40
4	3.90	3.81	3.72	3.63	3.55	3.47	3.39	3.31	3.24	3.17	3.10	3.04
5	4.85	4.71	4.58	4.45	4.33	4.21	4.10	3.99	3.89	3.79	3.70	3.60
6	5.80	5.60	5.42	5.24	5.08	4.92	4.77	4.62	4.49	4.36	4.23	4.11
7	6.73	6.47	6.23	6.00	5.79	5.58	5.39	5.21	5.03	4.87	4.71	4.56
8	7.65	7.33	7.02	6.73	6.46	6.21	5.97	5.75	5.53	5.33	5.15	4.97
9	8.57	8.16	7.79	7.44	7.11	6.80	6.52	6.25	6.00	5.76	5.54	5.33
10	9.47	8.98	8.53	8.11	7.72	7.36	7.02	6.71	6.42	6.14	5.89	5.65
11	10.37	9.79	9.25	8.76	8.31	7.89	7.50	7.14	6.81	6.50	6.21	5.94
12	11.26	10.58	9.95	9.39	8.86	8.38	7.94	7.54	7.16	6.81	6.49	6.19
13	12.13	11.35	10.63	9.99	9.39	8.85	8.36	7.90	7.49	7.10	6.75	6.42
14	13.00	12.11	11.30	10.56	9.90	9.29	8.75	8.24	7.79	7.37	6.98	6.63
15	13.87	12.85	11.94	11.12	10.38	9.71	9.11	8.56	8.06	7.61	7.19	6.81

Years	Discount rates (r)										
(n)	13%	14%	15%	16%	17%	18%	19%	20%	30%	40%	50%
1	0.88	0.88	0.87	0.86	0.85	0.85	0.84	0.83	0.77	0.71	0.67
2	1.67	1.65	1.63	1.61	1.59	1.57	1.55	1.53	1.36	1.22	1.11
3	2.36	2.32	2.28	2.25	2.21	2.17	2.14	2.11	1.82	1.59	1.41
4	2.97	2.91	2.85	2.80	2.74	2.69	2.64	2.59	2.17	1.85	1.60
5	3.52	3.43	3.35	3.27	3.20	3.13	3.06	2.99	2.44	2.04	1.74
6	4.00	3.89	3.78	3.68	3.59	3.50	3.41	3.33	2.64	2.17	1.82
7	4.42	4.29	4.16	4.04	3.92	3.81	3.71	3.60	2.80	2.26	1.88
8	4.80	4.64	4.49	4.34	4.21	4.08	3.95	3.84	2.92	2.33	1.92
9	5.13	4.95	4.77	4.61	4.45	4.30	4.16	4.03	3.02	2.38	1.95
10	5.43	5.22	5.02	4.83	4.66	4.49	4.34	4.19	3.09	2.41	1.97
11	5.69	5.45	5.23	5.03	4.84	4.66	4.49	4.33	3.15	2.44	1.98
12	5.92	5.66	5.42	5.20	4.99	4.79	4.61	4.44	3.19	2.46	1.98
13	6.12	5.84	5.58	5.34	5.12	4.91	4.71	4.53	3.22	2.47	1.99
14	6.30	6.00	5.72	5.47	5.23	5.01	4.80	4.61	3.25	2.48	1.99
15	6.46	6.14	5.85	5.58	5.32	5.09	4.88	4.68	3.27	2.48	2.00

BPP Publishing

1 BASIC MATHEMATICS

Signpost

The aim of this chapter is to introduce some mathematical tools which you will use frequently in your studies. Percentages are often used in business contexts, for example in quoting interest rates. Powers and roots are a useful way of expressing problems where a number is to be multiplied by itself several times. Equations show how different amounts, such as the quantity of goods and the cost of making those goods, are related to each other. Matrices are tables of figures, such as the numbers of different types of workers in different factories, written out so as to make it easy to perform mathematical operations on the figures.

Your objectives

After completing this chapter you should:

(a) be able to deal with percentages;

(b) be able to deal with powers and roots;

(c) be able to solve linear equations, simultaneous linear equations and quadratic equations;

(d) be able to write down, add and multiply matrices;

(e) be able to use matrices to solve simultaneous equations.

---

1 Basic mathematical skills

'Business mathematics' covers a wide range of topics. However, there are some techniques which come up again and again, so it is important for you to feel at ease with them. You may already be very familiar with them, but even if you are do glance through this chapter and try some of the exercises. Getting the basics right really will make life much easier later on.

2 Percentages and proportions

Percentages are used to indicate the *relative* size or proportion of items, rather than their absolute sizes. For example, if one branch of a bank employs ten clerks, six office secretaries and four managers, the *absolute* values of staff numbers and the *percentage* of the total workforce in each type would be as follows.

BPP Publishing

	Clerks	Secretaries	Managers	Total
Absolute numbers	10	6	4	20
Percentages	50%	30%	20%	100%

The idea of percentages is that the whole of something can be thought of as 100%. The whole of a cake, for example, is 100%. If you share it equally with a friend, you will get half each, or 100%/2 = 50% each.

Because percentages are based on the number one hundred (100%), working out something in percentages is the same as working it out in hundredths. For instance, 30% is the same as $\frac{30}{100}$, which is the same as 0.3. Other examples are:

(a) $20\% = \frac{20}{100} = 0.20$;

(b) $87\% = \frac{87}{100} = 0.87$;

(c) $2\% = \frac{2}{100} = 0.02$;

(d) $0.3\% = \frac{0.3}{100} = \frac{3}{1,000} = 0.003$.

So to turn a percentage into a fraction or decimal, you put the percentage over 100: in other words, you *divide* by 100. To turn a fraction or decimal back into a percentage you *multiply* by 100%. For example:

(a) $0.16 = 0.16 \times 100\% = 16\%$;

(b) $\frac{4}{5} = \frac{4}{5} \times 100\% = \frac{400}{5}\% = 80\%$

3 Powers and roots

Powers and roots are a sort of mathematical shorthand. They can be used to make difficult calculations much simpler.

A power of a number is that number written out as many times as the power with × signs in all the gaps. For example, 6 to the power 3 is written 6^3 and equals $6 \times 6 \times 6$ (which equals 216).

There are three important rules to remember about powers.

(a) Any number to the power 1 is just the number itself. For example, $3^1 = 3$ and $429^1 = 429$.

(b) Any number to the power 0 is 1. For example $3^0 = 1$ and $429^0 = 1$.

(c) Any number to a negative power is the reciprocal ('one over') of the number to the positive power.

For example $3^{-2} = \dfrac{1}{3^2} = \dfrac{1}{3} \times \dfrac{1}{3} = \dfrac{1}{9}$ and $(\dfrac{4}{5})^{-3} = (\dfrac{5}{4})^3 = \dfrac{125}{64}$

The powers 2 and 3 crop up so often that they have been given special names: 'square' and 'cube'. For example:

(a) 4 squared $= 4^2 = 4 \times 4 = 16$;
(b) 6 cubed $= 6^3 = 6 \times 6 \times 6 = 216$.

Powers of numbers are worked out in exactly the same way whether the number is an integer (a whole number like 4 or –3), a fraction or a decimal.

Exercise 1

Work out the following, *without* using a calculator.

(a) 3.2^2

(b) $(\dfrac{1}{4})^3$

(c) 3^{-3}

Adding and subtracting powers

Suppose you had to work out $2^3 \times 2^4$. This is the same as $(2 \times 2 \times 2) \times (2 \times 2 \times 2 \times 2)$. But this is just 2 multiplied by itself seven times, or 2^7. So $2^3 \times 2^4 = 2^7$.

The principle demonstrated in this example is always true. When a number to a power is multiplied by the *same number* to a power, all you have to do is add the powers together and then work out the answer.

(a) $3^2 \times 3^3 = 3^{2+3} = 3^5 = 243$.
(b) $(0.5)^4 \times (0.5)^2 = (0.5)^{4+2} = (0.5)^6 = 0.015625$.

Similarly, when a number to a power is to be divided by the *same number* to a power, all you have to do is to subtract the powers, and then work out the answer.

(a) $3^3 \div 3^2 = 3^{3-2} = 3^1 = 3$.

(b) $(0.5)^4 \div (0.5)^2 = (0.5)^{4-2} = (0.5)^2 = 0.25$.

Exercise 2

Work out the following, without using a calculator.

BPP Publishing

    (a) $(0.52)^{16} \times (0.52)^{-14}$
    (b) $(3.6)^8 \div (3.6)^6$
    (c) $(4.1)^2 \times (4.2)^2$

Roots

So far in this chapter, we have seen what it means if a number has a power which is a positive integer, a negative integer, or 0. But can a power be a fraction?

The answer is yes. A fractional power is called a *root* and effectively it reverses the effect of a power. For example:

(a) $2^3 = 8$, so $8^{\frac{1}{3}} = 2$;

(b) $5^2 = 25$, so $25^{\frac{1}{2}} = 5$.

So if you were asked to work out $64^{\frac{1}{3}}$, you would need to calculate what number, to the power 3, comes out at 64. In this case, the answer is 4 (because $4 \times 4 \times 4 = 64$).

Just as the powers of 2 and 3 are called 'square' and 'cube', so the roots of $\frac{1}{2}$ and $\frac{1}{3}$ are called 'square root' and 'cube root'. For example:

(a) the square root of 4 means $4^{\frac{1}{2}}$ (usually written $\sqrt{4}$), and works out at 2;

(b) the cube root of 27 means $27^{\frac{1}{3}}$ (usually written $\sqrt[3]{27}$), and works out at 3.

-2 is also a square root of 4, because $(-2) \times (-2) = 4$. Every positive number has two square roots, one positive and one negative. However, this does not happen with cube roots: $-3^3 = -27$, not 27.

Indices

Indices is just a word used to mean roots and powers. For example:

(a) in the expression 2^4, the *index* of 2 is 4;

(b) in the expression $9^{\frac{1}{4}}$, the *index* of 9 is $\frac{1}{4}$.

Finding powers and roots on a calculator

Suppose you are asked to work out the following.

(a) $4^{2.6}$

(b) $7^{\frac{1}{2}}$

(c) $(\frac{1}{4})^{2.6}$

Your calculator can handle such problems easily, provided all the figures are in decimals, not fractions. We will work through (a) to (c) in order to demonstrate this principle.

(a) $4^{2.6}$. Just press the keys:

    4 | x^y | 2.6 | = |

and the answer 36.7583 should appear.

(b) $7^{\frac{1}{2}}$. Before we can work this out, the power has to be written as a decimal. So we alter the question to read $7^{0.5}$. Then we use the calculator in the normal way.

7 $\boxed{x^y}$ 0.5 $\boxed{=}$

should give an answer of 2.64575 (the positive square root of 7).

(c) $(\frac{1}{4})^{2.6}$. In this problem, the power is satisfactorily expressed as a decimal, but the part to be powered is not. We have to change the $\frac{1}{4}$ into 0.25, so that the question reads $(0.25)^{2.6}$.

Then

0.25 $\boxed{x^y}$ 2.6 $\boxed{=}$

should yield the answer 0.0272.

We can find roots on a calculator, either by converting the root to a power (1/the root) and using the power button, or by using the root button. Here is an example, showing both methods.

$$\sqrt[3.8]{16} = 16^{1/3.8} = 16^{0.2632} = 16 \boxed{x^y} 0.2632 \boxed{=} 2.07$$

$$\sqrt[3.8]{16} = 16 \boxed{\sqrt[y]{x}} \quad (\text{or} \quad \boxed{x^{1/y}}) \quad 3.8 \boxed{=} 2.07$$

Exercise 3

Work out the following, using a calculator.

(a) $(18.6)^{2.6}$
(b) $(18.6)^{-2.6}$

(c) $\sqrt[2.6]{18.6}$

4 Variables and formulae

So far, all our problems have been formulated entirely in terms of specific numbers. However, when we looked at the use of calculators to work out powers, we referred to the x^y key. x and y stood for whichever numbers we happened to have in our problem, for example 3 and 4 if we wanted to work out 3^4. When we use letters like this to stand for any numbers, we call them *variables*. When we work out 3^4, x stands for 3. When we work out 7^2, x will stand for 7. Its value can *vary*.

The use of variables enables us to state general truths about mathematics.

For example:

x = x
$x^2 = x \times x$
If $x = 2 \times y$, then $y = 0.5 \times x$

These will be true *whatever* values x and y have.

For example, let y = 0.5 × x
If y = 3, x = 2 × y = 6.
If y = 7, x = 2 × y = 14.
If y = 1, x = 2 × y = 2 and so on for any other choice of a value for y.

We can use variables to build up useful *formulae*. We can then put in values for the variables and get out a value for something we are interested in.

Let us consider an example. For a business, profit = revenue - costs. Since revenue = selling price × units sold, we can say that

    profit = selling price × units sold - costs.

'Selling price × units sold - costs' is a *formula* for profit.

We can then use single letters to make the formula quicker to write.

Let x   =   profit
      p   =   selling price
      u   =   units sold
      c   =   cost

    Then x = p × u - c.

If we are then told that in a particular month, p = £5, u = 30 and c = £118, we can find out the month's profit.

Profit   =   x = p × u - c = £5 × 30 - £118
           = £150 - £118 = £32.

It is usual when writing formulae to leave out multiplication signs between letters. Thus p × u - c can be written as pu - c. We will also write (for example) 2x instead of 2 × x.

5   Equations

In the above example, pu - c was a *formula* for profit. If we write x = pu - c, we have written an *equation*. It says that one thing (profit, x) is equal to another (pu - c).

Sometimes, we are given an equation with numbers filled in for all but one of the variables. The problem is then to find the number which should be filled in in the place of the last variable. This is called *solving* the equation.

Returning to x = pu - c, we could be told that for a particular month p = £4, u = 60 and c = £208. We would then have the *equation* x = £4 × 60 - £208. We can solve this easily by working out £4 × 60 - £208 = £240 - £208 = £32. Thus x = £32.

On the other hand, we might have been told that in a month when profits were £172, 50 units were sold and the selling price was £7. The thing we have not been told is the month's costs, c. We can work out c by writing out the equation.

£172 = £7 × 50 - c
£172 = £350 - c

We need c to be such that when it is taken away from £350 we have £172 left. With a bit of trial and error, we can get to c = £178.

Trial and error takes far too long in more complicated cases, however, and we will now go on to look at a rule for solving equations, which will take us directly to the answers we want.

The rule for solving equations

To solve an equation, we need to get it into the form:

Unknown variable = something with just numbers in it, which we can work out.

We therefore want to get the unknown variable on one side of the = sign, and everything else on the other side.

The rule is that you can do what you like to one side of an equation, so long as you do the same thing to the other side straightaway. The two sides are equal, and they will stay equal so long as you treat them in the same way.

For example, you can do any of the following.

> Add 37 to both sides.
> Subtract 3x from both sides.
> Multiply both sides by -4.329.
> Divide both sides by (x + 2).
> Take the reciprocals of both sides.
> Square both sides.
> Take the cube root of both sides.

Thus in our earlier example, we had £172 = £350 - c.

We can then get

£172 + c = £350	(add c to each side)
c = £350 - £172	(subtract £172 from each side)
c = £178	(work out the right hand side).

Here are two more examples.

450 = 3x + 72	(initial equation: x unknown)
450 - 72 = 3x	(subtract 72 from each side)

$$\frac{450 - 72}{3} = x \qquad \text{(divide each side by 3)}$$

126 = x	(work out the left hand side).

3y + 2 = 5y - 7	(initial equation: y unknown)
3y + 9 = 5y	(add 7 to each side)
9 = 2y	(subtract 3y from each side)
4.5 = y	(divide each side by 2).

BPP Publishing

Our first example of an equation was x = pu - c. We could change this, so as to make it easy to find p.

$$x = pu - c$$

$$x + c = pu \qquad \text{(add c to each side)}$$

$$\frac{x + c}{u} = p \qquad \text{(divide each side by u)}$$

$$p = \frac{x + c}{u} \qquad \text{(swap the sides for ease of reading)}$$

Given values for x, c and u we can now find p. We have *re-arranged* the equation to give p *in terms of* x, c and u.

6 Linear and quadratic equations

The equations we are most interested in involve two variables. Such equations, for example y = 2x, will describe a relationship which holds between the two variables. Two of the most common types that you will encounter are *linear equations* and *quadratic equations*.

Linear equations

A linear equation has the general form

y = a + bx

where   y   is a dependent variable, depending for its value on the value of x
           x   is an independent variable whose value helps to determine the corresponding value of y
           a   is a constant, that is, a fixed amount
           b   is also a constant. It is the coefficient of x (that is, the number by which the value of x should be multiplied in deriving the value of y).

Typical linear equations are as follows.

(a)   y = 78 + 3x
      (If x = 1, y = 81; if x = 2, y = 84; if x = 3, y = 87.)

(b)   y = -12 + 2x
      (If x = 1, y = -10; if x = 5, y = -2; if x = 8, y = 4.)

(c)   p = 16 - 3q
      (If q = 2, p = 10; if q = 4, p = 4.)

Note from the last example that the letters used do not have to be x and y. It may be sensible to use other letters, for example where p is price and q is quantity.

A linear equation can be plotted on a graph as a straight line. Thus the graph of y = 5 + 2x and the graph of y = 10 - x would be as follows.

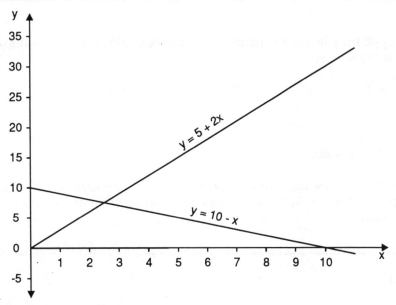

Simultaneous linear equations

Simultaneous equations are two or more equations which are satisfied together. For example, we might have these two linear equations.

$$y = 3x + 16$$
$$2y = x + 72$$

There are two unknown values, x and y, and there are two different equations for x and y. Because there are as many equations as there are unknowns, we can find the values of x and y.

(a) We have:

$$y = 3x + 16 \qquad (1)$$
$$2y = x + 72 \qquad (2)$$

(b) Rearranging these, we have:

$$y - 3x = 16 \qquad (3)$$
$$2y - x = 72 \qquad (4)$$

(c) If we now multiply equation (4) by 3, so that the coefficient for x becomes the same as in equation (3) we get:

$$6y - 3x = 216 \qquad (5)$$
$$y - 3x = 16 \qquad (3)$$

(d) Subtracting (3) from (5) we get:

$$5y = 200$$
$$y = 40$$

Notes

(e) Substituting 40 for y in any equation, we can derive a value for x. Thus substituting in equation (4) we get:

$$2 \times 40 - x = 72$$
$$80 - 72 = x$$
$$8 = x$$

(f) The solution is y = 40, x = 8.

You should now try to draw the lines for the two equations we started with on a graph. They should intersect at x = 8, y = 40, because the intersection of the lines is where both equations hold.

Exercise 4

Solve the following simultaneous equations to derive values for x and y.

$$4x + 3y = 23 \quad (1)$$
$$5x - 4y = -10 \quad (2)$$

Quadratic equations

In quadratic equations, one variable varies with the square (or second power) of the other variable. Thus:

$$y = x^2$$
$$y = 3x^2 + 2$$
$$2y = 5x^2 - 6$$
$$y = -x^2 + 3$$

are all quadratic equations.

A quadratic equation may include both a term involving the square and also a term involving the first power of a variable. Here are some examples.

$$y = x^2 + 6x + 10$$
$$2y = 3x^2 - 4x - 8$$
$$y = -2x^2 + 3x + 6$$

All quadratic equations can be expressed in the form $y = ax^2 + bx + c$. For instance, in the equation $y = x^2$, a is 1, b is 0 and c is 0.

Solving a quadratic equation

Quadratic equations often have two values of x (called 'solutions for x', or 'roots of the equation') which satisfy the equation for any particular value of y. These values can be found using the following formula.

If $ax^2 + bx + c = 0$, then

$$x = \frac{-b \pm \sqrt{[b^2 - 4ac]}}{2a}$$

Example: quadratic equations

Solve $x^2 + x - 2 = 0$

Solution

$$x = \frac{-1 \pm \sqrt{[1^2 - (4 \times 1 \times (-2))]}}{2 \times 1}$$

$$= \frac{-1 \pm \sqrt{(1 + 8)}}{2}$$

$$= \frac{-1 \pm 3}{2}$$

$$= \frac{-4}{2} = -2 \text{ or } \quad \frac{2}{2} = 1. \text{ So } x = -2 \text{ or } x = 1.$$

Exercise 5

Solve $3x^2 - 8x - 11 = 0$.

Quadratic equations with a single value for x

Sometimes, $b^2 - 4ac = 0$, and there is only one solution. For example, if we solve

$x^2 + 2x + 1 = 0$, we get

$$x = \frac{-2 \pm \sqrt{[2^2 - (4 \times 1 \times 1)]}}{2 \times 1}$$

$$= \frac{-2 \pm 0}{2} = -1$$

Quadratic equations without solutions

If $b^2 - 4ac$ is negative, there are no solutions of the quadratic equation unless we resort to what are called complex numbers. You can ignore this topic at this stage in your studies.

7 Matrices

A *matrix* (plural *matrices*) is an array or table of numbers or variables. For example, the table below is a matrix.

		Labour	
	Skilled	*Semi-skilled*	*Unskilled*
Factory P	100	75	250
Factory Q	40	40	200
Factory R	25	10	100

This table, showing the numbers of skilled, semi-skilled and unskilled workers in each of three factories, is a matrix with three rows and three columns; that is, its size is 3 × 3. A matrix with m rows and n columns is called an m × n matrix.

A table of numbers or variables which has just one row or column is called a *vector*. A row vector is one row of numbers, and a column vector is a single column of numbers.

A matrix is shown in large brackets. The example above would be written as follows.

$$\begin{pmatrix} 100 & 75 & 250 \\ 40 & 40 & 200 \\ 25 & 10 & 100 \end{pmatrix}$$

This takes some time to write out in full, so we may refer to a matrix by a single letter. For example, we could call the matrix above 'X'.

Each figure in a matrix is called an element. An element is identified by the row and column in which it falls. For example, in the above matrix X, the element X_{32} is that in the third row and the second column, namely the number of semi-skilled workers at factory R, which is 10.

Matrix addition

Two matrices may be added together (or subtracted) provided they are of the same size. The addition is performed by adding the corresponding elements together. Continuing our first example of workers in factories, we might have a matrix A showing the effects on staffing levels of changing to new working practices, and a matrix B showing the effects of changing from gas power to electric power. A + B would show the effects of changing working practices *and* changing to electric power, while A − B would show the effects of changing working practices and changing back from electric to gas power.

Thus if A $= \begin{pmatrix} 2 & 9 & -1 \\ 3 & -6 & -4 \\ -1 & 7 & 2 \end{pmatrix}$

and B $\quad=\begin{pmatrix} 3 & 6 & 2 \\ -1 & -5 & 9 \\ 7 & -2 & -1 \end{pmatrix}$

then A + B $\quad=\begin{pmatrix} 2+3 & 9+6 & -1+2 \\ 3-1 & -6-5 & -4+9 \\ -1+7 & 7-2 & 2-1 \end{pmatrix}$

$\quad=\begin{pmatrix} 5 & 15 & 1 \\ 2 & -11 & 5 \\ 6 & 5 & 1 \end{pmatrix}$

The revised matrix X for the total workforce, after both changes, would be

X + (A + B) $\quad=\begin{pmatrix} 105 & 90 & 251 \\ 42 & 29 & 205 \\ 31 & 15 & 101 \end{pmatrix}$

A - B $\quad=\begin{pmatrix} 2-3 & 9-6 & -1-2 \\ 3+1 & -6+5 & -4-9 \\ -1-7 & 7+2 & 2+1 \end{pmatrix}$

$\quad=\begin{pmatrix} -1 & 3 & -3 \\ 4 & -1 & -13 \\ -8 & 9 & 3 \end{pmatrix}$

Matrix multiplication

Matrix multiplication is known as scalar multiplication. A scalar is an ordinary single number. If an entire matrix is multiplied by a scalar the effect is to multiply each element in the matrix by the scalar. Thus if:

A $\quad=\begin{pmatrix} 2 & 9 & -1 \\ 3 & -6 & -4 \\ -1 & 7 & 2 \end{pmatrix}$

then 3A = $\begin{pmatrix} 6 & 27 & -3 \\ 9 & -18 & -12 \\ -3 & 21 & 6 \end{pmatrix}$

Two matrices can be multiplied together *provided* that the first matrix has the same number of columns as the second matrix has rows.

Thus if matrix A has four rows and two columns, and matrix B has two rows and three columns, the two can be multiplied together to get a product AB.

Since A is a 4 × 2 matrix and B is a 2 × 3 matrix, a product AB can be found, but a product matrix BA does not exist. B has three columns and A has four rows, therefore multiplication is impossible.

The elements in a product matrix are calculated as follows.

(a) Take the elements in the first row of the first matrix (say, matrix A) and multiply them by the corresponding elements in the first column of the second matrix (say, matrix B). The sum of the products then becomes the element in the first row and the first column of the product matrix.

(b) Similarly, the elements in row 2 of matrix A should be multiplied by the corresponding elements in column 1 of matrix B, and the sum of the products then becomes the element in row 2 and column 1 of the product matrix.

(c) This process must be repeated m × p times. The general rule is that the elements in row m of the first matrix should be multiplied by the corresponding elements in column p of the second matrix, and the sum of the products then becomes the element in row m and column p of the product matrix.

Example: matrix multiplication

Matrix A is a 2 × 3 matrix

$$\begin{pmatrix} 5 & 6 & 4 \\ 4 & 9 & 7 \end{pmatrix}$$

Matrix B is a 3 × 4 matrix

$$\begin{pmatrix} 3 & 5 & 5 & 5 \\ 6 & 4 & 4 & 0 \\ 0 & 3 & 5 & 5 \end{pmatrix}$$

Calculate matrix C where C = AB

Solution

Matrix C will be a 2 × 4 matrix. C_{12} will be used for the number in row 1, column 2, and similarly for other numbers.

Element in matrix C	Elements in xth row of A	Elements in xth column of B	
C_{11}	1st	1st	= (5 × 3) + (6 × 6) + (4 × 0) = 51
C_{12}	1st	2nd	= (5 × 5) + (6 × 4) + (4 × 3) = 61
C_{13}	1st	3rd	= (5 × 5) + (6 × 4) + (4 × 5) = 69
C_{14}	1st	4th	= (5 × 5) + (6 × 0) + (4 × 5) = 45
C_{21}	2nd	1st	= (4 × 3) + (9 × 6) + (7 × 0) = 66
C_{22}	2nd	2nd	= (4 × 5) + (9 × 4) + (7 × 3) = 77
C_{23}	2nd	3rd	= (4 × 5) + (9 × 4) + (7 × 5) = 91
C_{24}	2nd	4th	= (4 × 5) + (9 × 0) + (7 × 5) = 55

$$\text{Matrix C} = \begin{pmatrix} 51 & 61 & 69 & 45 \\ 66 & 77 & 91 & 55 \end{pmatrix}$$

Exercise 6

Let A $= \begin{pmatrix} 2 & 1 \\ 0 & 3 \end{pmatrix}$

B $= \begin{pmatrix} 5 & 1 & 0 \\ 2 & 3 & 1 \end{pmatrix}$

C $= \begin{pmatrix} 3 & 1 \\ 0 & 2 \\ 1 & 4 \end{pmatrix}$

Find AB, CA, BC and CB.

Null matrices

A null matrix is one in which every element is 0. The null matrix behaves like the number 0 in calculations. Thus, if any matrix is multiplied by a null matrix the solution will also be a null matrix.

$$\begin{pmatrix} 0 & 0 \\ 0 & 0 \end{pmatrix} \times \begin{pmatrix} 6 & -1 \\ 2 & 3 \end{pmatrix} = \begin{pmatrix} 0 & 0 \\ 0 & 0 \end{pmatrix}$$

Identity matrices

An identity or unit matrix (often designated by I) is a square matrix which behaves like the number 1 in multiplication. Each element on the main diagonal (top left to botttom right) of a unit matrix is 1 and all other elements are 0.

A unit matrix must be square, and the effect of multiplying a matrix by a unit matrix is to leave it unchanged.

$$\begin{pmatrix} 1 & 0 & 0 \\ 0 & 1 & 0 \\ 0 & 0 & 1 \end{pmatrix} \times \begin{pmatrix} 1 & 2 & 3 \\ 4 & 5 & 6 \\ 7 & 8 & 9 \end{pmatrix} = \begin{pmatrix} 1 & 2 & 3 \\ 4 & 5 & 6 \\ 7 & 8 & 9 \end{pmatrix}$$
$$\quad\quad\ \text{I} \quad\quad \times \quad\quad\quad \text{A} \quad\quad\ = \quad\quad\quad \text{A}$$

Inverse of a matrix

The inverse of a square matrix (A) is represented by A^{-1} and can be defined by the equation:

$$AA^{-1} = A^{-1}A = I$$

This means that if A is multiplied by its inverse or vice versa the product is an identity matrix.

The inverse of a 2 × 2 matrix can be found as follows.

If A $= \begin{pmatrix} a & b \\ c & d \end{pmatrix}$ then A^{-1} = $\dfrac{1}{ad - bc}$ $\begin{pmatrix} d & -b \\ -c & a \end{pmatrix}$

Exercise 7

Find the inverse of matrix A $= \begin{pmatrix} 7 & 9 \\ 3 & 2 \end{pmatrix}$

Solving simultaneous equations using matrices

Matrices are widely used for solving simultaneous equations. The following example illustrates how this is done.

Example: solving simultaneous equations

Solve the equations

$$5x + 9y = -30$$
$$6x - 2y = 28$$

using matrix algebra.

Solution

In a matrix format the equations can be stated as:

$$\begin{pmatrix} 5 & 9 \\ 6 & -2 \end{pmatrix} \begin{pmatrix} x \\ y \end{pmatrix} = \begin{pmatrix} -30 \\ 28 \end{pmatrix}$$

Invert the square matrix, to get:

$$\frac{1}{5 \times (-2) - 9 \times 6} \begin{pmatrix} -2 & -9 \\ -6 & 5 \end{pmatrix}$$

$$= \frac{-1}{64} \begin{pmatrix} -2 & -9 \\ -6 & 5 \end{pmatrix}$$

$$= \begin{pmatrix} 2/64 & 9/64 \\ 6/64 & -5/64 \end{pmatrix}$$

Multiply both sides of the equation by this inverse.

$$\begin{pmatrix} 2/64 & 9/64 \\ 6/64 & -5/64 \end{pmatrix} \begin{pmatrix} 5 & 9 \\ 6 & -2 \end{pmatrix} \begin{pmatrix} x \\ y \end{pmatrix} = \begin{pmatrix} 2/64 & 9/64 \\ 6/64 & -5/64 \end{pmatrix} \begin{pmatrix} -30 \\ 28 \end{pmatrix}$$

$$\begin{pmatrix} 1 & 0 \\ 0 & 1 \end{pmatrix} \begin{pmatrix} x \\ y \end{pmatrix} = \begin{pmatrix} 3 \\ -5 \end{pmatrix}$$

So x = 3 and y = -5.

Notes

Chapter roundup

(a) A number x to the power y is x multiplied by itself y times.

(b) Powers can be positive or negative, and can be whole numbers or fractions. Fractional powers are called roots.

(c) Powers can be found using a calculator, but any fractions should first be converted to decimals.

(d) A linear equation has the form $y = a + bx$, and can be represented by a straight line on a graph. Two simultaneous linear equations can be solved to find values for x and y.

(e) A quadratic equation has the form $ax^2 + bx + c = 0$. It can be solved using a formula.

(f) A table of figures can be represented as a matrix. Two matrices of the same size can be added, a matrix can be multiplied by a single figure (a scalar) or two matrices can be multiplied (provided that the first matrix has the same number of columns as the second matrix has rows).

(g) Important matrices are the null matrix, the identity matrix and the inverse of a matrix. Inverses of matrices can be used to solve simultaneous equations.

Quick quiz

1   What is $(^2/_5)^2 + 0.5^2$?

2   What is $4^5 \times (\frac{1}{4})^3$?

3   What is $14.2^4 + 14.2^{1/4}$?

4   Solve the following simultaneous equations.

$$y = 3x + 7$$
$$4y = -12x + 11$$

5   Solve the equation $2x^2 + 6x - 56 = 0$.

6   Find $\begin{pmatrix} 3 & 2 & 9 \\ 6 & -4 & -2 \end{pmatrix} \begin{pmatrix} 1 & -2 \\ 4 & -1 \\ 6 & 12 \end{pmatrix}$

7   Find the inverse of $\begin{pmatrix} -2 & 4 \\ 1 & -4 \end{pmatrix}$

BPP Publishing

Solutions to exercises

1   (a) $3.2^2 = 3.2 \times 3.2 = 10.24$

   (b) $(\frac{1}{4})^3 = \frac{1}{4} \times \frac{1}{4} \times \frac{1}{4} = \frac{1}{64}$

   (c) $3^{-3} = (\frac{1}{3})^3 = \frac{1}{27}$

2   (a) $(0.52)^{16} \times (0.52)^{-14} = (0.52)^2 = 0.2704$

   (b) $(3.6)^8 \div (3.6)^6 = (3.6)^8 \times (3.6)^{-6} = 3.6^2 = 12.96$

   (c) $(4.1)^2 \times (4.2)^2 = 16.81 \times 17.64 = 296.5284$. (You cannot add the powers because 4.1 and 4.2 are different numbers.)

3   (a) $(18.6)^{2.6} = 1,998.64$

   (b) $(18.6)^{-2.6} = (\frac{1}{18.6})^{2.6} = 0.0005$

   (c) $\sqrt[2.6]{18.6} = 3.0780$

4   (a)   If we multiply equation (1) by 4 and equation (2) by 3, we will obtain coefficients of +12 and -12 for y in our two products.

      $16x + 12y = 92$ (3)
      $15x - 12y = -30$ (4)

   (b)   Add (3) and (4)

      $31x = 62$
      $x = 2$

   (c)   Substituting in equation (1)

      $4(2) + 3y = 23$
           $3y = 23 - 8 = 15$
            $y = 5$

   (d)   The solution is $x = 2$, $y = 5$.

5    $3x^2 - 8x - 11 = 0$

$$x = \frac{-(-8) \pm \sqrt{[64 - (4 \times 3 \times (-11))]}}{2 \times 3} = \frac{8 \pm \sqrt{196}}{6}$$

$$= \frac{8 + 14}{6} \text{ or } \frac{8 - 14}{6}$$

$$= 3\tfrac{2}{3} \text{ or } -1.$$

6    $AB = \begin{pmatrix} 12 & 5 & 1 \\ 6 & 9 & 3 \end{pmatrix}$

$CA = \begin{pmatrix} 6 & 6 \\ 0 & 6 \\ 2 & 13 \end{pmatrix}$

$BC = \begin{pmatrix} 15 & 7 \\ 7 & 12 \end{pmatrix}$

$CB = \begin{pmatrix} 17 & 6 & 1 \\ 4 & 6 & 2 \\ 13 & 13 & 4 \end{pmatrix}$

7    $A = \begin{pmatrix} 7 & 9 \\ 3 & 2 \end{pmatrix}$

$A^{-1} = \frac{1}{(14-27)} \begin{pmatrix} 2 & -9 \\ -3 & 7 \end{pmatrix}$

$$= \begin{pmatrix} -2/13 & 9/13 \\ 3/13 & -7/13 \end{pmatrix}$$

Solutions to quick quiz

1    $(\frac{2}{5})^2 + 0.5^2 = 0.4^2 + 0.5^2 = 0.16 + 0.25 = 0.41$

2    $4^5 \times (\frac{1}{4})^3 = \frac{4^5}{4^3} = 4^2 = 16$

3    $14.2^4 + 14.2^{\frac{1}{4}}$ $= 40,658.69 + 1.94$

     $= 40,660.63$

4 y $= 3x + 7$ (1)
    $4y$ $= -12x + 11$ (2)
    $4y$ $= 12x + 28$ (3) $((1) \times 4)$
    $8y$ $= 39$ (4) $((2) + (3))$
    y $= 4.875$ (5)
    $4.875 = 3x + 7$ (6) (from (1))
    $-2.125 = 3x$ (7)
    x $= -0.70833$ (8)

5 $2x^2 + 6x - 56 = 0$

$$x = \frac{-6 \pm \sqrt{[6^2 - 4 \times 2 \times (-56)]}}{2 \times 2}$$

$$= (-6 \pm \sqrt{484})/4$$

$$= (-6 \pm 22)/4$$

$$= 4 \text{ or } -7$$

6 $\begin{pmatrix} 3 + 8 + 54 & -6 - 2 + 108 \\ 6 - 16 - 12 & -12 + 4 - 24 \end{pmatrix} = \begin{pmatrix} 65 & 100 \\ -22 & -32 \end{pmatrix}$

7 $\dfrac{1}{(-2) \times (-4) - 4 \times 1} \begin{pmatrix} -4 & -4 \\ -1 & -2 \end{pmatrix} = \begin{pmatrix} -1 & -1 \\ -0.25 & -0.5 \end{pmatrix}$

2 COLLECTING DATA

Signpost

This chapter introduces statistics, which is all about collecting and manipulating data to get useful information. We will classify types of data according to the type of information they give. We can say whether an animal is a dog or a cat without taking a measurement - its species is an attribute. But we measure its length, and its length is a variable. We will also classify data according to whether they were collected for the current purpose (primary data) or for some other purpose (secondary data). Finally, we will look at how to take a sample (a selection of data) when we cannot look at all of the available data.

Your objectives

After completing this chapter you should:

(a) understand the different meanings of the word 'statistics';

(b) be able to distinguish between attributes, discrete variables and continuous variables, and between primary and secondary data;

(c) know how a random sample is selected;

(d) know several other methods of sampling.

1 Using statistics

The word 'statistics' has three meanings.

(a) Firstly, it is used to describe a group of figures. For example, figures relating to a country's imports and exports are often referred to as 'trade statistics' and the figures kept by cricket commentators on past matches are called 'statistics'.

(b) Secondly, it means the methods by which data (that is, *numbers* obtained as a result of counting or measuring something) are presented. A large mass of meaningless data can be condensed into a more readily understandable form.

(c) Thirdly, it has come to mean the way in which the data are interpreted, once they have been presented in a satisfactory form.

The subject called statistics therefore covers collecting data, presenting them in a useful form and interpreting them.

BPP Publishing

The main advantage of statistics is that it offers methods which can be used to make sense of numbers. In a business environment, for example, a manager may collect all sorts of data on production levels, costs or sales, but on their own the numbers are unlikely to mean very much. By using statistics, a manager can try to make sense out of the numbers, which in turn should help in making sensible business decisions.

Statistical results can rarely be completely certain. For example, suppose light bulbs are produced by a factory in batches of 100. Using data on past batches, statistics might show that seven out of every batch of bulbs are faulty and fail to light up. But nobody could say that there will *always* be seven faulty bulbs in a batch. Sometimes there will be fewer, and sometimes more. But at least statistics can give some guidance on how many bulbs are wasted, which can help a manager to estimate production costs.

2   Types of data

The data gathered for a particular purpose may be of several types. The first major distinction is between *attributes* and *variables*.

(a)   An attribute is something an object has either got or not got. It cannot be measured on a scale. For example, an individual is either male or female. There is no measure of *how* male or *how* female somebody is: the sex of a person is an attribute. Data on attributes may be called *categorical data* or *nominal data*.

(b)   A variable is something which can be measured. For example, the height of a person can be measured according to some scale (such as centimetres).

Variables can be further classified as discrete or continuous.

(a)   *Discrete* variables can only take specific values. The range of possible values is split into a series of steps. For example, the number of cars made in a factory may be 1,000 or 1,005 but it cannot be 1,000.3 or 1,005.27.

(b)   *Continuous* variables may take on any value within a range. They are measured rather than counted. For example, it may be considered sufficient to measure the quantity of paint used on a car to the nearest millilitre but there is no reason why the measurements should not be made to the nearest microlitre.

An alternative classification of variables, which can apply to both discrete and continuous variables, is into those measured on an ordinal scale, those measured on an interval scale and those measured on a ratio scale.

(a)   An *ordinal scale* is one which puts items in order, but does not allow comparisons to be made between values. Thus five athletes might be ranked first, second, third, fourth and fifth, but we cannot (on the basis of this information alone) say anything such as that the difference between the performances of the athletes who came first and second was half as great as the difference between the performances of the athletes who came third and fifth. It would be silly to reach such a conclusion on the basis that 5 - 3 = 2 is twice as big as 2 - 1 = 1.

(b)   An *interval scale* is one where the differences between pairs of values can be compared, but there is no meaningful zero point. Thus if you measure the positions of emergency telephones on the M25 (an orbital motorway around London) by taking their distances clockwise around the motorway from the junction for Brighton, you might find that telephone A is 30km from that junction, telephone B is 40km from that junction and telephone C is 70km from that junction. It is meaningful to say that the distance between telephones B and C is three times the distance between telephones A and B, but there is nothing significant about the values 30km, 40km and 70km. We could just as easily have measured from the junction for Woking, and come up with 10km, 20km and 50km.

(c)   A *ratio scale* is one where the differences between pairs of values can be compared, *and* there is a meaningful zero. Thus salaries are measured on a ratio scale, because there is a meaningful zero, a salary of £0, and we can say that a salary of £17,500 is 1.75 times as high as one of £10,000.

Exercise 1

Look through the following list of surveys and decide whether each is collecting data on attributes, discrete variables, or continuous variables.

(a)   A survey of statistics books, to determine how many diagrams they contain

(b)   A survey of cans on a supermarket shelf, to determine whether or not each has a price sticker on it

(c)   A survey of athletes, to find out how long they take to run a mile

(d)   A survey of the results of an examination, to determine what percentage marks the students obtained

(e)   A survey of the heights of telegraph poles in England, to find out if there is any variation across the country

Primary data and secondary data

The data used in a statistical survey, whether variables or attributes, can be either primary data or secondary data.

(a)   Primary data are data collected especially for the purpose of whatever survey is being conducted. Thus a production manager might collect data on overtime hours worked especially for a report on the cost of overtime. *Raw data* are primary data which have not been processed at all, but are still just (for example) a list of numbers.

(b)   *Secondary data* are data which have already been collected elsewhere, for some other purpose, but which can be used or adapted for the survey being conducted. Thus a marketing manager might use published trade statistics to evaluate possible markets abroad.

An advantage of using primary data is that the investigator knows where the data came from, the circumstances under which they were collected, and any limitations or inadequacies in the data.

In contrast, with secondary data:

(a) any limitations in the data might not be known to the investigator, because he or she did not collect them;

(b) the data might not be entirely suitable for the purpose they are being used for.

Secondary data are sometimes used despite their inadequacies, simply because they are available cheaply whereas the extra cost of collecting primary data would far outweigh their extra value.

Primary data have to be gathered from a source. Methods of collecting primary data include:

(a) personal investigation;
(b) teams of investigators;
(c) questionnaires.

Collecting primary data: personal investigation

Personal investigation involves the investigator collecting all the data himself, for example by interviewing people, or by looking through historical records. Interviews might include questions like 'How much do you earn?' and 'Do you drive a Ford motor car?'

This method of collecting data is time consuming, expensive and limited to the amount of data a single person can collect. On the other hand, personal investigation has the advantage that the data collected are likely to be accurate and complete, because the investigator knows exactly what he wants and how to get it. He is not relying on other people to do the survey work.

Collecting primary data: teams of investigators

A survey could be carried out by a team of investigators who collect data separately and then pool their results.

A team of investigators can cover a larger field than personal investigation but will still be expensive. The members of the team must be carefully briefed to ensure that the data they collect are satisfactory. This method is sometimes called delegated personal investigation.

Collecting primary data: questionnaires

With a questionnaire, the questions which need to be answered for the survey are listed and are either sent to a number of people (so that they can fill in their answers and send the questionnaires back) or used by investigators to interview people (perhaps by approaching people in the street and asking them the questions).

Questionnaires can provide a quick and cheap method of conducting a survey but suffer from several defects which may lead to biased results.

(a)   The people completing the forms (the respondents) may place different interpretations on the questions. This problem will be aggravated if the questions are badly phrased.

(b)   Large numbers of forms may not be returned or may only be returned partly completed. This may well lead to biased results as the people replying are likely to be those most interested in the survey.

(c)   Respondents may give false or misleading information if, for example, they have forgotten material facts or want to give a favourable impression.

In addition, if the questionnaire is being used by an interviewer (on the telephone or in the street), then the following problems could arise.

(a)   The interviewer may not really understand the questions.

(b)   The interviewer may not understand the replies, or may note down replies wrongly because of personal bias.

Before a questionnaire is designed the following points should be clarified.

(a)   The target population

(b)   The main items of information required and the form it should be in for subsequent analysis

(c)   Any subsidiary information which would be of interest (for example so that the responses of men and women or old and young can be compared)

(d)   Whether the questionnaire will be filled in by the respondent or by an interviewer. This determines how 'user-friendly' it needs to be.

Each question to be included in the questionnaire should be considered in detail.

(a)   Is it really necessary?

(b)   Is it posed in a way that will provide the information and any subsequent analysis that is required?

(c)   Will interviewers be able to read out the words, or will they need to 'ad lib', which might introduce bias?

(d)   Is the question posed in a neutral, unbiased way or is it a 'leading' question which inclines respondents towards a particular answer?

(e)   Are respondents likely to find the question too personal or offensive? Can it be reworded to reduce the risk of this happening?

(f)   Is it unambiguous?

(g)   Is the question worded in a way that the respondents will understand?

(h) Open questions are difficult to analyse. An open question might be worded like this.

'How did you travel to work today?'

The responses may be so numerous that analysis becomes onerous and time consuming. The designer of the questionnaire should instead try to offer a full range of possible responses to the question, perhaps like this.

'Please indicate how you travelled to work today.

By bus	☐
By train	☐
By private car	☐
On foot	☐
By bicycle/motorcycle	☐
I did not go to work today (illness, holidays etc)	☐
I work at home	☐
I do not work	☐

Other (please give details) ....

The responses from this closed question will be much easier to analyse. It is important, however, to avoid putting such lists of responses in order of supposed popularity.

(i) Questions that require respondents to perform calculations should be avoided. A list of options would remove or reduce this.

Other general points to be borne in mind when designing a questionnaire are as follows.

(a) If respondents have to complete the questionnaire themselves, it must be approachable and as short as possible. The use of lines, boxes, different type faces, print sizes and small pictures should be considered. Plenty of space should be used.

(b) Tick boxes can be used but it must be clear where ticks should go and how to respond in each case. For analysis, it should be easy to transfer responses from the forms to a summary sheet or a computer.

(c) The purpose of the survey should be explained at the beginning of the questionnaire and where possible confidentiality should be guaranteed. The date by which it must be returned must be emphasised.

(d) The first questions should be quota control questions so that the interviewer can rapidly determine whether the interviewee is the right type of person. Quota control questions might, for example, identify whether the interviewee is employed or unemployed, under 40 or over 40 and so on. Such questions enable the interviewer to terminate worthless interviews as early as possible.

(e)   Questions should be in logical order as far as possible, but if difficult questions are necessary it may be more appropriate to put them at the end.

(f)   At the end of the questionnaire, the respondent should be thanked and it should be clear what should be done with the completed questionnaire.

(g)   A record of interviews that fail (for example not willing to respond, not in quota and so on) may need to be kept. If so, the interviewer should be provided with a form to note the failures and their responses or a space should be provided on the questionnaire for the interviewer to explain the termination of interviews.

Secondary data sources

Secondary data are data that were originally collected as primary data for one purpose, or for general use, but are now being used for another purpose. The Government, for example, collects data to help with making decisions about running the country, and makes these data available to the public.

Examples of secondary data include the following.

(a)   *Published statistics.* For example, the Government publishes statistics through the Central Statistical Office (CSO). The European Union (EU) and the United Nations also publish statistics. So do various newspapers.

(b)   *Historical records.* The type of historical record used for a survey obviously depends on what survey is being carried out. Someone producing an estimate of future company sales might use historical records of past sales.

Exercise 2

Which of the following are secondary data sources?

(a)   The *Monthly Digest of Statistics* published by the Central Statistical Office.

(b)   *Economic Trends* published by the Central Statistical Office.

(c)   Data collected for a survey of consumers through personal interviews with those consumers.

---

3   Sampling

Sampling is one of the most important subjects in statistics. In most practical situations the population (that is, everyone or everything we could collect data from) will be too large to carry out a complete survey and only a sample will be examined. An example of this is a poll taken to try to predict the results of an election. It is not possible to ask everyone of voting age how they are going to vote: it would take too long and cost too much. So a sample of voters is taken, and the results from the sample are used to estimate the voting intentions of the whole population. Occasionally a population is small enough that all of it can be examined: for example, the examination results of one class of students. When all of the population is examined, the survey is called a *census*. This type of survey is quite rare, however, and usually the investigator has to choose some sort of sample.

You may think that using a sample is very much a compromise, but you should consider the following points.

(a) In practice, a 100% survey (a census) never achieves the completeness required.

(b) A census may require the use of semi-skilled investigators, resulting in a loss of accuracy in the data collected.

(c) It can be shown mathematically that once a certain sample size has been reached, very little extra accuracy is gained by examining more items.

(d) It is possible to ask more questions with a sample.

(e) The higher cost of a census may exceed the value of results.

(f) Things are always changing. Even if you took a census it could well be out of date by the time you completed it.

One of the most important requirements of data is that they should be *complete*. That is, the data should cover all areas of the population to be examined. If this requirement is not met, then the sample will be biased.

For example, suppose you wanted to survey the productivity of workers in a factory, and you went along every Monday and Tuesday for a few months to measure their output. Would the data be complete? The answer is no. You might have gathered very thorough data on what happens on Mondays and Tuesdays, but you would have missed out the rest of the week. It could be that the workers, keen and fresh after the weekend, work better at the start of the week than at the end. If this is the case, then your data will give you a misleadingly high productivity figure.

Random sampling

A *random sample* is a sample selected in such a way that every item in the population has an equal chance of being included. The point of taking a random sample is to remove *bias*. A biased sample is unlikely to give us a good basis for learning about the population we are sampling from.

For example, if you wanted to take a random sample of library books, it would not be good enough to pick them off the shelves, even if you picked them at random. This is because the books which were out on loan would stand no chance of being chosen. You would either have to make sure that all the books were on the shelves before taking your sample, or find some other way of sampling (for example, using the library index cards).

A random sample is not necessarily a perfect sample. For example, you might pick what you believe to be a completely random selection of library books, and find that every one of them is a detective thriller. It is a remote possibility, but it could happen. The only way to eliminate the possibility altogether is to take a 100% survey (a census) of the books, which, unless it is a tiny library, is impractical.

Sampling frames

A sampling frame is simply a numbered list of all the items in the population. Once such a list has been made, it is easy to select a random sample, simply by generating a list of random numbers.

For instance, if you wanted to select a random sample of children from a school, it would be useful to have a list of names:

0   J Absolam
1   R Brown
2   S Brown
...

Now the numbers 0, 1, 2 and so on can be used to select the random sample. It is normal to start the numbering at 0, so that when 0 appears in a list of random numbers it can be used.

Sometimes it is not possible to draw up a sampling frame. For example, if you wanted to take a random sample of Americans, it would take too long to list all Americans.

Exercise 3

You want to take a random sample of all people who live in a particular area. Why would the electoral register not be an adequate sampling frame?

Assuming that a sampling frame *can* be drawn up, then a random sample can be picked from it by:

(a)   the lottery method, which amounts to picking numbered pieces of paper out of a box;
(b)   the use of random number tables.

Random number tables

Set out below is part of a typical random number table.

93716	16894	98953	73231
32886	59780	09958	18065
92052	06831	19640	99413
39510	35905	85244	35159
27699	06494	03152	19121
92962	61773	22109	78508
10274	12202	94205	50380
75867	20717	82037	10268
85783	47619	87481	37220

Example: random sampling

An investigator wishes to select a random sample from a population of 800 people, who have been numbered 000, 001, ...799. As there are three digits in 800 the random numbers will be selected in groups of three. Working along the first line of the table given above, the first few groups are as follows.

937   161   689   498   953   732

Numbers over 799 are discarded. The first four people in the sample will therefore be those numbered 161, 689, 498 and 732.

You should note the following points about random number tables.

(a) The sample is found by selecting groups of random numbers with numbers of digits reflecting the total population size, as follows.

Total population size	*Number of random digits*
1 - 10	1
11 - 100	2
101 - 1,000	3

The items selected for the sample are those corresponding to the random numbers selected.

(b) The starting point on the table should be selected at random. After that, however, numbers must be selected in a consistent manner. In other words, you should use the table row by row or column by column. By jumping around the table from places to place personal bias may be introduced.

(c) In many practical situations it is more convenient to use a computer to generate a list of random numbers, especially when a large sample is required.

Non-random sampling

In many situations it is either not possible or else too expensive to obtain a random sample. For example, it may not be possible to draw up a sampling frame. In such cases, non-random sampling has to be used.

The main methods of non-random sampling are:

(a) systematic sampling;
(b) stratified sampling;
(c) multistage sampling;
(d) quota sampling;
(e) cluster sampling.

Systematic sampling

Systematic sampling may provide a good approximation to random sampling. It works by selecting every nth item after a random start. For example, if it was decided to select a sample of 20 from a population of 800, then every 40th (800 ÷ 20) item after a random start in the first 40 should be selected. The starting point could be found using the lottery method or random number tables. If (say) 23 was chosen, then the sample would include the 23rd, 63rd, 103rd, 143rd ... 783rd items.

The gap of 40 is known as the *sampling interval.*

The investigator must ensure that there is no regular pattern to the population which, if it coincided with the sampling interval, might lead to a biased sample. In practice, this problem is often overcome by choosing multiple starting points and using varying sampling intervals whose size is selected at random.

Stratified sampling

In many situations *stratified sampling* is a good method of choosing a sample. The population must be divided into strata or categories.

If we took a random sample of all students in a university, it is conceivable that the entire sample might consist of business studies students. Stratified sampling removes this possibility as random samples could be taken from each type of student, the number in each sample being proportional to the total number of students of each type (for example students of business studies, engineering, languages and so on).

Example: stratified sampling

The number of students of each type in a particular university are as follows.

Business studies	500
Engineering	500
Languages	700
Mathematics	800
	2,500

If a sample of 250 is required, then 10% of each type should be selected by a random selection method, as follows.

50	business studies students
50	engineering students
70	languages students
80	mathematics students
250	

Exercise 4

An accountant is selecting a sample of invoices for checking. The invoices are numbered sequentially. The first invoice is selected randomly and is invoice number 3. He then selects invoice numbers 7, 11, 15, 19 and 23 to complete the sample. Is this stratified sampling or systematic sampling? What would you have said if the accountant had taken samples in the same way from invoices up to £500, invoices over £500 and up to £1,000 and invoices over £1,000?

Quantitative methods

Notes

Multistage sampling

Multistage sampling is normally used to cut down the number of investigators and the costs of obtaining a sample. An example will show how the method works.

Example: multistage sampling

A survey of spending habits is being planned to cover the whole of Britain. It is obviously impractical to draw up a sampling frame, so random sampling is not possible. Multi-stage sampling is to be used instead.

The country is divided into a number of areas and a small sample of these is selected at random. Each of the areas selected is subdivided into smaller units and again, a smaller number of these is selected at random. This process is repeated as many times as necessary and finally, a random sample of the relevant people living in each of the smallest units is taken. A fair approximation to a random sample can be obtained.

Thus, we might choose a random sample of eight areas, and from each of these areas, select a random sample of five towns. From each town, a random sample of 200 people might be selected so that the total sample size is 8 × 5 × 200 = 8,000 people.

Quota sampling

In *quota sampling*, investigators are told to interview all the people they meet up to a certain quota. A large degree of bias can be introduced accidentally. For example, an interviewer in a shopping centre may fill his quota by only meeting people who can go shopping during the week. In practice, this problem is partly overcome by subdividing the quota into different types of people, for example on the basis of age, sex and income.

Example: quota sampling

Consider the figures above, but with the following additional information relating to the sex of students.

	Male	Female
Business studies	300	200
Engineering	400	100
Languages	300	400
Mathematics	300	500

An investigator's quotas would be as follows.

	Male	Female	Total
Business studies	30	20	50
Engineering	40	10	50
Languages	30	40	70
Mathematics	30	50	80
			250

Using quota sampling, the investigator would interview the first 30 male business studies students that he met, the first 20 female business studies students that he met and so on.

One major advantage of quota sampling is that, although a fairly detailed knowledge of the characteristics of a population is required, it is not necessary to establish a sampling frame because the interviewer questions every person he meets up to the quota. In many practical situations, it will be either impossible or too expensive to compile a complete list of the population under study, and so quota sampling offers a cheaper and satisfactory alternative to random sampling.

Cluster sampling

Cluster sampling is similar to multistage sampling in that the population is divided up into small areas, but *every* item in a random selection of small areas is examined.

Cluster sampling benefits from low costs in the same way as multistage sampling.

Exercise 5

A publishing company carries out a national survey of adults' reading habits. To reduce travelling costs, the country is first divided into constituencies. A sample of 50 constituencies is then selected at random. Within each of these constituencies, 5 polling districts are selected, again using random techniques. Interviewers will visit a random selection of 30 people on the electoral register in each of the districts selected. What sampling method is the company using?

Chapter roundup

(a) 'Statistics' may refer to a group of figures, to ways of presenting them or to ways of interpreting them.

(b) Data may be collected on attributes or on variables. Variables may be either discrete or continuous. Variables may be measured on an ordinal scale, an interval scale or a ratio scale.

(c) Data may be primary or secondary. Primary data are more expensive to collect, but are more likely to suit the collector's precise purpose.

(d) Primary data may be collected using personal investigation, teams of investigators or questionnaires.

Quick quiz

1   What is the difference between an attribute and a variable?

2   Distinguish between discrete and continuous variables.

3   What is the difference between primary and secondary data?

4   What is a census?

5   What is a sampling frame?

6   What is quota sampling?

Solutions to exercises

1   (a)   The number of diagrams in a textbook is a *discrete variable*, because it can only be counted in whole number steps. You cannot, for example, have 26½ diagrams or 47.32 diagrams in a book.

    (b)   Whether or not a can possesses a sticker is an *attribute*. It is not something which can be measured. A can either possesses the attribute or it does not.

    (c)   How long an athlete takes to run a mile is a *continuous variable*, because the time recorded can in theory take any value, for example 4 minutes 2.0643 seconds.

    (d)   The percentage obtained in an examination is a *discrete variable*, taking whole number values between 0% and 100%. The discrete values might include half percent steps, if the examination is the sort where you could be awarded ½%. But it would not be possible to score, say, 62.32%, so the variable is not continuous.

    (e)   The height of a telegraph pole is a *continuous variable*.

2   Sources (a) and (b).

3   Children and people who have recently moved into the area are omitted; people who have recently left the area are still included.

4   Systematic sampling is being used. The alternative method proposed would be stratified sampling, with systematic sampling being used to select a sample from each stratum.

5   Multistage sampling.

---

3 PRESENTING DATA

Signpost

Once data have been collected, they need to be presented so as to make their significance clear. We will start this chapter by seeing how to present data in rows and columns (tables), and how to show how often different values occur (frequency distributions). We will then look at the use of repeated pictures to represent numbers (pictograms) and at how to show a total carved up into its components (pie charts). Bar charts use the lengths of bars to represent totals, and histograms use bars to show how often different values occur. A graph is a line (or several lines) drawn to show values by reference to two scales (axes). An ogive shows how the numbers of times values occur build up as we move through the values. Lorenz curves also show totals building up, and a Z chart shows a total building up over time.

Your objectives

After completing this chapter you should:

(a) know how to present data in tables and frequency distributions;
(b) be able to prepare and interpret pictograms, pie charts and bar charts;
(c) know how a histogram is drawn;
(d) know how graphs may be drawn to represent mathematical relationships;
(e) be able to draw ogives, and use them to find the median and the quartiles;
(f) know how Lorenz curves and Z charts are drawn.

1 Tables

Raw data (the list of results from a survey) need to be summarised and analysed, to give them meaning. This chapter is concerned with several different ways of presenting data to convey their meaning. We will start with one of the most basic ways, the preparation of a table.

Tabulation means putting data into tables. A table is a matrix of data in rows and columns, with the rows and the columns having titles.

Since a table is two-dimensional, it can only show two variables. For example, the resources required to produce items in one week in a factory could be tabulated, with one dimension (rows or columns) representing the items produced and the other dimension representing the resources.

                                                                 BPP Publishing

Quantitative methods

Resources for production, week 24: all figures in thousands of pounds
Product items

Resources	A	B	C	Total
Material A	20	14	7	41
Material B	35	20	18	73
Labour grade 1	7	12	8	27
Labour grade 2	3	9	19	31
Supervision	1	1	2	4
Machine time	12	3	4	19
Total	78	59	58	195

To tabulate data, you need to recognise what the two dimensions should represent, prepare rows and columns accordingly with suitable titles, and then insert the data into the appropriate places in the table.

Guidelines for tabulation

There are certain guidelines which you should apply when presenting data in tabular form. They are as follows.

(a) The table should be given a clear title.

(b) All columns should be clearly labelled.

(c) Where appropriate, there should be clear sub-totals.

(d) A total column may be presented; this would usually be the right-hand column.

(e) A total figure is often advisable at the bottom of each column of figures.

(f) Tables should not be packed with too much data so that reading the information is difficult.

Example: tables

The total number of employees in a certain trading company is 1,000. They are employed in three departments: production, administration and sales. 600 people are employed in the production department and 300 in administration. There are 110 male juveniles in employment, 110 female juveniles, and 290 adult females. The remaining employees are adult males.

In the production department there are 350 adult males, 150 adult females and 50 male juveniles, whilst in the administration department there are 100 adult males, 110 adult females and 50 juvenile males.

Draw up a table to show all the details of employment in the company and its departments and provide suitable secondary statistics to describe the distribution of people in departments.

Solution

The basic table required has the following two dimensions.

(a) Departments
(b) Age/sex analysis

Secondary statistics (not the same thing as secondary data) are supporting figures that are supplementary to the main items of data, and which clarify or amplify the main data. A major example of secondary statistics is percentages. In this example, we could show one of the following.

(a) The percentage of the total work force in each department belonging to each age/sex group.

(b) The percentage of the total of each age/sex group employed in each department.

In this example, (a) has been selected but you might consider that (b) would be more suitable. Either could be suitable, depending of course on what purposes the data are being collected and presented for.

Analysis of employees

	Production		Administration		Sales		Total	
	No	*%*	*No*	*%*	*No*	*%*	*No*	*%*
Adult males	350	58.4	100	33.3	40 **	40	490 *	49
Adult females	150	25.0	110	36.7	30 **	30	290	29
Male juveniles	50	8.3	50	16.7	10 **	10	110	11
Female juveniles	50 *	8.3	40 *	13.3	20 **	20	110	11
	600	100.0	300	100.0	100	100	1,000	100

*   Balancing figure to make up the column total

**   Balancing figure then needed to make up the row total

Exercise 1

(a) Convert the information given below into tabulur form.

The number of telephones installed in a country in 1960 was 5,246,000. Ten years later in 1970 the number was 6,830,000, and by 1980 the total installed in that year was 12,654,000. Another ten years later the number for 1990 was 10,194,000. In 1960 B Co Ltd saw 2,114,000 of its telephones installed, more than any other kind; A Co Ltd was second with 1,810,000; C Co Ltd third with 448,000; and the 'all others' group accounted for 874,000. In 1970 A Co Ltd was in first position with 3,248,000; C Co Ltd was second with 1,618,000; B Co Ltd third with 1,288,000; and the 'all others group' installed fewer telephones than ten years earlier: 676,000. In 1980 A Co Ltd installations alone, 5,742,000, exceeded total installations of just 20 years earlier. B Co Ltd was in second position with 3,038,000; C Co Ltd third with 2,228,000; and the 'all others' group installed just 1,646,000. 1990 data indicated that relative positions remained the same as 1980 with A Co Ltd at 4,932,000, B Co Ltd at 3,138,000, C Co Ltd at 1,506,000 and 'all others' at 618,000.

(b)   Interpret the data in (a) by calculating and further tabulating appropriate percentages to show comparisons of the telephone installations by the producers in the four years given.

(c)   Comment on the percentage trends in (b).

Tally marks

Tally marks are another simple way of presenting data. If we measured the number of jobs completed by each employee during one week, the data could be collected and presented as follows.

Employee	*Jobs completed*	
A	///// ////	= 9
B	///// ///// ////	= 14
C	///// //	= 7
D	///	= 3

2   Frequency distributions

If a large number of measurements of a particular variable is taken (for example the number of units produced per employee per week) some values may occur more than once. A *frequency distribution* is obtained by recording the number of times each value occurs.

Example: a frequency distribution

The output in units of 20 employees during one week was as follows.

```
65   69   70   71   70   68   69   67   70   68
72   71   69   74   70   73   71   67   69   70
```

If the number of occurrences is placed against each output quantity, a frequency distribution is produced.

Output of employees in one week in units

Output Units	*Number of employees (frequency)*
65	1
66	0
67	2
68	2
69	4
70	5
71	3
72	1
73	1
74	1
	20

The number of employees corresponding to a particular volume of output is called a *frequency*.

Exercise 2

What are the most common and the least common (but achieved at least once) volumes of output in the above frequency distribution?

Grouped frequency distributions

It is often convenient to group frequencies together into bands or classes. For example, suppose that the output produced by each of 20 employees during one week was as follows, in units.

1,087	850	1,084	792
924	1,226	1,012	1,205
1,265	1,028	1,230	1,182
1,086	1,130	989	1,155
1,134	1,166	1,129	1,160

An ungrouped frequency distribution would not be a helpful way of presenting the data, because each employee has produced a different number of units in the week.

The range of output from the lowest to the highest producer is 792 to 1,265, a range of 473 units. This range could be divided into classes of say, 100 units (the *class width* or *class interval*), and the number of employees producing output within each class could then be grouped into a single frequency, as follows.

Output Units	Number of employees (frequency)
700 - 799	1
800 - 899	1
900 - 999	2
1,000 - 1,099	5
1,100 - 1,199	7
1,200 - 1,299	4
	20

Stem-and-leaf diagrams

A stem-and-leaf diagram is an alternative to a grouped frequency distribution. It has the merit of showing the exact values but still gives a good idea of the overall shape of the distribution. Each class of values is given a line, and the digits common to all values in that class are shown at the start of the line. The remaining digits for each actual value are then shown along the line with the values in ascending order. Thus for the above example, the class 900-999 includes 924 and 989, and its line would be shown as follows.

09   24 89

The complete diagram for the above example would be as follows.

07	92					
08	50					
09	24	89				
10	12	28	84	86	87	
11	29	30	34	55	60	66	82
12	05	26	30	65		

Grouped frequency distributions of continuous variables

Grouped frequency distributions can be used to present data for continuous variables.

Example: a grouped frequency distribution for a continuous variable

Suppose we wish to record the heights of 50 different individuals. The information might be presented as a grouped frequency distribution, as follows.

Height cm	*Number of individuals (frequency)*
Up to and including 154	1
Over 154, up to and including 163	3
Over 163, up to and including 172	8
Over 172, up to and including 181	16
Over 181, up to and including 190	18
Over 190	4
	50

Note the following points.

(a)   It would be wrong to show the ranges as 0 - 154, 154 - 163, 163 - 172 and so on, because 154 cm and 163 cm would then be values in two classes, which is not permissible.

(b)   There is an *open ended class* at each end of the range. This is because heights up to 154 cm and over 190 cm are thought to be uncommon, so that a single 'open ended' class is used to group all the frequencies together.

Preparing grouped frequency distributions

To prepare a grouped frequency distribution, a decision must be made about how wide each class should be. You should generally observe the following guidelines.

(a)   The upper and lower limits of each class interval should be suitable 'round' numbers, for class intervals which are in multiples of 5, 10, 100, 1,000 and so on. For example, if the class interval is 10, and data items range in value from 23 to 62 (discrete values) the class intervals should be 20-29, 30-39, 40-49, 50-59 and 60-69, rather than 23-32, 33-42, 43-52 and 53-62.

(b) With continuous variables, either:

(i) the upper limit of a class should be 'up to and including ...' (the mathematical symbol for which is ≤) and the lower limit of the next class should be 'over ...' (symbol >); or

(ii) the upper limit of a class should be 'less than ...' (symbol <), and the lower limit of the next class should be 'at least ...' (symbol ≥).

Exercise 3

The commission earnings for May 1993 of the assistants in a department store were as follows (in pounds).

60	35	53	47	25	44	55	58	47	71
63	67	57	44	61	48	50	56	61	42
43	38	41	39	61	51	27	56	57	50
55	68	55	50	25	48	44	43	49	73
53	35	36	41	45	71	56	40	69	52
36	47	66	52	32	46	44	32	52	58
49	41	45	45	48	36	46	42	52	33
31	36	40	66	53	58	60	52	66	51
51	44	59	53	51	57	35	45	46	54
46	54	51	39	64	43	54	47	60	45

Prepare a grouped frequency distribution classifying the commission earnings into categories of £5 commencing with '£25 and under £30'.

Cumulative frequency distributions

A cumulative frequency distribution can be used to show the total number of times that a value above or below a certain amount occurs.

Example: cumulative frequency distributions

The volume of output produced in one day by each of 20 employees is as follows, in units.

18	29	22	17
30	12	27	24
26	32	24	29
28	46	31	27
19	18	32	25

Notes

We could present a grouped frequency distribution as follows.

Output Units	Number of employees (frequency)
Under 15	1
15 or more, under 20	4
20 or more, under 25	3
25 or more, under 30	7
30 or more, under 35	4
35 or more	1
	20

The two possible cumulative frequency distributions for the same data are as follows.

	Cumulative frequency		Cumulative frequency
$\geq$ 0	20	<15	1
$\geq$ 15	19	<20	5
$\geq$ 20	15	<25	8
$\geq$ 25	12	<30	15
$\geq$ 30	5	<35	19
$\geq$ 35	1	<47	20

Notes

(a) The symbol > means 'greater than' and $\geq$ means 'greater than or equal to'.
The symbol < means 'less than' and $\leq$ means 'less than or equal to'.

These symbols provide a convenient method of stating classes.

(b) The first cumulative frequency distribution shows that of the total of 20 employees:

(i)   19 produced 15 units or more;
(ii) 15 produced 20 units or more;
(iii) 12 produced 25 units or more;

and so on.

Exercise 4

Using the second cumulative frequency distribution, how many employees produced:

(a)   under 15 units?
(b)   under 20 units?
(c)   under 25 units?

---

3   Charts

Instead of presenting data in a table, it might be preferable to give a visual display in the form of a chart.

The purpose of a chart is to convey the data in a way that will demonstrate its meaning or significance more clearly than a table of data would. Charts are not always more appropriate than tables, and the most suitable way of presenting data will depend on:

(a)   what the data are intended to show. Visual displays usually make one or two points quite forcefully, whereas tables usually give more detailed information;

(b)   who is going to use the data. Some individuals might understand visual displays more readily than tabulated data.

Types of chart that might be used to present data are:

(a)   pictograms;
(b)   pie charts;
(c)   bar charts.

We shall look at each of these in turn.

Pictograms

A pictogram is a statistical diagram in which quantities are represented by pictures or symbols.

Example: pictograms

A pictogram showing the number of employees at a factory would represent the quantities of employees using pictures of people.

Number of employees

In this example, each picture represents ten employees, and to represent a smaller quantity, a part-picture can be drawn. Here, there were 45 men employed in 19X6.

The advantage of pictograms is that they present data in a simple, readily understood way. Pictograms convey their message to the reader at a glance, and are consequently often used on television and in advertisements.

The disadvantages of pictograms are that they can only convey a limited amount of information, and that they lack precision. Each symbol must represent quite a large number of items, otherwise a pictogram would contain too many symbols. Using portions of a symbol to represent smaller quantities gives some extra precision, but not much.

Pie charts

A pie chart is used to show pictorially the relative size of component elements of a total. It is called a pie chart because it is circular, and so has the shape of a pie in a round pie dish and because the 'pie' is then cut into slices. Each slice represents a part of the total.

Pie charts have sectors of varying sizes, and you need to be able to draw sectors fairly accurately. To do this, you need a protractor. Working out sector sizes involves converting parts of the total into equivalent degrees of a circle.

Example: pie charts

The costs of production at Factory A and Factory B during March 1992 were as follows.

	Factory A		Factory B	
	£'000	%	£'000	%
Direct materials	70	35	50	20
Direct labour	30	15	125	50
Production overhead	90	45	50	20
Office costs	10	5	25	10
	200	100	250	100

Show the costs for the factories in pie charts.

Solution

To convert the components into degrees of a circle, we can use either the percentage figures or the actual cost figures. We will use the former.

Using the percentage figures, the total percentage is 100%, and the total number of degrees in a circle is 360°. To convert from one to the other, we multiply each percentage value by 360°/100% = 3.6.

	Factory A		Factory B	
	%	Degrees	%	Degrees
Direct materials	35	126	20	72
Direct labour	15	54	50	180
Production overhead	45	162	20	72
Office costs	5	18	10	36
	100	360	100	360

Exercise 5

Using the actual cost figures, we would multiply each cost by

$\dfrac{\text{Number of degrees}}{\text{Total cost}}$

Prepare tables of workings using this method.

A pie chart could be drawn for each factory, as follows. A protractor is used to measure the degrees accurately to obtain the correct sector sizes.

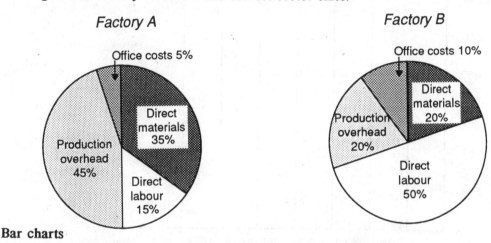

Bar charts

The bar chart is one of the most common methods of presenting data in a visual form. It is a chart in which quantities are shown in the form of bars. The three main types of bar chart are:

(a) simple bar charts
(b) component bar charts, including percentage component bar charts;
(c) multiple (or compound) bar charts.

Simple bar charts

A simple bar chart is a chart consisting of one or more bars, in which the length of each bar indicates the size of the corresponding data item.

Example: a simple bar chart

A company's total sales for the years from 19X1 to 19X6 are as follows.

Year	£'000
19X1	800
19X2	1,200
19X3	1,100
19X4	1,400
19X5	1,600
19X6	1,700

The data could be shown on a simple bar chart as follows.

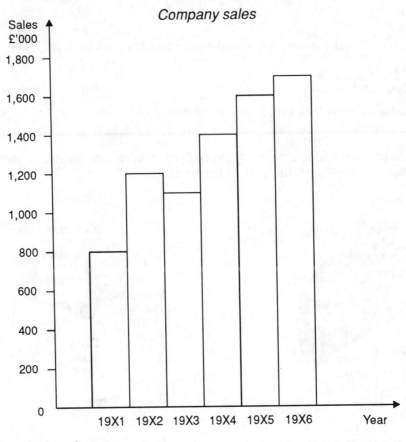

Company sales

Component bar charts

A component bar chart is a bar chart that gives a breakdown of each total into its components.

Example: a component bar chart

Charbart plc's sales for the years from 19X7 to 19X9 are as follows.

	19X7 £'000	19X8 £'000	19X9 £'000
Product A	1,000	1,200	1,700
Product B	900	1,000	1,000
Product C	500	600	700
Total	2,400	2,800	3,400

A component bar chart would show:

(a) how total sales have changed from year to year;
(b) the components of each year's total.

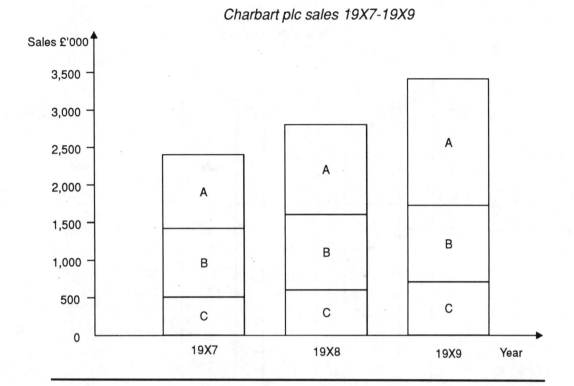

Charbart plc sales 19X7-19X9

Exercise 6

In what way is it hard to interpret the above component bar chart?

The bars in a bar chart can either be drawn side by side, with no gap between them, or with gaps between them, as in the diagram here. It does not matter which method is used.

Percentage component bar charts

The difference between a component bar chart and a percentage component bar chart is that with a component bar chart, the total length of each bar (and the length of each component in it) indicates magnitude. A bigger amount is shown by a longer bar. With a percentage component bar chart, total magnitudes are not shown. If two or more bars are drawn on the chart, the total length of each bar is the same. The only varying lengths in a percentage component bar chart are the lengths of the sections of a bar, which vary according to the relative sizes of the components.

Example: a percentage component bar chart

The information in the previous example of sales of Charbart plc could have been shown in a percentage component bar chart as follows.

BPP Publishing

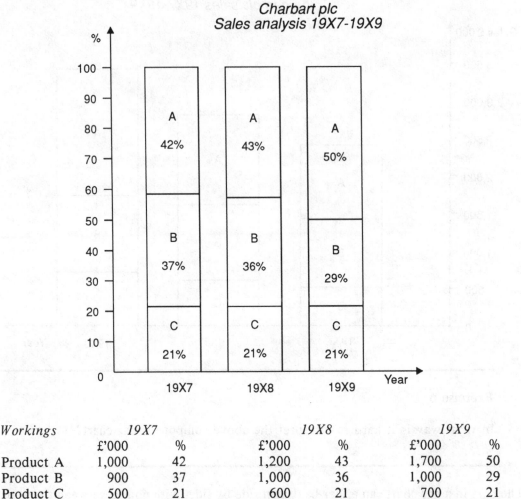

Charbart plc
Sales analysis 19X7-19X9

Workings	19X7		19X8		19X9	
	£'000	%	£'000	%	£'000	%
Product A	1,000	42	1,200	43	1,700	50
Product B	900	37	1,000	36	1,000	29
Product C	500	21	600	21	700	21
Total	2,400	100	2,800	100	3,400	100

Multiple bar charts (compound bar charts)

A multiple bar chart (or compound bar chart) is a bar chart in which two or more separate bars are used to present sub-divisions of data.

Example: a multiple bar chart

The output of Rodd Ltd in the years from 19X6 to 19X8 is as follows.

	19X6 '000 units	19X7 '000 units	19X8 '000 units
Product X	180	130	50
Product Y	90	110	170
Product Z	180	180	125
Total	450	420	345

The data could be shown in a multiple bar chart as follows.

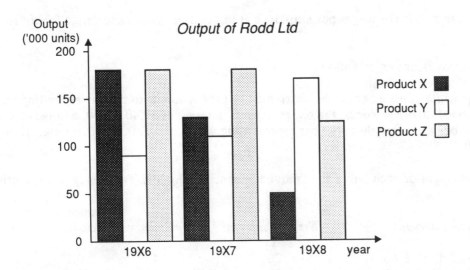

A multiple bar chart uses several bars for each total. In the above example, the sales in each year are shown as three separate bars, one for each product, X, Y and Z.

Exercise 7

Which important figures are not immediately obvious from the above chart, although available in the data?

Multiple bar charts are sometimes drawn with the bars horizontal instead of vertical.

4   Histograms

Histograms look rather like bar charts, but there are important differences. They are used when *grouped data of a continuous variable* are presented. They can also be used for discrete data, by treating the data as continuous so there are no gaps between class intervals: for example with a   cricketer's scores in various games, using ⩾ 0 < 10, ⩾ 10 < 20 and so on, instead of 0-9, 10-19 and so on.

The number of observations in a class is represented by the *area* covered by the bar, rather than   by its height.

Example: a histogram

The weekly wages of employees of Salt Lake Ltd are as follows.

Wages per employee	Number of employees
> £ 40 ⩽ £ 60	4
> £ 60 ⩽ £ 80	6
> £ 80 ⩽ £ 90	6
> £ 90 ⩽ £120	6
> £120 ⩽ £150	3

49

The class intervals for wages per employee are not all the same, and range from £10 to £30.

A histogram is drawn as follows.

(a) The *width* of each bar on the chart must be proportionate to the corresponding class interval. In other words, the bar representing wages of > £40 ≤ £60, a range of £20, will be twice as wide as the bar representing wages of > £80 ≤ £90, a range of only £10.

(b) The *height* of each bar is the frequency density which is (frequency/class width).

Class interval	Size of interval £	Frequency	Frequency density
> £ 40 ≤ £ 60	20	4	0.2
> £ 60 ≤ £ 80	20	6	0.3
> £ 80 ≤ £ 90	10	6	0.6
> £ 90 ≤ £120	30	6	0.2
> £120 ≤ £150	30	3	0.1

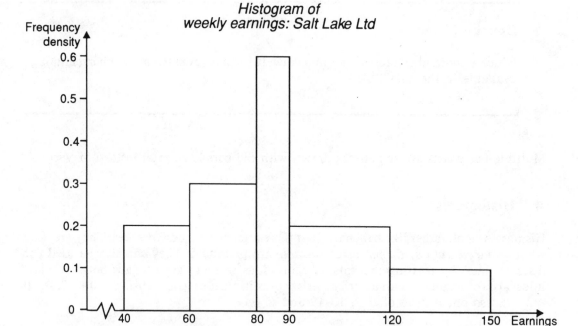

Histogram of weekly earnings: Salt Lake Ltd

Exercise 8

The sales force of a company just completed a successful sales campaign. The performances of individual sales staff have been analysed as follows, into a grouped frequency distribution.

Sales £'000	Number of sales staff
> 4 ≤ 10	1
> 10 ≤ 12	10
> 12 ≤ 14	12
> 14 ≤ 18	8
> 18 ≤ 22	4
> 22 ≤ 28	1

Draw a histogram from this information.

5 Drawing graphs

Graphs are a form of visual display. A graph shows, by means of either a straight line or a curve, the relationship between two variables. In particular, it shows how the value of one variable changes given changes in the value of the other variable.

For example, a graph might show how:

(a) sales turnover changes over time;
(b) a country's population changes over time;
(c) total costs of production vary with the number of units produced.

The variable whose value is influenced by the value of the other variable is referred to as the *dependent variable*. In the examples above, sales turnover, population and total costs would be the dependent variables in (a), (b) and (c) respectively.

The variable whose value affects the value of the dependent variable is known as the *independent variable*. In the examples above, these are time in (a) and (b) and number of units produced in (c).

The relationship between variables can often be presented more clearly in graph form than in a table of figures, and this is why graphs are so commonly used.

The rules for drawing graphs

A graph has a horizontal axis, the x axis and a vertical axis, the y axis. The x axis is used to represent the independent variable (the one which varies of its own accord) and the y axis is used to represent the dependent variable (the one which is influenced by the other variable). Thus if a graph of sales against advertising expenditure were drawn, advertising expenditure would be the independent variable and sales would be the dependent variable, because advertising affects sales.

If time is one variable, it is always treated as the independent variable. When time is represented by the x axis on a graph, we have a *time series*.

The scales on each axis should be selected so as to use as much of the graph paper as possible. Do not cramp a graph into one corner. In some cases it is best not to start a scale at zero so as to avoid having a large area of wasted paper. This is perfectly acceptable as long as the scale adopted is clearly shown on the axis. One way of avoiding confusion is to break the axis concerned, as follows.

BPP Publishing

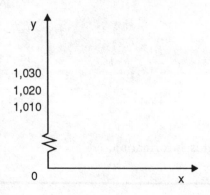

Example: drawing graphs

Plot the graph for $y = x^2 + 110$. Consider the range of values from $x = 0$ to $x = 10$

Solution

The first step is to draw up a table of values. Although the problem mentions $x = 0$ to $x = 10$, it is not necessary to calculate values of y for $x = 1, 2, 3$ etc. Start with a few values, calculating more only if it appears that this will lead to a smoother graph.

x	y
0	110
2	114
4	126
6	146
8	174
10	210

Graph of y = x²+ 110

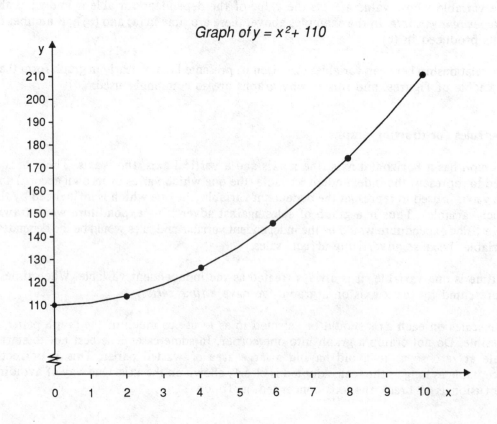

In this graph we are only interested in the range y = 110 to y = 210. For this reason, the y axis has been broken so as to avoid a large area of unused graph paper.

Exercise 9

If, in the graph above, we had wanted to go up to x = 20, what would have been the greatest value of y we would have had to allow for?

---

6 Types of graph

Having considered the rules for constructing graphs, we shall now turn to various ways of presenting statistical data in graphical form.

We shall look at:

(a) ogives;
(b) Lorenz curves;
(c) Z charts.

Ogives

An ogive, also known as a cumulative frequency curve, shows the cumulative number of items with a value less than or equal to, or alternatively greater than or equal to a certain amount.

Example: a 'less than' ogive

Consider the following frequency distribution derived from a quality control process in a factory.

Number of faulty units (per box of 100 units) rejected on inspection	Frequency	Cumulative frequency
1	5	5
2	5	10
3	3	13
4	1	14
	14	

An ogive would be drawn as follows.

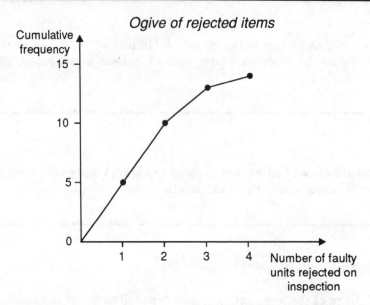

The ogive is drawn by plotting the cumulative frequencies on the graph, and joining them with straight lines.

For grouped frequency distributions, where we work up through values of the variable, the cumulative frequencies are plotted against the *upper* limits of the classes. For example:

(a) for the class 'over 200, up to and including 250', the cumulative frequency should be plotted against 250;

(b) for the class 'from 100 up to but not including 150' the cumulative frequency for a continuous variable should be plotted against 150. For a discrete variable, it would be plotted against the highest value less than 150, probably 149.

Exercise 10

A grouped frequency distribution for the volume of output produced at a factory over a period of 40 weeks is as follows.

Output Units	Number of times output achieved
> 0 ≤ 200	4
> 200 ≤ 400	8
> 400 ≤ 600	12
> 600 ≤ 800	10
> 800 ≤ 1,000	6
	40

Draw an appropriate ogive, and estimate the number of weeks in which output was 550 units or less.

We can also draw ogives to show the cumulative number of items with values greater than or equal to some given value.

Example: a 'greater than' ogive

Output at a factory over a period of 80 weeks is shown by the following frequency distribution.

Output per week Units	Number of times output achieved
> 0 ≤ 100	10
> 100 ≤ 200	20
> 200 ≤ 300	25
> 300 ≤ 400	15
> 400 ≤ 500	10
	80

If we wished to draw an ogive to show the number of weeks in which output exceeded a certain value, the cumulative total would begin at 80 and drop to 0.

In drawing an ogive when we work down through values of the variable, the descending cumulative frequency should be plotted against the lower limit of each class interval.

Lower limit of interval	Frequency	Cumulative ('more than') frequency
0	10	80
100	20	70
200	25	50
300	15	25
400	10	10
500	0	0

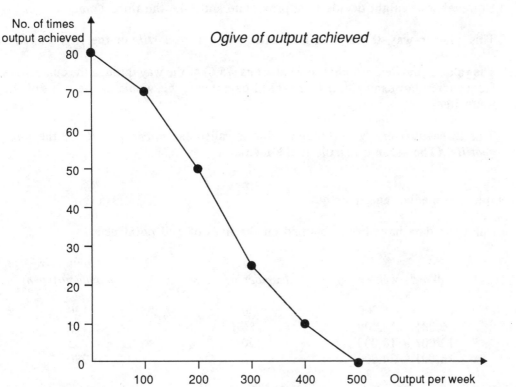

Ogive of output achieved

Make sure that you understand what this curve shows. For example, 350 on the x axis corresponds with about 18 on the y-axis. This means that output of 350 units *or more* was achieved 18 times out of the 80 weeks.

BPP Publishing

What information does an ogive provide?

An ogive represents a cumulative frequency distribution and it can be used to show what range of values contain given proportions of the total population. For example, it can be used to find:

(a)   the range of values which includes the first 50% of the population;
(b)   the range of values which includes the middle 50% of the population.

These particular pieces of information can be obtained by finding the following from the ogive (whether a 'greater than' ogive or a 'less than' ogive).

(a)   The value of the middle item in the range, corresponding to a cumulative frequency of 50% of the *total*. For example, if there are 11 data items, the middle item would be the sixth. If there are ten data items, we would take the fifth item.

   The middle item of n data items is the [(n + 1)/2]th where n is an odd number and the (n/2)th where n is an even number (it is not usually worth worrying about the fact that when n is even, there are two items which are equally 'in the middle').

   The value of the middle item is called the *median* value.

(b)   The value of the item which is a quarter (25%) of the way through the cumulative frequencies (running from low values up to high values). For example, if there are 11 data items, this would be the third item. If there are ten data items, it would be taken as the mid-way point between the second and third items: the '2½th' item. However, one might decide to approximate and take the third item.

   This quarter-way-through item is called the *lower quartile* or the *first quartile*.

(c)   The value of the item which is three quarters (75%) of the way through the cumulative frequencies. For example, if there are 11 data items, this would be the value of the ninth item.

   This three-quarters-way-through value is called the *upper quartile* or the *third quartile*. (The second quartile is the median.)

Example: the median and quartiles

The following data have been obtained on the lives of ball point pens.

Words written	Number of pens	Cumulative number of pens
0 - 6,000	30	30
6,001 - 12,000	85	115
12,001 - 18,000	120	235
18,001 - 24,000	45	280

Draw an ogive and find the median and first quartile number of words.

Solution

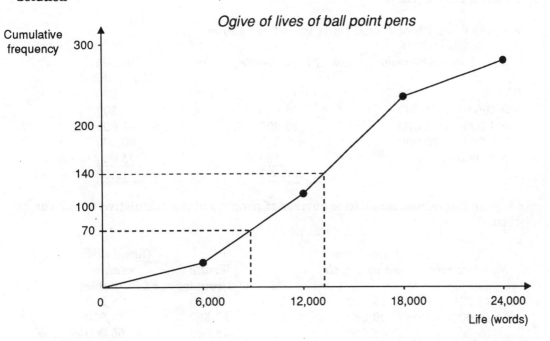

Ogive of lives of ball point pens

The median is found by drawing a line across from 280/2 = 140 and then down. It is about 13,250 words.

The first quartile is found by drawing a line across from 280/4 = 70 and then down. It is about 8,800 words.

Exercise 11

Use the last ogive above to find the third quartile.

Lorenz curves

A Lorenz curve is a form of cumulative frequency curve, which measures one cumulative amount against another. It is normal, though not essential, for both the x axis and the y axis to be shown in terms of percentages (each up to 100%).

A Lorenz curve shows degree of concentration. A common application of the Lorenz curve is to show the distribution of wealth. If the distribution is completely even, then there is no concentration of wealth in the population, and everyone has the same wealth. If the distribution is uneven, then the poorest half of the population will own less than half of the wealth between them.

Example: a Lorenz curve

The national wealth of Ruritania is spread as follows.

Wealth in roubles per person	No of people	Wealth '000 roubles
< 500	13,000	5,200
⩾ 500 < 1,000	16,000	12,800
⩾ 1,000 < 5,000	16,000	48,000
⩾ 5,000 < 40,000	2,000	50,000
⩾ 40,000	500	25,000
	47,500	141,000

From these figures the cumulative number of people and the cumulative wealth can be calculated.

No of people	Cumulative no of people	%	Wealth '000 roubles	Cumulative wealth '000 roubles	%
13,000	13,000	27	5,200	5,200	4
16,000	29,000	61	12,800	18,000	13
16,000	45,000	95	48,000	66,000	47
2,000	47,000	99	50,000	116,000	82
500	47,500	100	25,000	141,000	100

The graph is plotted from the percentage columns.

Lorenz curve showing the distribution of wealth in Ruritania

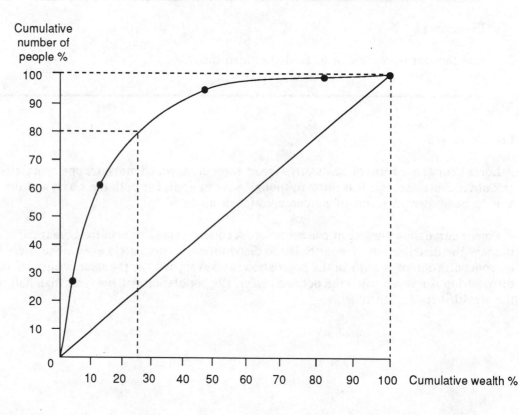

A straight line is also drawn, joining the origin of the graph with the point (100%, 100%). This is the line we would expect if there were no concentration of wealth in the population, that is, if everyone had the same wealth. It is drawn to show how much concentration there actually is. The more the curve deviates from this diagonal line (called the *line of uniform distribution*), the greater the concentration.

In this case it appears that a large proportion of the wealth of Ruritania belongs to a fairly small section of the population. The dotted lines on the graph show that 80% of the population own only 25% of the wealth, so the richest 20% of the population own 75% of the wealth.

The main application of Lorenz curves is in making comparisons. For instance, researchers may wish to see whether in subsequent years the concentration of wealth in Ruritania changes. If Lorenz curves for subsequent years are plotted on the same graph it can be seen whether the degree of concentration has increased (in which case the curve will be further from the diagonal) or decreased (in which case the curve will be nearer the diagonal).

Exercise 12

If in the above example we had plotted the cumulative number of people on the x axis and cumulative wealth on the y axis, how would the resulting curve have differed?

Z Charts

A Z chart is a time series graph which can be very useful for presenting business data. It can show:

(a) how results are changing from period to period;
(b) how results compare with the previous year;
(c) how results compare with the budget for the year to date.

A Z chart shows:

(a) the value of a variable plotted against time over the year;
(b) the cumulative sum of values for that variable over the year to date;
(c) the annual moving total for that variable.

The annual moving total is the total for the most recent 12 months.

A line for the budget for the year to date may be added to a Z chart, for comparison with the cumulative sum of actual values.

Example: a Z chart

The sales figures for a company for 19X2 and 19X3 are as follows.

	19X2 sales £m	*19X3 sales* £m
January	7	8
February	7	8
March	8	8
April	7	9
May	9	8
June	8	8
July	8	7
August	7	8
September	6	9
October	7	6
November	8	9
December	8	9
	90	97

Draw a Z chart to represent these data.

Solution

The first thing to do is to calculate the cumulative sales for 19X3 and the annual moving total for the year.

	Sales 19X2 £m	*Sales 19X3* £m	*Cumulative sales 19X3* £m	*Annual moving total* £m
January	7	8	8	91
February	7	8	16	92
March	8	8	24	92
April	7	9	33	94
May	9	8	41	93
June	8	8	49	93
July	8	7	56	92
August	7	8	64	93
September	6	9	73	96
October	7	6	79	95
November	8	9	88	96
December	8	9	97	97

The first figure in the annual moving total is arrived at by taking the sales for the year ended December 19X2, adding those for January 19X3 and subtracting those for January 19X2. This gives the sales for a 12 month period to the end of January 19X3: 90 + 8 - 7 = 91.

A similar approach is used for the rest of the year, by adding on the new 19X3 month and deducting the corresponding 19X2 month.

The Z chart is given below.

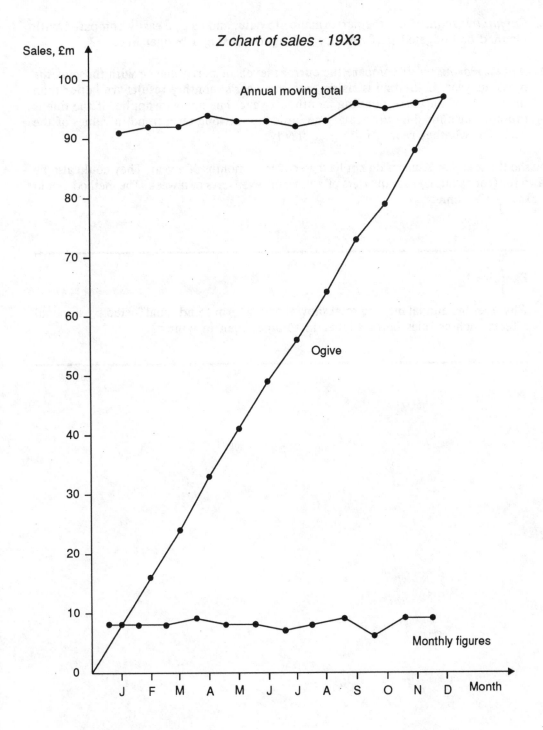

The interpretation of Z charts

The popularity of Z charts in practical applications derives from the wealth of information which they can contain.

(a) *Monthly totals* show the monthly results at a glance together with any seasonal variations.

(b) *Cumulative totals* show the performance to date, and can be easily compared with planned or budgeted performance by superimposing a budget line.

(c) *Annual moving totals* compare the current levels of performance with those of the previous year. If the line is rising then this year's monthly results are better than the results of the corresponding month last year. The opposite applies if the line is falling. The annual moving total line indicates the long term trend in values of the variable, whether rising, falling or steady.

You should note that Z charts do not have to cover 12 months of a year. They could also be drawn for (for example) four quarters of a year, or seven days of a week. The method would be exactly the same.

Exercise 13

Why does the annual moving total show the long term trend, unaffected by seasonal effects such as sales being higher in summer than in winter?

Chapter roundup

(a) One of the simplest forms of presentation of data is a table.

(b) Where there are several values of a single variable, a frequency distribution is often the clearest way of presenting the data. A grouped frequency distribution should be used if an ungrouped frequency distribution would have too many separate values.

(c) A cumulative frequency distribution shows the number of occurrences of values less than (or alternatively greater than) each chosen class boundary value.

(d) A pictogram uses several copies of a standard drawing to represent a value. A pie chart shows relative values by dividing a circle into sectors.

(e) Bar charts can be used to display frequency distributions. They may be simple bar charts, component bar charts or multiple bar charts.

(f) Histograms display grouped frequency distributions of continuous variables. Values of the variable are displayed on the horizontal axis, and frequency densities on the vertical axis.

(g) Graphs plot dependent variables (on the y axis) against independent variables (on the x axis).

(h) Ogives display cumulative frequency distributions. An ogive may be used to find the median and the quartiles of a distribution.

(i) A Lorenz curve plots one cumulative amount against another. It shows degree of concentration.

(j) A Z chart plots results for each period (such as each month), the cumulative total for the year to date and the annual moving total. It can be used to compare actual and budgeted results.

Quantitative methods

Notes

Quick quiz

1 How should classes be defined for a grouped frequency distribution of a continuous variable?

2 Distinguish between a component bar chart and a multiple bar chart.

3 How are the widths and heights of bars in a histogram determined?

4 Which axis on a graph represents the independent variable?

5 What does an ogive show?

6 What is the purpose of a Lorenz curve?

7 Which three lines are plotted on a Z chart?

Solutions to exercises

1 (a)

New telephone installations
(by company)

Company	1960	1970	1980	1990
	Installations (thousands)			
A Co Ltd	1,810	3,248	5,742	4,932
B Co Ltd	2,114	1,288	3,038	3,138
C Co Ltd	448	1,618	2,228	1,506
Others	874	676	1,646	618
Total	5,246	6,830	12,654	10,194

(b)

Company	1960	1970	1980	1990
	Installations (percentages)			
A Co Ltd	34.5	47.6	45.4	48.4
B Co Ltd	40.3	18.8	24.0	30.8
C Co Ltd	8.5	23.7	17.6	14.8
Others	16.7	9.9	13.0	6.0
Total	100.0	100.0	100.0	100.0

(c) A Co Ltd was the second largest installer in 1960, but was the market leader in 1970, 1980 and 1990, with an apparently secure grip on nearly half the market.

B Co Ltd's share of the market dropped sharply between 1960 and 1970, but the company has since been steadily recovering market share.

C Co Ltd did very well between 1960 and 1970, but has not been able to sustain its growth rate, and has lost market share since 1970.

Other companies have maintained a small and variable market share. There is no sign of a serious challenge to the three main companies.

2   Most common: 70 units
     Least common: 65, 72, 73 and 74 units

3   We are told what classes to use, so the first step is to identify the lowest and highest values in the data. The lowest value is £25 (in the first row) and the highest value is £73 (in the fourth row). This means that the class intervals must go up to '£70 and under £75'.

     We can now set out the classes in a column, and then count the number of items in each class using tally marks.

Class interval	Tally marks	Total
£25 and less than £30	///	3
£30 and less than £35	////	4
£35 and less than £40	### ###	10
£40 and less than £45	### ### ###	15
£45 and less than £50	### ### ### ///	18
£50 and less than £55	### ### ### ###	20
£55 and less than £60	### ### ///	13
£60 and less than £65	### ///	8
£65 and less than £70	### /	6
£70 and less than £75	///	3
	Total	100

4   Under 15 units: 1
     Under 20 units: 5
     Under 25 units: 8

5

	Factory A		Factory B	
	£'000	Degrees	£'000	Degrees
Direct materials	70	126	50	72
Direct labour	30	54	125	180
Production overhead	90	162	50	72
Office costs	10	18	25	36
	200	360	250	360

6   It is hard to see how the sales of products A and B are changing, because the bases of the components in each year are not lined up. It is much easier to see how sales of product C are changing.

7   Total units output each year.

8

Class interval £'000	Size of interval £'000	Frequency	Density
> 4 ≤ 10	6	1	0.167
> 10 ≤ 12	2	10	5.000
> 12 ≤ 14	2	12	6.000
> 14 ≤ 18	4	8	2.000
> 18 ≤ 22	4	4	1.000
> 22 ≤ 28	6	1	0.167

Notes

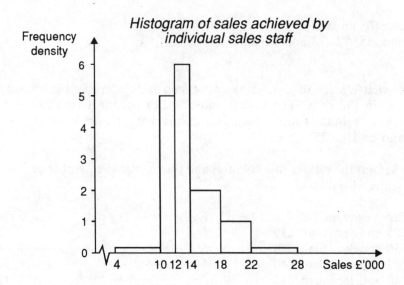

Histogram of sales achieved by individual sales staff

9    $y = 20^2 + 110 = 400 + 110 = 510$

10

Upper limit of interval	Frequency	Cumulative frequency
200	4	4
400	8	12
600	12	24
800	10	34
1,000	6	40

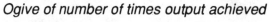

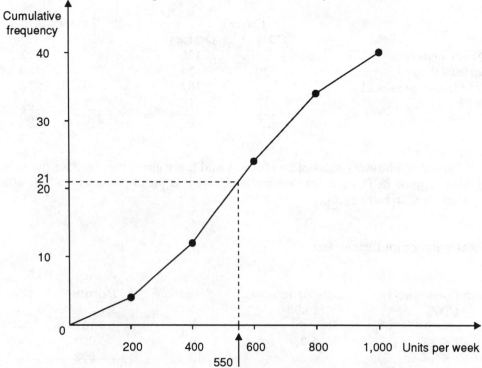

Ogive of number of times output achieved

The dotted lines indicate that output of up to 550 units was achieved in 21 out of the 40 weeks.

11   The third quartile is found by drawing a line across from 280 × 3/4 = 210 and then down. It is about 16,750 words.

12   The curve would have been the same shape, but it would have been on the other side of the diagonal line.

13   One example of each month is included in the annual moving total. Thus although July might be a very good month but January a very bad month, there will be one July and one January in the total, balancing each other.

                                              BPP Publishing

4 INDEX NUMBERS

Signpost

Index numbers show changes in prices or quantities over time. The Retail Prices Index is an example. Index numbers show relative changes (percentages, not numbers of pounds), and a price relative shows how much a price has changed in percentage terms. We will look at different ways of combining the changes in prices or quantities of several items (the aggregate index method, the Laspeyre method and the Paasche method), and at the practical problems of preparing useful index numbers.

Your objectives

After completing this chapter you should:

(a) know how an index shows relative changes in prices and quantities;
(b) understand how price relatives are computed;
(c) know how index numbers are computed using the aggregate index method;
(d) understand the main practical issues in the compilation of an index;
(e) be able to compute Laspeyre and Paasche index numbers;
(f) have an awareness of the Retail Prices Index (RPI) for the UK.

---

1 The construction of an index

An *index number* is a measure of the value (price or quantity) of a group of items. An index comprises a series of *index numbers*. Although it is possible to prepare an index for a single item, for example the price of an ounce of gold, such an index would probably be unnecessary. It is only when there is a group of items that a simple list of changes in their values over time becomes rather hard to interpret, and an index provides a useful single measure of comparison.

Price indices and quantity indices

An index may be a price index or a quantity index.

(a) A *price index* measures the change in the money value of a group of items over time. Perhaps the best known price index in the UK is the Retail Prices Index (RPI) which measures changes in the prices of items of expenditure of the average household.

(b) A *quantity index* (also called a *volume index)* measures the change in the non-monetary values of a group of items over time. An example is a productivity index, which measures changes in the productivity of various departments or groups of workers.

Index points

The term 'points' refers to the difference between the index values in two years.

For example, suppose that the index of food prices in 19X1 - 19X6 was as follows.

19X1	180
19X2	200
19X3	230
19X4	250
19X5	300
19X6	336

The index has risen 156 points between 19X1 and 19X6. This is an increase of $(156/180) \times 100 = 86.7\%$.

Similarly, the index rose 36 points between 19X5 and 19X6, a rise of 12%.

The base period, or base year

Index numbers normally take the value for a base date, usually the starting point of the series though it could be part way through the series, as 100.

When one commodity only is under consideration, we have the following formulae.

(a) Price index = $\dfrac{p_1}{p_0} \times 100$

where p_1 is the price for the period under consideration and p_0 is the price for the base period.

(b) Quantity index = $\dfrac{q_1}{q_0} \times 100$

where q_1 is the quantity for the period under consideration and q_0 is the quantity for the base period.

Example: single–item indices

If the price of a cup of coffee was 40p in 19X0, 50p in 19X1 and 76p in 19X2, then using 19X0 as a base year the price index numbers for 19X1 and 19X2 would be as follows.

19X1 price index = $\dfrac{50}{40} \times 100 = 125$

19X2 price index = $\dfrac{76}{40} \times 100 = 190$

If the number of cups of coffee sold in 19X0 was 500,000, in 19X1 700,000 and in 19X2 600,000, then using 19X0 as a base year, the quantity index numbers for 19X1 and 19X2 would be as follows.

19X1 quantity index = $\dfrac{700,000}{500,000} \times 100 = 140$

BPP Publishing

Quantitative methods

19X2 quantity index = $\dfrac{600,000}{500,000}$ × 100 = 120

Exercise 1

1 kg of raw material cost £80 in year 1 and £120 in year 2. Using year 1 as a base year, what was the price index number for year 2?

Multi-item indices

Most practical indices cover more than one item. For example, say that the cost of living index is calculated from only three commodities: bread, tea and caviar, and that the prices for 19X1 and 19X5 were as follows.

	19X1	*19X5*
Bread	20p a loaf	40p a loaf
Tea	25p a packet	30p a packet
Caviar	450p a jar	405p a jar

An examination of these figures reveals three main difficulties.

(a) Two prices have gone up and one has gone down. The index number must be a compromise.

(b) The quantities are given in different units.

(c) There is no indication of the relative importance of each item. Bread is probably more important than caviar.

Nothing can be done about difficulty (a): it is a feature of index numbers and must always be borne in mind; but (b) and (c) can be overcome by *weighting*.

Weighting an index

To decide the weightings of different items in an index, it is necessary to obtain information, perhaps by market research, about the relative importance of each item. Thus, in our example of a simple cost of living index, it would be necessary to find out how much the average person or household spends each week on each item.

Example: a multi-item index

Research may suggest that the average spending by each household in a year was as follows in 19X1.

	Quantity	Price (19X1)	Total spending £	%	Price (19X5)
Bread	90	20p	18.00	60	40p
Tea	30	25p	7.50	25	30p
Caviar	1	450p	4.50	15	405p
			30.00	100	

The weighting of each item in the index will depend on the proportion of total weekly spending taken up by the item. In our example, the weightings of bread, tea and caviar would be 60%, 25% and 15% respectively.

If 19X1 is chosen as the base year, the index for 19X5 can be obtained as follows.

(a) Calculate the price of each item in 19X5 as a percentage of the price in 19X1. This percentage figure is called a *price relative*, because it gives the new price level of each item relative to the base year price. (*Quantity relatives*, giving one quantity as a percentage of another, could be computed for a quantity index.)

(b) Multiply the price relative by the weighting for the item.

(c) Add the results.

It is assumed that the relative quantities of bread, tea and caviar consumed each year by the average household did not change between 19X1 and 19X5, so that the 'basket of goods': bread, tea and caviar, is still representative of the average household's consumption pattern.

In our example, we have the following computations.

(a) 19X5 price relatives are as follows.

   (i) Bread $\dfrac{40p}{20p} \times 100 = 200$

   (ii) Tea $\dfrac{30p}{25p} \times 100 = 120$

   (iii) Caviar $\dfrac{405p}{450p} \times 100 = 90$

(b)

Item	Weighting %	Price relative	Product
Bread	60	200	120.0
Tea	25	120	30.0
Caviar	15	90	13.5
	100		163.5

(c) The 19X5 index is 163.5.

BPP Publishing

Exercise 2

Constant Ltd uses three grades of labour. The rates paid in years 1 and 4 and the average weekly labour hours in year 1 were as follows.

Grade of labour	Year 1	Year 4	Average weekly labour hours in Year 1
	£ per hour	£ per hour	
Unskilled	2	2.32	180
Semi-skilled	3	3.60	140
Skilled	4	4.40	805

The company wishes to calculate a weighted index of price relatives for labour using year 1 as the base year. The weighting of the index is to be based on the proportions of total weekly wages incurred in year 1. What is the year 4 price index for labour, to the nearest whole number?

The aggregate index method

An alternative method of calculating index numbers is the *aggregate index* method. By this method, the formulae for calculating an index are as follows. Σ, used in both formulae, is the Greek capital letter sigma, which is used to mean 'the sum of'. Thus $\Sigma p_1 q_0$ means that we work out the values of $p_1 q_0$ for all the items and then add up the results.

(a) Price index: $\dfrac{\Sigma p_1 q_0}{\Sigma p_0 q_0} \times 100$

    where p_0 represents the prices of items in the base year
               p_1 represents the prices of items in the new year
               q_0 represents the quantities of the items consumed in the base year.

(b) Quantity index: $\dfrac{\Sigma p_0 q_1}{\Sigma p_0 q_0} \times 100$

    where q_1 represents the quantities consumed in the new year
               q_0 represents the quantities consumed in the base year
               p_0 represents the prices in the base year.

Example: the aggregate index method

In the previous example of the cost of living index, the 19X5 index value could have been calculated as follows.

Item	Quantity	Price in 1981		Price in 19X5	
	q_0	p_0	$p_0 q_0$	p_1	$p_1 q_0$
Bread	90	20	1,800	40	3,600
Tea	30	25	750	30	900
Caviar	1	450	450	405	405
			3,000		4,905

Index in 19X5 = $\dfrac{4,905}{3,000}$ × 100 = 163.5

Note that we get the same result as before. This is because the weights we used there were percentages of total expenditure in the base year, so the index number we computed was

$$\Sigma \left(\frac{p_1}{p_0} \times \frac{p_0 q_0}{\Sigma p_0 q_0} \right) = \Sigma \left(\frac{p_1 q_0}{\Sigma p_0 q_0} \right) = \frac{\Sigma p_1 q_0}{\Sigma p_0 q_0}$$

If we had weighted our price relatives on a different basis, we would have got a different result.

Exercise 3

The Falldown Construction Company uses four items of materials and components in a standard production job.

In 19X0 the quantities of each material or component used per job and their cost, were as follows.

	Quantity Units	Price per unit £
Material A	20	2
Material B	5	10
Component C	40	3
Component D	15	6

In 19X2 the quantities of materials and components used per job were as follows.

	Quantity Units
Material A	15
Material B	6
Component C	36
Component D	25

Using 19X0 as a base year and the aggregate index method, calculate the quantity index value in 19X2 for the amount of materials and components used in a standard job.

BPP Publishing

2   Practical issues

The main practical issues to consider when constructing or using an index are as follows.

(a)   What items to include
(b)   How and where to get the data
(c)   What weights to use
(d)   The choice of a base period
(e)   The limitations of index numbers and the scope for their misinterpretation.

What items to include

The purpose to which the index is to be put must be carefully considered. Once this has been done, the items selected must be as representative as possible, taking into account this purpose. Care must be taken to ensure that the items are unambiguously defined and that their values are readily ascertainable.

The Retail Prices Index is an excellent example of the problem. It would be impossible to include all items of domestic spending and a selective, representative basket of goods and services must be found, ranging from spending on mortgages and rents, to cars, public transport, food and drink, electricity, gas, telephone, clothing, leisure activities and so on.

How and where to get the data

Data are required to determine:

(a)   the values for each item;
(b)   the weight that will be attached to each item.

Consider as an example a cost of living index. The prices of a particular commodity will vary from place to place, from shop to shop and from brand to brand. Also the price will vary during the period under consideration. The actual prices used must obviously be some sort of average. The way in which the average is to be obtained should be clearly defined at the outset.

When constructing a price index, it is common practice to use the quantities consumed as weights; similarly, when constructing a quantity index, the prices may be used as weights. Care must be taken in selecting the basis for the weighting. For example, in a cost of living index, it may be decided to use the consumption of a typical family as the weights, but some difficulty may be encountered in defining a typical family.

What weights to use

Quantities consumed are often used as weights in price indices. Obviously, patterns of consumption change and a decision is necessary on whether to use:

(a)   quantities consumed in the base year; or
(b)   quantities consumed in the current year.

Laspeyre price index

An index using (a) is called a *Laspeyre price index*. In the notation already used it can be expressed as:

$$\text{Laspeyre Price index} = \frac{\Sigma\, p_1 q_0}{\Sigma\, p_0 q_0} \times 100$$

This is the same as the formula already given for aggregate indices where the weighting factor is q_0, the quantity of each item consumed in the base period.

Paasche price index

An index in which the weightings are changed each year to reflect consumption patterns in the current year is called a *Paasche price index*.

$$\text{Paasche price index} = \frac{\Sigma\, p_1 q_1}{\Sigma\, p_0 q_1} \times 100$$

Which to use - Paasche or Laspeyre?

The following points should be considered when deciding which type of index to use.

(a)   A Paasche index requires quantities to be ascertained each year. A Laspeyre index only requires them for the base year.

(b)   For the Paasche index the denominator $\Sigma\, p_0 q_1$ has to be recalculated each year because the quantities must be changed to current year consumption levels.

For the Laspeyre index, the denominator $\Sigma\, p_0 q_0$ is fixed.

(c)   Because of (b) the Laspeyre index numbers for several different years can be directly compared whereas with the Paasche index comparisons can only be drawn directly between the current year and the base year.

(d)   The weights for a Laspeyre index become out of date, whereas those for the Paasche index are updated each year.

In practice, it is common to use a Laspeyre index and revise the weights every few years.

Example: Laspeyre and Paasche price indices

The wholesale price index in Ruritania is made up from the prices of five items. The price of each item, and the average quantities purchased by manufacturing and other companies each week were as follows, in 19X0 and 19X2.

Quantitative methods

Item	19X0 Quantity ('000 units)	19X0 Price per unit Roubles	19X1 Quantity ('000 units)	19X1 Price per unit Roubles
P	60	3	80	4
Q	30	6	40	5
R	40	5	20	8
S	100	2	150	2
T	20	7	10	10

Calculate the price index in 19X2, if 19X0 is taken as the base year, using:

(a) a Laspeyre index;
(b) a Paasche index.

Solution

Workings

Item	p_0	q_0	p_1	q_1	Laspeyre p_0q_0	Laspeyre p_1q_0	Paasche p_1q_1	Paasche p_0q_1
P	3	60	4	80	180	240	320	240
Q	6	30	5	40	180	150	200	240
R	5	40	8	20	200	320	160	100
S	2	100	2	150	200	200	300	300
T	7	20	10	10	140	200	100	70
					900	1,110	1,080	950

19X2 index numbers are as follows.

(a) Laspeyre index $\dfrac{1,110}{900} \times 100 = 123.3$

(b) Paasche index $\dfrac{1,080}{950} \times 100 = 113.7$

The Paasche index for 19X2 reflects the decline in consumption of the relatively expensive items R and T since 19X0. The Laspeyre index for 1992 fails to reflect this change.

Quantity indices: the Laspeyre and Paasche methods

Quantity indices can be constructed in exactly the same way as price indices, but using the periods' prices as weights.

The formulae for quantity indices are as follows.

Laspeyre quantity index $= \dfrac{\Sigma\, q_1 p_0}{\Sigma\, q_0 p_0} \times 100$

Paasche quantity index $= \dfrac{\Sigma\, q_1 p_1}{\Sigma\, q_0 p_1} \times 100$

Exercise 4

Output Ltd prepares an annual index of quantity produced. There are four products, A, B, C and D.

Data for 19X0 and 19X2 were as follows.

Product	*19X0* Price	*19X0* Units	*19X1* Price	*19X1* Units
A	£3	120	£4	150
B	£6	95	£5	98
C	£1	140	£2	130
D	£4	110	£3	114

Calculate the quantity index for 19X2 (with 19X0 as the base year) using:

(a) a Laspeyre index;
(b) a Paasche index.

The choice of a base year

The choice of a base date, or base year is not significant, except that it should be representative. In the construction of a price index, the base year must not be one in which there were abnormally high or low prices for any items in the basket of goods making up the index. For example, a year in which there is a potato famine would be unsuitable as a base period for the Retail Prices Index.

The chain base method of indexing

In all the previous examples in this chapter, we have used a *fixed base* method of indexing, whereby a base year is selected (index 100) and all subsequent changes are measured against this base.

The *chain base* method of indexing is an alternative approach, whereby:

(a) in a price index, the changes in prices are taken as percentages of the prices of the period immediately before;

(b) in a quantity index, the changes in quantities are taken as percentages of the quantities of the period immediately before.

This method is suitable where weightings are changing rapidly, and new items are continually being brought into the index and old items taken out.

Example: the chain base method

Allowing for changes in the weighting of items included in a price index, average prices were 15% higher in 19X1 than in 19X0, 10% higher in 19X2 than in 19X1, and 12% higher in 19X3 than in 19X2.

(a)   Construct a chain base index for the years 19X0 to 19X3.

(b)   Construct a fixed base index for the years 19X0 to 19X3, using 19X0 as the base year. Ignore any changes in weightings over the years.

Solution

(a)   Chain base index:

19X0	100
19X1	115
19X2	110
19X3	112

(b)   Fixed base index:

19X0	100	
19X1	115	
19X2	126.5	(115 × 110%)
19X3	141.7	(126.5 × 112%)

The chain base index shows the rate of change in prices from year to year, whereas the fixed base index shows changes relative to prices in the base year.

The limitations of index numbers

Index numbers are usually only approximations of changes in price or quantity over time, and must be interpreted with care.

As we have seen, weightings become out of date over time. Unless a Paasche index is used, the weightings will gradually cease to reflect current reality.

New products or items may appear, and old ones may cease to be significant. For example, spending has changed in recent years, to include new items such as personal computers and video recorders, whereas the demand for twin tub washing machines has declined. These changes would make the weightings of a price index for such goods out of date.

The data used to calculate index numbers might be incomplete, out of date, or inaccurate. For example, the quantity indices of imports and exports are based on records supplied by traders which may be prone to error or even deliberate falsification.

The base year of an index should be a normal year, but there is probably no such thing as a perfectly normal year. Some error in the index will be caused by a typical values in the base period.

The 'basket of items' in an index is often selective. For example, the Retail Prices Index (RPI) is constructed from a sample of households and from a basket of less than 400 items.

A national index may not be very relevant to an individual town or region. For example, if the national index of wages and salaries rises from 100 to 115, we cannot conclude that the wages and salaries of people in, say, Glasgow, have gone up by 15%.

An index may exclude important items: for example, the RPI excludes payments of income tax out of gross wages.

The misinterpretation of index numbers

You must be careful not to misinterpret index numbers. Some possible mistakes will be explained using the following example of the UK's RPI.

1991		*1992*	
February	130.9	February	136.3
March	131.4	March	136.7

(a) It would be wrong to say that prices rose by 0.4% between February and March 1992. It is correct to say that prices rose 0.4 points, or $(0.4/136.3) \times 100\% = 0.3\%$.

(b) It would be correct to say that the annual rate of price increases (the rate of inflation) fell between February and March 1992. It would be a mistake, however, to suppose that a fall in the rate of inflation means that prices are falling, therefore the price index is falling.

The rate of price increases has slowed down, but the trend of prices is still upwards.

(i) The annual rate of inflation from February 1991 to February 1992 is

$$\frac{136.3 - 130.9}{130.9} = 4.1\%$$

(ii) The annual rate of inflation from March 1991 to March 1992 is

$$\frac{136.7 - 131.4}{131.4} = 4.0\%$$

Thus the annual rate of inflation has dropped, even though prices went up in the month between February and March 1992 by 0.3%.

3 The Retail Prices Index for the United Kingdom

We will conclude our study of index numbers by looking at the construction of the UK Retail Prices Index (RPI) which measures the change in the cost of living. Since it measures the monthly change in the cost of living its principal use is as a measure of inflation.

The index measures the percentage change, month by month, in the average level of prices of 'a representative basket of goods' purchased by the great majority of households in the United Kingdom.

On one particular day of each month, data are collected about prices of the following groups of items.

(a) Food
(b) Alcoholic drink
(c) Tobacco

(d) Housing
(e) Fuel and light
(f) Durable household goods
(g) Clothing and footwear
(h) Transport and vehicles
(i) Miscellaneous goods
(j) Services
(k) Meals bought and consumed outside the home

Each group is sub-divided into sections: for example 'food' will be sub-divided into bread, butter, potatoes and so on. These sections may in turn be sub-divided into more specific items. The groups do not cover every item of expenditure (for example they exclude income tax, pension fund contributions and football pools).

The weightings given to each group, section and sub-section are based on information provided by the *Family Expenditure Survey*, which is a survey of over 10,000 households.

Each member of the selected households (aged 16 or over) is asked to keep a detailed record of their expenditure over a period of 14 days, and to provide information about longer-term payments (such as insurance premiums). Information is also obtained about their income.

The weightings used in the construction of the RPI are not revised every year, but are revised from time to time using information in the Family Expenditure Survey of the previous year.

Exercise 5

An extract from a country's retail prices index is as follows.

January Year 8	408.0
January Year 9	432.7
January Year 10	500.6

What was the average annual rate of inflation between January Year 8 and January Year 10?

Chapter roundup

(a) An index measures average changes over time in the prices or quantities of a group of items.

(b) Price or quantity relatives, showing changes since a base period, can be computed for the items in an index. These can then be combined in a weighted average.

(c) The aggregate index method is an alternative approach. Totals of products of prices and quantities are found, and then one total is divided by another.

(d) The two main aggregate index formulae are the Laspeyre index and the Paasche index. The former uses base period weights whereas the latter uses current period weights.

(e) Practical issues in the compilation of index numbers include the choice of items, the choice of weights and the choice of a base year.

(f) Index numbers are subject to various limitations and are open to misinterpretation.

(g) The RPI measures the change in the cost of living. Its principal use is as a measure of inflation.

Quick quiz

1   What is the usual index value for a base year?

2   What is a price relative?

3   Distinguish between a Laspeyre price index and a Paasche price index.

4   What is the formula for a Paasche quantity index?

5   What are the limitations of index numbers?

6   Give some examples of how index numbers may be misinterpreted.

Solutions to exercises

1   $\dfrac{120}{80} \times 100 = 150$

2   The weighting of the index is to be based on the proportions of total weekly wages incurred in year 1.

	£ per hour	Average weekly labour hours	Total weekly wages £	%
Unskilled	2	180	360	9.0
Semi skilled	3	140	420	10.5
Skilled	4	805	3,220	80.5
			4,000	100.0

Price relative of unskilled labour $= \dfrac{£2.32}{£2.00} \times 100 = 116$

Price relative of semi-skilled labour $= \dfrac{£3.60}{£3.00} \times 100 = 120$

Price relative of skilled labour $= \dfrac{£4.40}{£4.00} \times 100 = 110$

Grade of labour	Weighting (i)	Price relative (ii)	(i) × (ii)
Unskilled	9.0%	116	10.44
Semi-skilled	10.5%	120	12.60
Skilled	80.5%	110	88.55
			111.59

To the nearest whole number, the index number for year 4 is 112.

3

Item	p_0 £	q_0	$p_0 q_0$	q_1	$p_0 q_1$
Material A	2	20	40	15	30
Material B	10	5	50	6	60
Component C	3	40	120	36	108
Component D	6	15	90	25	150
			300		348

Quantity index $= \dfrac{348}{300} \times 100 = 116$

4

Product					Laspeyre		Paasche	
	p_0	q_0	p_1	q_1	$p_0 q_0$	$p_0 q_1$	$p_1 q_1$	$p_1 q_0$
A	3	120	4	150	360	450	600	480
B	6	95	5	98	570	588	490	475
C	1	140	2	130	140	130	260	280
D	4	110	3	114	440	456	342	330
					1,510	1,624	1,692	1,565

Index numbers for 19X2 are as follows.

(a)   Laspeyre method: $\dfrac{1,624}{1,510} \times 100 = 107.5$

(b)   Paasche method: $\dfrac{1,692}{1,565} \times 100 = 108.1$

5   Let the average annual rate of inflation over the two years be x%. If an item whose price moved exactly in line with inflation cost £408 in January year 8, its price two years later would be £408 $(1 + x)(1 + x) = £408(1 + x)^2$. Its price would (in accordance with the index figures given) have risen to £500.60. We can therefore work out the average annual rate of inflation as follows.

$$
\begin{aligned}
408 \quad (1 + x)^2 &= 500.6 \\
(1 + x)^2 &= 500.6\,/408.0 = 1.227 \\
1 + x &= \sqrt{1.227} = 1.108 \\
x &= 0.108
\end{aligned}
$$

The average annual rate of inflation is 10.8%.

BPP Publishing

5 AVERAGES AND DISPERSION

Signpost

Once data have been collected (and perhaps presented in some easily understood way), computations can be done on them. Index numbers are one sort of computation. In this chapter we will look at two other sorts. An average gives a general idea of how large the values in a set of data are: it may be the arithmetic mean (sum of values divided by number of values), the mode (the most common value) or the median (the middle value). A measure of dispersion shows how spread out the values in a set of data are: the standard deviation, which is the square root of the variance, takes account of the distances of all the values from the arithmetic mean.

Your objectives

After completing this chapter you should:

(a) understand the concept of an average;
(b) be able to compute the arithmetic mean for both ungrouped and grouped data;
(c) be able to find the mode using a formula or using a histogram;
(d) be able to compute the median using a formula;
(e) understand the concept of dispersion;
(f) be able to compute measures of dispersion based on quartiles;
(g) be able to compute the variance and the standard deviation.

---

1   The concept of an average

An average is a representative figure that is used to give some impression of the size of all the items in a population We could, for example, work out the average age of a workforce, or a company's average quarterly telephone bill over a five year period.

The three main types of average used are:

(a) the arithmetic mean;
(b) the mode;
(c) the median.

An average, whether it is a mean, a mode or a median, is a *measure of central tendency*. By this we mean that while a population may range in values, these values will be distributed around a central point. This central point, or average, is therefore in some way representative of the population as a whole. Averages are also called *measures of location* because they show roughly where data are located on a scale of values.

---

2 The arithmetic mean

This is the best known type of average. For ungrouped data, it is calculated by the formula

Arithmetic mean $= \dfrac{\text{Sum of values of items}}{\text{Number of items}}$

Example: the arithmetic mean

The demand for a product on each of 20 days was as follows (in units).

3 12 7 17 3 14 9 6 11 10 1 4 19 7 15 6 9 12 12 8

The arithmetic mean of daily demand is

$\dfrac{\text{Sum of demands}}{\text{Number of days}} = \dfrac{185}{20} = 9.25$ units

The arithmetic mean of a variable x is shown as $\bar{x}$ ('x bar').

Thus in the above example $\bar{x} = 9.25$ units.

In the above example, demand on any one day is never actually 9.25 units. The arithmetic mean is merely an average representation of demand on each of the 20 days.

The arithmetic mean of data in a frequency distribution

It is more likely that an arithmetic mean of a frequency distribution will be required. In our previous example, the frequency distribution would be shown as follows.

Daily demand x	Frequency f	Demand × frequency fx
1	1	1
3	2	6
4	1	4
6	2	12
7	2	14
8	1	8
9	2	18
10	1	10
11	1	11
12	3	36
14	1	14
15	1	15
17	1	17
19	1	19
	20	185

The mean, $\bar{x} = \dfrac{185}{20} = 9.25$

Exercise 1

If, in the above distribution, the frequency for x = 12 had been 7 and the frequencies for x = 14, 15, 17 and 19 had been 0, what would the mean have been?

Sigma, Σ

The statistical notation for the arithmetic mean of a set of data uses the symbol Σ (sigma). Σ means 'the sum of' and is used as shorthand to mean the sum of a set of values.

Thus, in the previous example:

(a) Σ f would mean the sum of all the frequencies, which is 20.

(b) Σ fx would mean the sum of all the values of 'frequency multiplied by daily demand', that is, all 14 values of fx, so Σ fx = 185.

The symbolic formula for the arithmetic mean

Using the Σ sign, the formula for the arithmetic mean of a frequency distribution is

$$\bar{x} = \frac{\Sigma fx}{n} \quad \text{or} \quad \frac{\Sigma fx}{\Sigma f}$$

where n is the number of values recorded, or the number of items measured.

The arithmetic mean of grouped data in class intervals

Another common problem is to calculate (or at least approximate) the arithmetic mean of a frequency distribution, where the frequencies are shown in class intervals.

Example: grouped data

The frequency distribution above might have been shown as follows.

Daily demand	Frequency
> 0 ⩽ 5	4
> 5 ⩽ 10	8
> 10 ⩽ 15	6
> 15 ⩽ 20	2
	20

An arithmetic mean is calculated by taking the mid point of each class interval, on the assumption that the frequencies occur evenly over the class interval range. Note that the variable is discrete, so the first class includes 1, 2, 3, 4 and 5, giving a mid point of 3. With a continuous variable (such as quantities of fuel consumed in litres), the mid points would have been 2.5, 7.5 and so on.

Daily demand	Mid point x	Frequency f	fx
> 0 ⩽ 5	3	4	12
> 5 ⩽ 10	8	8	64
> 10 ⩽ 15	13	6	78
> 15 ⩽ 20	18	2	36
		Σf = 20	Σfx = 190

Arithmetic mean $\bar{x} = \dfrac{\Sigma fx}{\Sigma f} = \dfrac{190}{20} = 9.5$ units

Because the assumption that frequencies occurred evenly within each class interval is not quite correct in this example, our approximate mean of 9.5 is not exactly correct, and is in error by 0.25.

As the frequencies become larger, the size of this approximating error should become smaller.

Exercise 2

For the week ended 29 May, the wages earned by the 69 operators employed in the machine shop of Mechaids Ltd were as follows.

Wages at least £	less than £	Number of operators
50	60	3
60	70	11
70	80	16
80	90	15
90	100	10
100	110	8
110	120	6
		69

Calculate the arithmetic mean wage of the machine operators of Mechaids Ltd for the week ended 29 May.

3 The mode

The mode is an average which means 'the most frequently occurring value'. It is possible for there to be two modes (a *bimodel* frequency distribution) or several modes (a *multimodal* frequency distribution).

BPP Publishing

Example: the mode

The daily demand for stock in a ten day period is as follows.

Demand Units	Number of days
6	3
7	6
8	$\underline{1}$
	$\underline{\underline{10}}$

The mode is 7 units, because it is the value which occurs most frequently.

The mode in grouped frequency distributions

In a grouped frequency distribution, the mode can only be estimated approximately.

The method of making this estimate is as follows.

(a)   Establish which is the class with the highest frequency (the modal class).

(b)   The mode is taken as

$$L + \frac{(F_1 - F_0) \times c}{2F_1 - F_0 - F_2}$$

where L =   the lower limit of the modal class
          F_0 =   the frequency of the next class below the modal class
          F_1 =   the frequency of the modal class
          F_2 =   the frequency of the next class above the modal class
          c =   the width of the modal class.

This formula only works if the modal class, the next class below it and the next class above it all have the same width (class interval).

Example: the formula for the mode

Calculate the mode of the following frequency distribution.

Value		
at least	less than	Frequency
10	25	6
25	40	19
40	55	12
55	70	7
70	85	3

Solution

The modal class is the class interval with the highest frequency, that is, the class $\geqslant 25$ and < 40. The class interval is 15. F_1 is 19, the frequency of the modal class. F_0 is the frequency of the class below 25-40, the class 10-25, which is 6. F_2 is the frequency of the class 40-55, which is 12.

The estimated mode is

$$25 + \frac{(19 - 6) \times 15}{(2 \times 19) - 6 - 12}$$

$$= \quad 25 + \frac{(13 \times 15)}{(38 - 18)}$$

$$= \quad 25 + 9.75$$

$$= \quad 34.75$$

Finding the mode from a histogram

The mode of a grouped frequency distribution can also be calculated from a histogram. Using this method, it does not matter if the class intervals vary.

Example

Consider the following histogram.

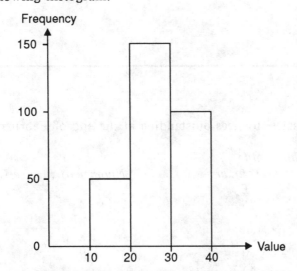

The mode is in the range 20-30. The modal class is the class with the tallest bar (which may not be the class with the highest frequency if the classes do not all have the same width).

We can estimate the mode graphically as follows.

(a)   Join with a straight line the top left hand corner of the bar for the modal class and the top left hand corner of the next bar to the right.

(b) Join with a straight line the top right hand corner of the bar for the modal class and the top right hand corner of the next bar to the left.

Where these two lines intersect, we find the estimated modal value. In this example it is 26.7.

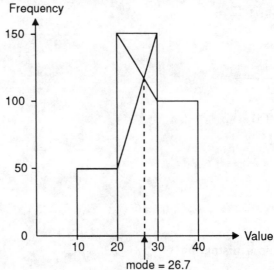

Using the formula for the mode, we would arrive at the same answer.

$$\text{Mode} = 20 + \frac{(150 - 50) \times 10}{(2 \times 150) - 50 - 100}$$

$$= 20 + \frac{1,000}{150}$$

$$= 26.7.$$

Exercise 3

An analysis of sales invoices outstanding at the end of February is as follows.

Invoice value		Number of invoices
at least £	less than £	
10	25	4
25	40	8
40	55	18
55	70	9
70	85	3

What is the approximate modal value of invoices outstanding at the end of February?

---

4 The median

The third type of average is the median. The median is the value of the middle member of a distribution. Thus the median wage of a workforce would be the wage of the middle member in wage order, with half the workforce earning more than that member and half earning as much or less.

The median of a set of ungrouped data is found by arranging the items in ascending or descending order of value, and selecting the item in the middle of the range. A list of items in order of value is called an *array*.

Example: the median

The median of the following nine values:

    8   6   9   12   15   6   3   20   11

is found by taking the middle item (the fifth one) in the array:

    3   6   6   8   9   11   12   15   20

The median is 9.

The median of the following ten values would be the fifth item in the array.

    8   6   7   2   1   11   3   2   5   2

    1   2   2   2   3   5   6   7   8   11

Median = 3

With an even number of items, we could take the arithmetic mean of the two middle ones (in this example, $(3 + 5)/2 = 4$), but when there are many items it is not worth doing this.

The median of an ungrouped frequency distribution

The median of an ungrouped frequency distribution is found in a similar way. We will need a column for the cumulative frequency, which is the total of frequencies up to and including each value of the variable in turn. Thus the median of the following distribution:

Value x	Frequency f	Cumulative frequency
8	3	3
12	7	10
16	12	22
17	8	30
19	5	35
	35	

would be the $(35 + 1)/2 = $ 18th item. The 18th item has a value of 16, as we can see from the cumulative frequencies in the right hand column of the above table.

BPP Publishing

The median of a grouped frequency distribution

The median of a grouped frequency distribution, like the arithmetic mean and the mode, can only be estimated approximately.

First, we must find the class interval to which the middle item belongs.

We then use the following formula.

Median = value of lower limit to the class $+ (\frac{R}{f} \times c)$

where
- c is the size of the class interval
- f is the frequency of the class
- R is the difference between the middle member ($(n + 1)/2$ for odd n, $n/2$ for even n) and the cumulative total of frequencies up to the end of the preceding class.

Example: the median of a grouped frequency distribution

The average monthly earnings of 135 employees of Comedian Ltd have been analysed as a grouped frequency distribution as follows.

Average monthly earnings			
more than £	not more than £	No of employees	Cumulative frequency
120	140	12	12
140	160	49	61
160	180	25	86
180	200	18	104
200	220	17	121
220	240	14	135
		135	

What are the median monthly earnings of employees of Comedian Ltd?

Solution

The middle member is the $(135 + 1)/2 = 68$th item. This occurs in the class £160 – £180.

Median $= £160 + (\frac{68 - 61}{25} \times £20)$

$= £165.60$

Finding the median from an ogive

Instead of using the formula to estimate the median of a grouped frequency distribution, we could establish the median from an ogive. The method of doing this was described in Chapter 3.

Exercise 4

The following grouped frequency distribution gives the annual wages of 200 employees in an engineering firm.

Wages		Number of employees
at least £	less than £	
5,000	5,500	4
5,500	6,000	26
6,000	6,500	133
6,500	7,000	35
7,000	7,500	2

Calculate the mean, the median and the mode of annual wages.

5 Dispersion

Averages are a method of determining the 'location' or central point of a distribution, but they give no information about the spread of values in the distribution.

For example, consider the following frequency distributions.

Value x	Distribution X frequency f	Distribution Y frequency f
1	3	0
2	6	0
3	10	10
4	12	30
5	10	10
6	6	0
7	3	0
	50	50

Both distributions have the same mean, median and mode (4).

Although distributions X and Y have the same averages, they are noticeably different. Distribution X is more spread out, and values range from 1 to 7; in distribution Y, the range of values is restricted to 3, 4 and 5.

The differences between the distributions are caused by their spread or dispersion.

Measures of dispersion give some idea of the spread of a variable about its average. The most basic measure is the *range* (highest value - lowest value) but there are other more sophisticated measures.

Quantitative methods

Notes

Quartiles and other quantiles

Quartiles are one means of identifying the range within which most of the values in the population occur. The lower quartile is the value below which 25% of the population fall and the upper quartile is the value above which 25% of the population fall. It follows that 50% of the total population fall between the lower and the upper quartiles. The quartiles and the median also divide the population into four groups of equal size.

In a similar way, a population could be divided into ten equal groups, and the value of each dividing point is referred to, not as a quartile, but as a *decile*. When a population is divided into 100 parts, the value of each dividing point is referred to as a *percentile*. For example, in a population of 201 values, the percentiles would be the second, fourth, sixth, eighth and so on, up to the 200th item, in rising order of values.

Quartiles, deciles and percentiles, and any other similar dividing points for analysing a frequency distribution, are referred to collectively as *quantiles*. The purpose of quantiles is to analyse the dispersion of data values.

The quartile deviation and the inter-quartile range

A measure of dispersion in a frequency distribution is the *quartile deviation*. The quartile deviation is *half the difference* between the two quartiles and is sometimes called the semi-inter-quartile range.

For example, if the lower and upper quartiles of a frequency distribution were 6 and 11, the quartile deviation of the distribution would be $(11 - 6)/2 = 2.5$ units.

This shows that the average distance of a quartile from the median is 2.5. The smaller the quartile deviation, the less dispersed is the distribution.

We could also have used the *inter-quartile range*, which in the above example would be $11 - 6 = 5$. This would show that the range of values of the middle half of the population is 5 units.

Example: quartiles

(a) Calculate the lower and upper quartiles and the median of the following grouped frequency distribution of values of sales made at a shop till.

(b) Calculate the quartile deviation.

Value (x) more than £	not more than £	Frequency (f)	Cumulative frequency
0	10	3	3
10	20	6	9
20	30	11	20
30	40	15	35
40	50	12	47
50	60	7	54
60	70	6	60
		60	

BPP Publishing 94

Solution

(a) The lower quartile is the $\frac{1}{4} \times$ 60th = 15th item, which is in the class £20 - £30.

It is calculated in the same way as the median of a grouped frequency distribution, using the formula

Q_1 = value of lower limit of class $+ (\frac{R}{f} \times$ c)

where Q_1 is the lower quartile
  f is the frequency of occurrences in the quartile class
  R is the quartile member minus the cumulative frequency up to the end of the preceding class
  c is the width of the quartile class.

Lower quartile Q_1 =   20 + $(\frac{15 - 9}{11} \times$ 10)

    =   25.45, say £25

The median is the 30th item, which is in the class £30 - £40. It is

30 + $(\frac{30 - 20}{15} \times$ 10) = 36.67, say £37.

The upper quartile (Q_3) is the 45th item, which is in the class interval £40 - £50.

Q_3 =   40 + $(\frac{45 - 35}{12} \times$ 10) = 48.33, say £48.

(b) The quartile deviation is $\frac{Q_3 - Q_1}{2}$ = $\frac{48 - 25}{2}$ = £11.50.

The quartile coefficient of dispersion

The *quartile coefficient of dispersion* is another measure of dispersion using quartiles. It differs from the quartile deviation because it is expressed as a *proportion* and not in units of the value of the variable. The lower the proportion, the less dispersed is the distribution.

Quartile coefficient of dispersion = $\frac{Q_3 - Q_1}{Q_3 + Q_1}$

where Q_1 is the lower quartile
  Q_3 is the upper quartile.

Exercise 5

The following table shows the values of deliveries made to customers last week.

	Value of delivery	
at least	*less than*	*Frequency*
£	£	
0	10	4
10	20	7
20	30	10
30	40	25
40	50	20
50	60	6
60	70	4

What is the quartile deviation?

The variance and the standard deviation

The most important measure of dispersion in statistics is the *standard deviation*. It is denoted by s or σ. σ is a lower case Greek letter sigma. The symbol s is used for the standard deviation of a sample, and σ is used for the standard deviation of a population.

The reason why the standard deviation is so important is that it is easy to use in further statistical analysis. In Chapter 8, for example, we will see how to use it to test theories like 'the average salary in the UK is £13,000'.

The standard deviation is *the square root of the variance*.

The *variance* is the average of the squared deviation $f(x - \bar{x})^2$ for each value in the distribution. It is denoted by s^2 or σ^2.

Thus the variance $= \dfrac{\Sigma f(x - \bar{x})^2}{n} = \dfrac{\Sigma fx^2}{n} - (\bar{x})^2$

The second of these formulae can be easily remembered as 'mean of squares minus square of mean'. Both of the formulae will always give the same value for the variance. With a frequency distribution, n = Σf.

The standard deviation $= \sqrt{\dfrac{\Sigma f(x - \bar{x})^2}{n}} = \sqrt{\dfrac{\Sigma fx^2}{n} - (\bar{x})^2}$

Example: the variance and the standard deviation

Calculate the variance and the standard deviation of the following frequency distribution of rates per hour charged for temporary secretaries.

Value x £	Frequency f
6	4
7	6
8	10
9	11
10	8
11	1
	40

It has a mean, $\bar{x}$, of £8.40.

Solution

Value x £	f	x^2	fx^2
6	4	36	144
7	6	49	294
8	10	64	640
9	11	81	891
10	8	100	800
11	1	121	121
	40		2,890

$$\text{Variance} = \frac{\Sigma fx^2}{n} - \bar{x}^2 = \frac{2,890}{40} - 8.4^2 = 72.25 - 70.56 = 1.69.$$

Standard deviation = $\sqrt{1.69}$ = £1.30.

Exercise 6

The durations of the telephone calls made by an employee were recorded for a month. The results are shown in the following table.

Duration at least Minutes	less than Minutes	Number of calls
0	3	45
3	6	59
6	9	38
9	12	31
12	15	19
15	18	8

Calculate the arithmetic mean, the variance and the standard deviation of the durations of these calls. Use the formula $\Sigma f(x - \bar{x})^2 / n$ for the variance.

BPP Publishing

Quantitative methods

The main properties of the standard deviation

The standard deviation's main properties are as follows.

(a) It is based on all the values in the distribution and so is more comprehensive than dispersion measures based on quantiles, such as the quartile deviation.

(b) It emphasises the effect of large deviations, because it squares all the deviations: $x - \bar{x}$.

(c) It is suitable for further statistical analysis.

The coefficient of variation

It is sometimes useful to be able to compare the dispersions of two distributions.

This comparison can be done using the *coefficient of variation.*

$$\text{Coefficient of variation} = \frac{\text{standard deviation}}{\text{mean}}$$

The coefficient of variation is sometimes known as the coefficient of relative dispersion.

The bigger the coefficient of variation, the wider the dispersion. For example, suppose that two sets of data, A and B, have the following mean and standard deviation.

	A	*B*
Mean	120	125
Standard deviation	50	51
Coefficient of variation	0.417	0.408

Although B has a higher standard deviation in absolute terms (51 compared to 50) its relative dispersion is a bit less than A's since the coefficient of variation is a bit smaller.

Exercise 7

A maintenance manager has recorded the time taken by maintenance staff to repair a particular type of equipment fault. The following table shows the time taken in minutes to repair 250 recent faults.

Time taken		
at least	*less than*	*Frequency*
Minutes	Minutes	
0	10	28
10	20	54
20	30	81
30	40	57
40	50	23
50	60	7

(a) Calculate the mean and the standard deviation of the time taken.
(b) Calculate the coefficient of variation.

The variance and the standard deviation of several items together

You may need to calculate the variance and standard deviation for n items together, given the variance and standard deviation for one item alone.

Example: several items together

The daily demand for an item of stock has a mean of 6 units, with a variance of 4 and a standard deviation of 2 units. Demand on any one day is unaffected by demand on previous days or subsequent days.

What will be the arithmetic mean, the variance and the standard deviation of demand for a five day week?

Solution

The mean is simply 6 units a day × 5 days = 30 units.

The *variance* is also calculated as the sum of the variances for each day of the week: 4 a day × 5 days = 20.

The *standard deviation* is $\sqrt{20}$ = 4.47 units. (It is *not* 2 units a day × 5 days = 10 units.)

The rules demonstrated in this example apply whenever we add values of variables which are independent of each other: add means and add variances (*not* standard deviations).

Exercise 8

The weights of three items X, Y and Z vary independently and have the following means and standard deviations.

	Mean weight	Standard deviation
	kg	kg
X	10	2
Y	14	2
Z	6	1

The three items are sold together in a single packet. What is the mean weight of a packet of one unit each of X, Y and Z, and what is the standard deviation of the weights of packets?

Notes

Chapter roundup

(a) Averages give an idea of the values of variables in a set of data.

(b) The arithmetic mean is found by adding all the values found (values × frequencies in a grouped frequency distribution) and dividing by the total number of items of data.

(c) The mode is the most frequently occurring value. In a grouped frequency distribution, it may be estimated using either a formula or a histogram.

(d) The median is the value below which 50% of items fall. In a grouped frequency distribution, it may be estimated using either a formula or an ogive.

(e) Measures of dispersion indicate how spread out values of a variable in a set of data are.

(f) Quartiles are one type of quantile. The quartile deviation and the quartile coefficient of dispersion are two measures of dispersion.

(g) The most important measure of dispersion is the standard deviation, which is the square root of the variance. The coefficient of variation is based on the standard deviation, but it facilitates comparisons between two sets of data.

(h) Where we have several independent variables, the variance of their sum is the sum of their variances.

Quick quiz

1   State a formula for the arithmetic mean of a frequency distribution.

2   Define the mode.

3   Explain how to estimate the mode from a histogram of a distribution.

4   Define the median.

5   What is the purpose of measures of dispersion?

6   What are quantiles?

7   Give a formula for the standard deviation.

8   Define the coefficient of variation of a distribution.

Solutions to exercises

1 The total of demands × frequencies would have been 168, giving $\bar{x} = 168/20 = 8.4$

2 Note that the mid points of the classes are half way between their end points, because wages can vary in steps of only 1p so are virtually a continuous variable.

Mid point of class	Frequency	
x	*f*	*fx*
£		
55	3	165
65	11	715
75	16	1,200
85	15	1,275
95	10	950
105	8	840
115	6	690
	69	5,835

Arithmetic mean $= \dfrac{£5,835}{69} = £84.57$

3 The model class is $\geqslant 40 < 55$.

An estimate of the mode is:

$$40 + \frac{(18-8) \times 15}{(2 \times 18) - 8 - 9} = 40 + \frac{150}{19} = £47.89$$

4 (a) The mean is calculated as follows.

Mid point	Frequency		Cumulative frequency
x	*f*	*fx*	
£			
5,250	4	21,000	4
5,750	26	149,500	30
6,250	133	831,250	163
6,750	35	236,250	198
7,250	2	14,500	200
	200	1,252,500	

Mean $= \dfrac{1,252,500}{200} = £6,262.50$

BPP Publishing

(b) The median value is the value of the 100th item. This is estimated as

$$£6,000 + \frac{100 - 30}{133} \times £500$$

=   £6,000 + £263.16

=   £6,263.16

(c) The modal value is in the range £6,000 and less than £6,500. It is estimated as

$$£6,000 + \frac{(133 - 26) \times £500}{(2 \times 133) - 26 - 35}$$

= $£6,000 + \dfrac{£53,500}{205}$

=   £6,260.98

5

Value of delivery			
at least £	less than £	Frequency	Cumulative frequency
0	10	4	4
10	20	7	11
20	30	10	21
30	40	25	46
40	50	20	66
50	60	6	72
60	70	4	76

The lower quartile is the $\frac{1}{4} \times$ 76th = 19th item, which is in the class £20 to £30.

Lower quartile Q_1 = $£20 + [(19 - 11)/10] \times £10 = £28.00$

The upper quartile is the $\frac{3}{4} \times$ 76th = 57th item. The 57th item is in the class interval £40 to £50.

Upper quartile, Q_3 = $£40 + [(57 - 46)/20] \times £10 = £45.50$

Quartile deviation   = $\dfrac{£(45.50 - 28.00)}{2}$ = £8.75

6

Mid point x Minutes	f	fx	$x - \bar{x}$	$f(x - \bar{x})^2$
1.5	45	67.5	-5.16	1,198.1520
4.5	59	265.5	-2.16	275.2704
7.5	38	285.0	0.84	26.8128
10.5	31	325.5	3.84	457.1136
13.5	19	256.5	6.84	888.9264
16.5	8	132.0	9.84	774.6048
	200	1,332.0		3,620.8800

$$\bar{x} = \frac{\Sigma fx}{\Sigma f} = \frac{1,332}{200} = 6.66$$

$$\text{Variance} = \frac{3,620.88}{200} = 18.1044$$

Standard deviation $= \sqrt{18.1044} = 4.255$ minutes.

7

Mid point x	f	fx	$x - \bar{x}$	$f(x - \bar{x})^2$
5	28	140	-20.56	11,835.98
15	54	810	-10.56	6,021.73
25	81	2,025	-0.56	25.40
35	57	1,995	9.44	5,079.48
45	23	1,035	19.44	8,692.01
55	7	385	29.44	6,067.00
	250	6,390		37,721.60

$$\text{Mean} = \frac{6,390}{250} = 25.56 \text{ minutes}$$

$$\text{Standard deviation} = \sqrt{\frac{37,721.6}{250}} = 12.28 \text{ minutes}$$

$$\text{Coefficient of variation} = \frac{12.28}{25.56} = 0.48$$

8   Mean of X + Y + Z $\quad = \quad (10 + 14 + 6) \text{ kg} = 30 \text{ kg}$

Variance of X + Y + Z $\quad = \quad (2^2 + 2^2 + 1^2) = 9$

Standard deviation of X + Y + Z $= \sqrt{9} = 3$ kg.

Packets of one of each of X, Y and Z have a mean weight of 30 kg and a standard deviation of weights of 3 kg.

6 PROBABILITY

1 The concept of probability

Probability is the likelihood or chance of something happening. For example, we might be concerned that it will rain tomorrow. Call 'rain tomorrow' outcome A. We might decide that there is an 80% chance (or a 0.8 chance) that outcome A will happen. We would then be implying that there is a 20%, or 0.2 chance, that A will not occur (that it will be dry tomorrow). It is four times more likely that A will occur than that A will not occur, and the total of probabilities adds up to 100% or 1.

Something which is certain to happen has a probability of 1. For example, it is certain that it will either rain or not rain tomorrow (but we do not know which). Something which is impossible has a probability of 0. For example, it is impossible for it both to rain tomorrow and be dry all day tomorrow.

In statistics, probabilities are more commonly expressed as proportions than as percentages: for example, if there are four possible different outcomes following the launch of a new product, the probabilities might be expressed as follows.

Possible outcome	Probability as a percentage %	Probability as a proportion
A: very high demand	15.0	0.150
B: high demand	45.0	0.450
C: low demand	32.5	0.325
D: no demand	7.5	0.075
	100.0	1.000

Consider a simple repetitive experiment, such as tossing a coin. There are two possible outcomes for each throw, heads or tails, each of which is equally likely. If the letter P is used to denote the probability of an outcome occurring, then

$$P \text{ (heads)} = P \text{ (tails)}$$

Probabilities are expressed in fractions or proportions and the sum of the probabilities of all possible outcomes must equal one.

$P (H) + P (T) = 1$ and
$P (H) = P (T) = 0.5$

Probability is concerned with *uncertainty* about what will happen. An estimate can be made about the *likelihood* of something happening, but what actually happens cannot be predicted with certainty. As you may imagine, in business, where future events are always uncertain, probability theory has many potential applications.

Probability is a measure of the likelihood of an event happening *in the long run*, or over a large number of times. If we toss a coin eight times, we cannot predict that it will necessarily come down heads four times and tails four times. Heads may occur any number of times between zero and eight. We can say, however, that in the long run heads will occur about 50% of the time if a coin is tossed often enough.

2   The rules of probability

To formulate the rules of probability, we need to consider certain types of outcomes and events.

Two outcomes are *mutually exclusive* when one of them cannot happen if the other occurs. Several outcomes are mutually exclusive if the occurrence of one of them excludes the possibility of any of the others happening. If, for example, five different firms tender for the same contract, any one of the five might win the contract, to the exclusion of the other four. There would be five possible outcomes, all mutually exclusive.

Independent events are events where the outcome of one of them in no way affects the outcome of the others. For example, whether or not it rains in Australia has no effect on whether or not a cricket match is cancelled in England.

A *conditional event* is one in which the outcome is influenced by the outcome of another event. For example, the probability of someone's getting a pay rise would depend on whether or not they had impressed their employer.

The probability of a particular outcome of a conditional event is usually written as $P_A(B)$ or $P(B|A)$, which refers to the probability that B will occur if A occurs. Thus if 'A' is someone's having impressed their employer, 'not A' is their having failed to impress their employer and 'B' is their getting a pay rise, we might have $P(B|A) = 0.9$ but $P(B|\text{not } A) = 0.2$.

Example: mutually exclusive outcomes

Customers in a clothes shop might require clothes in any one of five different sizes, with the following probabilities.

Size	Probability
10	0.1
12	0.3
14	0.3
16	0.2
18	0.1
	1.0

The probability that a customer will want clothes in size 10 or size 12 or size 14 is 0.1 + 0.3 + 0.3 = 0.7.

This example illustrates the rule that if several outcomes, X, Y and Z are *mutually exclusive*, then the probability that either X or Y or Z may occur is given by:

$$P(X \text{ or } Y \text{ or } Z) = P(X) + P(Y) + P(Z).$$

Example: outcomes which are not mutually exclusive

A company is bringing two new products, J and K onto the market. The demands for the two products are unrelated. The probability that demand for J will be high is 0.4, and the probability that demand for K will be high is 0.7.

The probability that either demand for J or demand for K (or both) will be high is not 0.4 + 0.7 = 1.1. That cannot be right, because probabilities cannot exceed 1. The probability we want is $0.4 + 0.7 - (0.4 \times 0.7) = 0.82$.

This example illustrates the rule that if A and B are two possible outcomes of an event then

$$P(A \text{ or } B \text{ or both}) = P(A) + P(B) - P(A \text{ and } B)$$

The deduction of $P(A \text{ and } B)$ is required to eliminate double counting, as the combination A and B will be considered in the calculation both of $P(A)$ and of $P(B)$. If A and B are mutually exclusive, then $P(A \text{ and } B) = 0$ and we have the same rule as we gave for mutually exclusive outcomes.

Exercise 1

If one card is drawn from a normal pack of 52 playing cards, what is the probability of getting an ace or a spade?

Example: independent events

The probability of throwing a 5 on a die is 1/6.
The probability of a tossed coin coming up heads is 1/2.

The probability of throwing a 5 and getting heads on a coin is

$$\frac{1}{6} \times \frac{1}{2} = \frac{1}{12}$$

The rule applied here is that if the outcome of one event will not influence the outcome of the other, the probability of one event having outcome A *and* the other event having outcome B is

$$P(A \text{ and } B) = P(A) \times P(B)$$

Example: conditional events

A company has an 0.8 probability of increasing its sales if extra sales staff are recruited but only a 0.1 probability of doing so if extra sales staff are not recruited. There is a 0.35 probability that extra sales staff will be recruited. If outcome A is that extra sales staff are recruited and outcome B is that sales are increased, then the probability that both will happen is

$$P(A \text{ and } B) = 0.35 \times 0.8 = 0.28$$

The rule applied here is that if the outcome of one event is dependent, or conditional, upon the outcome of another event, then the probability that both outcomes A (from one event) and B (from the other event) will occur is

$$P(A \text{ and } B) = P(A) \times P(B|A)$$

$$= P(B) \times P(A|B)$$

Exercise 2

The independent probabilities that the three sections of a costing department will encounter one computer error in a week are respectively 0.1, 0.2 and 0.3. There is never more than one computer error encountered by any one section in a week. Calculate the probability that there will be:

BPP Publishing

(a) at least one computer error;
(b) one and only one computer error;

encountered by the costing department next week.

A method of calculating conditional probabilities

It is possible to calculate the conditional probability of an outcome, using the formula:

$$P(B|A) = \frac{P(A \text{ and } B)}{P(A)} = \frac{P(B)P(A|B)}{P(A)}$$

This is called *Bayes' theorem*.

Example: Bayes' theorem

The estimated probability that the labour force in a factory will improve its productivity over both of the next two years is 0.6. It is also thought that there is a 0.8 probability that productivity will improve in the first year.

Given that productivity does rise in the first year, what is the probability that productivity will also rise in the second year?

Solution

Let outcome A = an increase in productivity in Year 1
    outcome B = an increase in productivity in Year 2

$$P(B|A) = \frac{P(A \text{ and } B)}{P(A)}$$

$$= \frac{0.6}{0.8}$$

$$= 0.75$$

3 Prior and posterior probabilities

Consider a factory in which two machines produce the same product. The older machine produces 35% of the total output but eight units in every 100 are defective. The newer machine produces 65% of the total output but two units in every 100 are defective. Thus if a unit came from the older machine, the probability that it is defective is 0.08. This is a *prior probability:* we get it straight from the data.

Looking at the situation in reverse, we can find the probability that a defective unit picked at random was produced by the older machine. This is a *posterior probability*, and we can find it using Bayes' theorem.

Let A be a unit's being defective.
Let B be a unit's having come from the older machine.

P(B)   = 0.35
P(A|B)   = 0.08
P(A)   = $(0.35 \times 0.08) + (0.65 \times 0.02) = 0.041$

Then P(B|A) = $\dfrac{P(B)\,P(A|B)}{P(A)}$ = $\dfrac{0.35 \times 0.08}{0.041}$ = 0.68

Exercise 3

Two sales staff, Jane and Alison, sell the same product. Jane makes 40% of all calls on potential customers, and Alison makes 60% of all calls. 70% of Jane's calls and 55% of Alison's calls are successful. Given that a successful call has been made, what is the probability that it was made by Alison?

---

4   Expected values

An expected value is a weighted average, based on probabilities. For a variable called X, it is denoted by E(X).

For example, suppose that the probability that a transistor is defective is 0.02. How many defectives would we expect to find in a batch of 4,000 transistors? Call the number of defectives in a batch X.

E(X) = $4,000 \times 0.02$
     = 80 defectives would be expected.

If the probability of an outcome of an event is p, then the expected number of times that this outcome will occur in n events (the expected value) is equal to $n \times p$.

Example: expected values

The daily sales, S, of Product T may be as follows.

Units	Probability
1,000	0.2
2,000	0.3
3,000	0.4
4,000	0.1
	1.0

What are the expected daily sales?

Solution

The expected value of daily sales may be calculated by multiplying each possible outcome (volume of daily sales) by the probability that this outcome will occur.

Units	Probability	Expected value
1,000	0.2	200
2,000	0.3	600
3,000	0.4	1,200
4,000	0.1	400
	E(S)	2,400

In the long run the expected value should be approximately the actual average, if the event occurs many times over. In the example above, we do not expect sales on any one day to equal 2,400 units, but in the long run, over a large number of days, average sales should equal 2,400 units a day.

Expected values and single events

The point made in the preceding paragraph is an important one. An expected value can be calculated when the event will only occur once or twice, but it will not be a true long-run average of what will actually happen, because there is no long run.

Suppose, for example, that a businessman is trying to decide whether to invest in a project. He estimates that there are three possible outcomes.

Outcome	Profit/(loss) £	Probability
Success	10,000	0.2
Moderate success	2,000	0.7
Failure	(4,000)	0.1

The expected value of profit may be calculated as follows.

Profit/(loss) £	Probability	Expected value £
10,000	0.2	2,000
2,000	0.7	1,400
(4,000)	0.1	(400)
	Expected value of profit	3,000

In this example, the project is a one-off event, and as far as we are aware, it will not be repeated. The actual profit or loss will be £10,000, £2,000 or £(4,000), and the average value of £3,000 will not actually happen. There is no long-run average of a single event.

Nevertheless, the expected value can be used to help the manager decide whether or not to invest in the project. All other things being equal a project with a positive expected value (an expected value which is a profit) should be accepted, and a project with a negative expected value (an expected value which is a loss) should be rejected.

Exercise 4

A company manufactures and sells product D. The selling price of the product is £6 per unit, and estimates of demand and variable costs of sales (the cost per unit made) are as follows.

Probability	Demand	Probability	Variable cost per unit
	Units		£
0.3	5,000	0.1	3.00
0.6	6,000	0.3	3.50
0.1	8,000	0.5	4.00
		0.1	4.50

The unit variable costs do not depend on the volume of sales.

Fixed costs (incurred however many units are made) will be £10,000.

What is the expected profit?

5 Decision trees

Decision trees are diagrams which illustrate the choices and possible outcomes of a decision. They are particularly useful when working out expected values.

The two stages in preparing a decision tree are:

(a) drawing the tree itself, to show all the choices and outcomes;
(b) putting in the numbers: the probabilities, outcome values and expected values.

Drawing a decision tree: the basic rules

Every decision tree starts from a decision point with the decision options that are currently being considered.

(a) There should be a line, or branch, for each option or alternative, for example for each level of advertising which a company could choose to undertake.

(b) It helps to identify the decision point, and any subsequent decision points in the tree, with a symbol. Here, we shall use a square shape.

It is conventional to draw decision trees from left to right, and so a decision tree will start as follows.

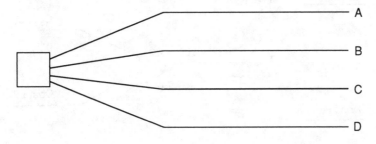

The square is the decision point, and A, B, C and D represent four alternatives from which a choice must be made.

If the outcome from any choice is certain, the branch of the decision tree for that alternative is complete.

If, on the other hand, the outcome of a particular choice is uncertain, the various possible outcomes must be shown. We show this on a decision tree by inserting an *outcome point* on the branch of the tree. Each possible outcome is then shown as a subsidiary branch, coming out from the outcome point. The probability of each outcome occurring should be written on to the branch of the tree which represents that outcome.

To distinguish decision points from outcome points, a circle will be used as the symbol for an outcome point. Thus a choice between abandoning a product (option A) and continuing with it could be shown as follows.

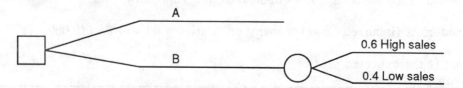

The outcome if A is chosen is known with certainty, but if B is chosen, there are two possible outcomes, high sales (0.6 probability) or low sales (0.4 probability).

When several outcomes are possible, it is usually simpler to show two or more stages of outcome points on the decision tree.

Example: several possible outcomes

A company can choose to launch a new product XYZ or not. If the product is launched, expected sales and expected unit costs might be as follows.

Sales			Unit costs	
Units	Probability		£	Probability
10,000	0.8		6	0.7
15,000	0.2		8	0.3

The decision tree could be drawn as follows.

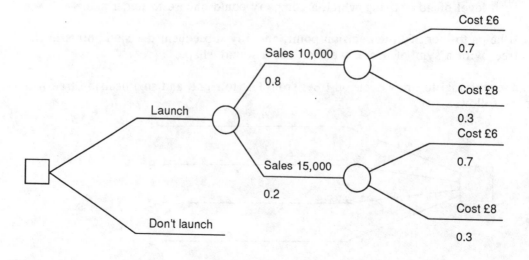

Sometimes, a decision taken now will lead to other decisions to be taken in the future. When this situation arises, the decision tree can be drawn as a two-stage tree, as follows.

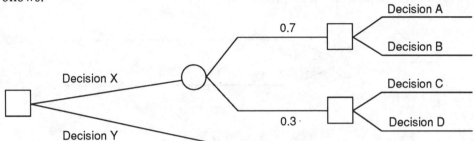

In this tree, either a choice between A and B or else a choice between C and D will be made, depending on the outcome which occurs after choosing X.

The decision tree should be in chronological order from left to right. When there are two-stage decision trees, the first decision in time should be drawn on the left.

Exercise 5

Beethoven Ltd has a new wonder product, the vylin, of which it expects great things. At the moment the company has two courses of action open to it, to test market the product or abandon it. If the company test markets it, the cost will be £100,000 and the market response could be positive or negative with probabilities of 0.60 and 0.40. If the response is positive the company could either abandon the product or market it full scale. If it markets the vylin full scale, the outcome might be low, medium or high demand, and the respective net payoffs would be (200), 200 or 1,000 in units of £1,000. (The result could range from a net loss of £200,000 to a gain of £1,000,000. The brackets in '(200)' indicate a loss, that is a profit of –200.) These outcomes have probabilities of 0.20, 0.50 and 0.30 respectively.

If the result of the test marketing is negative and the company goes ahead and markets the product, estimated losses would be £600,000. If, at any point, the company abandons the product, there would be a net gain of £50,000 from the sale of scrap.

(a)   Draw a decision tree.

(b)   Include figures for cost, loss or profit on the appropriate branches of the tree.

Evaluating the options with a decision tree

The expected value of each decision option can be evaluated, using the decision tree to help with keeping the logic properly sorted out. The basic rules are as follows.

We start on the right hand side of the tree and work back towards the left hand side and the current decision under consideration. Working from right to left, we calculate the expected value of revenue, cost, contribution or profit at each outcome point on the tree.

Example: evaluating the options

The following decision tree has been produced.

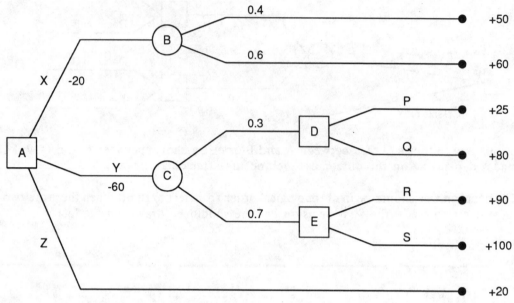

Key

All values in £'000

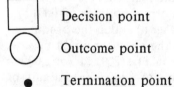
    Decision point

    Outcome point

    Termination point

Evaluate this tree.

Solution

The value at B is (0.4 × 50) + (0.6 × 60) = 56, so the value at A of decision X is 56 – 20 = 36.

At D, Q would be chosen rather than P, giving a value at D of 80.

AT E, S would be chosen rather than R, giving a value at E of 100.

The value at C is (0.3 × 80) + (0.7 × 100) = 94, so the value at A of decision Y is 94 – 60 = 34.

The value at A of decision Z is 20.

The best decision at A appears to be X, with an expected value of £36,000.

Exercise 6

Evaluate the options on the decision tree you prepared in Exercise 5.

Chapter roundup

(a) Probability is the likelihood of something happening. Probabilities may range from 0 to 1. The total of the probabilities of all of the outcomes of an event add up to 100% or 1.

(b) P (A or B) = P(A) + P(B) where A and B are mutually exclusive outcomes.

(c) P(A or B) = P(A) + P(B) - P(A and B), where A and B are non-mutually exclusive outcomes.

(d) P (A and B) = P(A) $\times$ P(B) where A and B are independent events.

(e) P(A and B) = P(A) $\times$ P(B/A) for conditional events.

(f) Conditional probabilities may be found using Bayes' theorem.

(g) Posterior probabilities work backwards from a known result (such as a part's being defective) to the likelihood of a particular cause (such as the part's having been produced on a particular machine).

(h) An expected value is a weighted average, based on probabilities. Expected values can be used to decide whether or not to proceed with a project, but it should be remembered that there is no long-run average for a one-off decision.

(i) Decision trees set out options and possible outcomes. They may be evaluated to find the expected value of each option.

Quick quiz

1 Define mutually exclusive outcomes, independent events and conditional events.

2 What is the formula for the conditional probability of B given A?

3 How do you calculate an expected value?

4 Are there any drawbacks to always selecting the option with the highest expected value of profit?

5 Sketch the symbols used to depict decision points and outcome points in a decision tree.

6 How is a decision tree evaluated?

Solutions to exercises

1 There are four aces in the pack, so P (ace) $= \dfrac{4}{52}$

There are 13 spades in the pack, so P (spade) $= \dfrac{13}{52}$

There is only one ace of spades, so P (ace of spades) $= \dfrac{1}{52}$

It follows that P (ace or spade) $= \dfrac{4}{52} + \dfrac{13}{52} - \dfrac{1}{52} = \dfrac{16}{52}$

The same result could, of course, have been obtained by working as follows.

Number of spades   13
Number of other aces   3
                                     16

Therefore P (ace or spade) $= \dfrac{16}{52}$ as before

2 (a) The probability of at least one computer error is 1 minus the probability of no errors. The probability of no error is $0.9 \times 0.8 \times 0.7 = 0.504$.

(Since the probability of an error is 0.1, 0.2 and 0.3 in each section, the probability of no error in each section must be 0.9, 0.8 and 0.7 respectively.)

The probability of at least one error is $1 - 0.504 = 0.496$.

(b) Y = yes, N = no

		Section 1	Section 2	Section 3
(i)	Error?	Y	N	N
(ii)	Error?	N	Y	N
(iii)	Error?	N	N	Y

Probabilities

(i)		$0.1 \times 0.8 \times 0.7$	=	0.056
(ii)		$0.9 \times 0.2 \times 0.7$	=	0.126
(iii)		$0.9 \times 0.8 \times 0.3$	=	0.216
		Total		0.398

The probability of one error only is 0.398.

3   Let A be a call's being successful
Let B be a call's being made by Alison

$P(A) = (0.4 \times 0.7) + (0.6 \times 0.55) = 0.61$
$P(B) = 0.6$
$P(A|B) = 0.55$

$P(B|A) = 0.6 \times 0.55 \, / \, 0.61 = 0.541$

4   The expected value of demand is as follows.

Demand	Probability	Expected value
Units		Units
5,000	0.3	1,500
6,000	0.6	3,600
8,000	0.1	800
		5,900

The expected value of the variable cost per unit is as follows.

Variable costs	Probability	Expected value
£		£
3.00	0.1	0.30
3.50	0.3	1.05
4.00	0.5	2.00
4.50	0.1	0.45
		3.80

		£
Sales	5,900 units × £6.00	35,400
Less variable costs	5,900 units × £3.80	22,420
Contribution		12,980
Less fixed costs		10,000
Expected profit		2,980

5

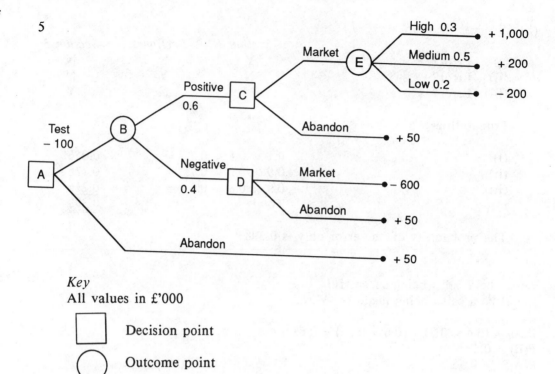

Key

All values in £'000

☐ Decision point

◯ Outcome point

● Termination point

6   The right-hand-most outcome point is point E, and the expected value is as follows.

	Profit (£'000)	Probability	
	x	*p*	*px*
High	1,000	0.3	300
Medium	200	0.5	100
Low	(200)	0.2	(40)
		Expected value	360

This is the expected value of the decision to market the product if the test shows a positive response. It may help you to write the expected value on the decision tree itself, at the appropriate outcome point (point E).

At decision point C, the choice is:

(a) market: expected value = +360 (the expected value at point E); or
(b) abandon: value = +50.

The choice would be to market the product, and so the expected value at decision point C is +360.

At decision point D, the choice is:

(a) market: value = -600; or
(b) abandon: value = +50.

The choice would be to abandon, and so the expected value at decision point D is +50.

The second stage decisions have therefore been made. If the original decision is to test market, the company will market the product if the test shows positive customer response, and will abandon the product if the test results are negative.

The evaluation of the decision tree is completed as follows.

(a)   Calculate the expected value at outcome point B.

$$0.6 \times 360 \text{ (expected value at C)}$$
$$+ \quad 0.4 \times \quad 50 \text{ (expected value at D)}$$
$$= \quad 216 + \quad 20 = 236.$$

(b)   Compare the options at point A, which are:

   (i)   test: expected value = expected value at B minus test marketing cost = 236 – 100 = 136;

   (ii)   abandon: value = 50.

The choice would be to test market the product, because it has a higher expected value of profit.

7 PROBABILITY DISTRIBUTIONS

Signpost

In the last chapter we looked at the probabilities of different outcomes separately. In this chapter we will look at probability distributions which collect together information on the probabilities of a whole range of different outcomes. We will first pause to look at permutations and combinations, which are a useful way of working out the number of different possible outcomes when a selection is made from a group of items. We will then look at three distributions.

The binomial distribution can answer questions like: what is the probability that 6 new cars in a batch of 100 will be faulty, given that 3% of all new cars are faulty? The Poisson distribution can answer questions like: what is the probability of receiving 5 letters tomorrow, given that on average 2 letters a day are received? The normal distribution can answer questions like: if the average hourly wage rate is £8, with a standard deviation of £2, what is the probability that a worker picked at random will earn between £7 and £10 an hour?

Your objectives

After completing this chapter you should:

(a) understand the concept of a probability distribution;

(b) be able to compute permutations and combinations;

(c) know when the binomial distribution applies, and be able to compute binomial probabilities;

(d) know when the Poisson distribution applies, and be able to compute Poisson probabilities;

(e) understand the importance of the normal distribution, and be able to use normal distribution tables.

1 Probability distributions

A frequency distribution shows how many times each particular value occurs in a set of items. A probability distribution simply replaces actual numbers (frequencies) with proportions of the total. For example, in a statistics test, the marks out of ten awarded to 50 students might be as follows.

Marks out of 10	Number of students (frequency distribution)	Proportion or probability (probability distribution)
0	0	0.00
1	0	0.00
2	1	0.02
3	2	0.04
4	4	0.08
5	10	0.20
6	15	0.30
7	10	0.20
8	6	0.12
9	2	0.04
10	0	0.00
	50	1.00

In this chapter, we shall look at three types of distribution commonly found in business applications. These are the binomial distribution, the Poisson distribution and the normal distribution. Before looking at the binomial distribution, however, we will take a little time to look at permutations and combinations. These can be useful in their own right and combinations are used directly in the binomial distribution.

2   Permutations and combinations

Permutations and combinations are important tools in working out probabilities. They give us a way of finding out the number of different possible outcomes of certain situations.

A *combination* is a set of items, selected from a larger collection of items, regardless of the order in which they are selected. For example, suppose that five people apply for two vacancies as accountants in Combo Ltd and these people are called A,B,C,D and E. The different possible combinations of people to fill the two posts from the five applicants would be AB, AC, AD, AE, BC, BD, BE, CD, CE and DE. We refer to the number of possible combinations of x items from n unlike items. In this example x = 2 and n = 5, and there are ten possible combinations.

A *permutation* is a set of items, selected from a larger group of items, in which the order of selection or arrangement is significant. We refer to the number of possible permutations of x items from n unlike items.

In the previous example, suppose that the two vacancies were for the post of senior accountant and junior accountant. The order of selection would be important and the possible permutations would be as follows.

Senior	Junior	Senior	Junior	Senior	Junior	Senior	Junior
A	B	B	C	C	D	D	E
A	C	B	D	C	E	E	A
A	D	B	E	D	A	E	B
A	E	C	A	D	B	E	C
B	A	C	B	D	C	E	D

Whereas there were ten combinations of two from five, there are 20 permutations of two from five.

BPP Publishing

The formula for the number of permutations

There is a formula to calculate the number of permutations of x items which are possible from a set of n unlike items. The number is denoted by $_nP_x$ and the formula is

$$_nP_x = \frac{n!}{(n-x)!}$$

The notation here is as follows.

n!	is the factorial of n ($1 \times 2 \times 3 \times 4 \times 5 \times ... \times n$)
(n-x)!	is the factorial of the difference between n and x.

There is a special rule that $0! = 1$.

Example: permutations

In the previous example of five candidates for two different jobs, the number of different permutations would be

$$_5P_2 = \frac{5!}{(5-2)!} = \frac{5 \times 4 \times 3 \times 2 \times 1}{3 \times 2 \times 1} = 5 \times 4 = 20$$

The formula for the number of combinations

There is also a formula to calculate the number of combinations of x items which are possible from a set of n unlike items. This formula is

$$_nC_x = \frac{n!}{(n-x)!x!}$$

(The notation $_nC_x$ means 'the number of different combinations of x items from a set of n items'.)

Example: combinations

In the example of five candidates applying for two jobs of equal status, the number of possible combinations of two applicants would be

$$_5C_2 = \frac{5!}{3!2!} = \frac{5 \times 4 \times 3 \times 2 \times 1}{(3 \times 2 \times 1)(2 \times 1)} = \frac{5 \times 4}{2 \times 1} = 10$$

Exercise 1

A class of 15 students is about to sit a statistics exam. They will subsequently be listed in descending order by reference to the marks scored. Assuming that there are no tied positions with two or more students having the same mark, calculate:

(a) the number of different possible orderings for the whole class;

(b)   the number of different possible results for the top three places;

(c)   the number of different possible ways of having three people taking the top three places (irrespective of order).

3   The binomial distribution

The binomial distribution applies where there are two possible outcomes, each with a constant probability. It follows that the outcome of one event has no effect on the outcomes of other events: the events are *independent*. For example, if we are considering the likelihood that a certain number of units of output are faulty, we may be able to use a binomial distribution because for any unit produced, there are only two possible outcomes.

(a)   The unit is faulty, probability p.
(b)   The unit is not faulty, probability q.

p + q equals 1, so q = 1 - p.

Binomial distributions are quite commonly found, since they usefully describe any situation in which we are considering the likelihood of something either happening or else not happening, so long as the probabilities (p and q) of the two outcomes are constant.

If there are n items and the outcome for each item must be either of two possible results, a binomial distribution will indicate the probability that one of the results will occur a certain number of times within the total of n.

For example, if a coin is tossed three times, the possible outcomes are as follows. (H is heads and T is tails.)

Number of heads	First toss	Second toss	Third toss	Probability
3	H	H	H	*0.125
2	H	T	H	
	H	H	T	**0.375
	T	H	H	
1	H	T	T	
	T	H	T	0.375
	T	T	H	
0	T	T	T	0.125
				1.000

*   (0.5 × 0.5 × 0.5)
** 3 × (0.5 × 0.5 × 0.5)

The right hand column gives the binomial distribution for three tosses of a coin.

Usually, one outcome (for example heads, or throwing a 6 on a die) is called a success, and the other outcome is called a failure.

BPP Publishing

If an experiment is performed n times then the probability of x successes is given by

$$P(x) = \frac{n!}{x!(n-x)!} \, p^x \, q^{n-x}$$

where p = the probability of success in a single trial
q = the probability of failure in a single trial
q = 1 - p

The first part of the expression, $\frac{n!}{x!(n-x)!}$ is the formula for the number of combinations $_nC_x$.

This is so because we need the number of different ways of picking x trials out of n to be the successes. Thus if x = 2 and n = 3, we could take trials 1 and 2, 2 and 3 or 1 and 3. For any one combination of trials, the probability of x successes and n - x failures is $p^x q^{n-x}$.

The formula could therefore be re-written as

$$P(x) = \, _nC_x \, p^x \, (1-p)^{n-x}$$

Example: the binomial distribution

A company is planning to sell a new product in four areas, North, South, East and West. The probability that the product will be successful in an area is 0.3. Success in one area will be independent of success or failure in the other areas. What is the probability of success in no area, one area, two areas, three areas or four areas?

Solution

The probabilities are p = 0.3 and q = 0.7. The number of areas, four, gives us our value for n.

Number of successes				Probability
0	P(0)	=	$\frac{4!}{0!4!} (0.3)^0 (0.7)^4$	=0.2401
1	P(1)	=	$\frac{4!}{1!3!} (0.3)^1 (0.7)^3$	=0.4116
2	P(2)	=	$\frac{4!}{2!2!} (0.3)^2 (0.7)^2$	=0.2646
3	P(3)	=	$\frac{4!}{3!1!} (0.3)^3 (0.7)^1$	=0.0756
4	P(4)	=	$\frac{4!}{4!0!} (0.3)^4 (0.7)^0$	=0.0081
				1.0000

Exercise 2

The demand for an item of raw material is usually less than eight units per month, but there is a 10% probability that demand in one month will be eight units or more.

In a six month period, what is the probability that demand will equal or exceed eight units in:

(a)   two of the six months?
(b)   three of the six months?

The mean and the standard deviation of a binomial distribution

The arithmetic mean of a binomial distribution is np. (This is the same as the expected value.)

The standard deviation of a binomial distribution $= \sqrt{npq} = \sqrt{np(1 - p)}$

The variance of a binomial distribution is therefore $npq = np(1-p)$

We will need these values later, when we look at approximations to the binomial distribution.

4   The Poisson distribution

The Poisson distribution is used:

(a)   where events occur randomly within an interval, for example defects in a 100m length of rope, or telephone sales orders received in an hour.

(b)   as an approximation to the binomial distribution, when n is large (say ten or more) and p is small (say 0.1 or less).

Like the binomial distribution the Poisson distribution is for *discrete* variables: when we estimate the probability P(x), the probability of an event happening no times at all, once, twice, or whatever, x must be a whole number.

There is a formula which can be used to calculate P(x).

$$P(x) = \frac{m^x e^{-m}}{x!}$$

where   P(x)   is the probability of an event occurring x times
        m   is the expected, or average number of times
        e   is a special constant whose value is approximately 2.71828. This is a value you ought to learn, or be able to get from your calculator.

   BPP Publishing

The standard deviation of a Poisson distribution is $\sqrt{m}$.

When a Poisson distribution is used to approximate a binomial distribution, m equals np, which is the mean of a binomial distribution.

Poisson tables

At the start of this text there is a table for the Poisson distribution. The table gives the probabilities for given values of x and m.

Example: the Poisson distribution

The mean number of calls received on a telephone per hour is 1.6. What is the probability that:

(a)   exactly two calls will be received in an hour;
(b)   more than two calls will be received in an hour;
(c)   exactly five calls will be received in a three hour period?

Solution

(a)   P(2)   =   0.2584 (from the table, using the row for m = 1.6)

(b)   P(>2) =   1 − (P(0) + P(1) + P(2))
          =   1 − (0.2019 + 0.3230 + 0.2584)
          =   1 − 0.7833
          =   0.2167

(c)   P(5 in 3 hours)

   If the mean per hour is 1.6, the mean per three hours is 3 × 1.6 = 4.8.

   $$\frac{4.8^5}{5!}\, e^{-4.8} = \frac{2,548.0397}{120} \times \frac{1}{121.5104}$$

   $$= 0.1747$$

Example: the Poisson distribution as an approximation to the Binomial distribution

Transistors are packed in boxes of 1,000. On average 0.1% will be defective. What proportion of boxes will contain:

(a)   0 defectives;
(b)   1 defective;
(c)   2 defectives;
(d)   3 or more defectives?

Solution

The binomial distribution applies, with n = 1,000 and np = 1,000 × 0.001 = 1.

Since n is large and p is small, the Poisson distribution will be used as an approximation to the binomial distribution. Any error will be small, and a lot of computational work will be saved.

(a) $P(0) = \dfrac{m^0}{0!} e^{-m} = \dfrac{1^0}{0!} e^{-1} = e^{-1} = 0.3679$

(b) $P(1) = \dfrac{1^1}{1!} e^{-1} = e^{-1}$ $=0.3679$

(c) $P(2) = \dfrac{1^2}{2!} e^{-1} = \dfrac{1}{2}(0.36788)$ $=0.1839$

(d) $P(3 \text{ or more})$ $= 1 - P(0) - P(1) - P(2)$
$= 1 - 0.3679 - 0.3679 - 0.1839$
$= 0.0803$

Exercise 3

The mean number of invoices received by a company on any one day is 2.6. What is the probability that seven invoices will be received over a two day period?

---

5   The normal distribution

The normal distribution is an important probability distribution which is often applied to 'continuous variables'. In other words, in calculating P(x), x can be any value, and does not have to be a whole number.

Examples of continuous variables include:

(a) the volume of paint produced each day by a machine. It need not be an exact number of litres, but can be anything within a range of possible figures;

(b) the temperature of a room. It need not be an exact number of degrees, but can fall anywhere within a range of possible values.

The normal distribution can also apply to discrete variables which can take many possible values. For example, the volume of sales, in units, of a product might be any whole number in the range 100 – 5,000 units. There are so many possibilities within this range that the variable is for all practical purposes continuous.

The normal distribution can be drawn as a graph, and it would be a bell-shaped curve. This means that there is a high probability of getting a value in the middle of the distribution, but a much lower probability of getting a value a long way from the middle.

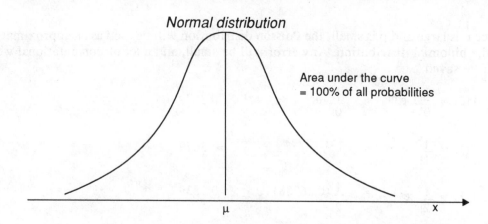

The normal curve is symmetrical. The left hand side of the area under the curve to the left of μ is the mirror image of the right hand side. μ is the mean, or average of the distribution. Because it is a probability distribution, the area under the curve (representing all possibilities) totals exactly 1. Thus if we take the example of the volume of paint produced each day by a machine, μ would be the mean output. Outputs close to the mean would be quite likely, but outputs a long way from the mean would be very unlikely.

The normal distribution is important because many probability distributions are close enough to a normal distribution to be treated as one.

The standard deviation and the normal distribution

For *any normal distribution*, the probability of getting values within any given range depends only on the mean μ and the standard deviation σ.

The entire curve represents all the possible outcomes. The normal curve is symmetrical; therefore 50% of occurrences have a value greater than the mean, and 50% of occurrences have a value less than the mean.

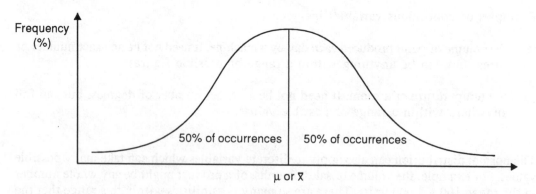

About 68% of frequencies have a value within one standard deviation either side of the mean.

Thus if a normal distribution has a mean of 80 and a standard deviation of 3, 68% of the total frequencies would occur within the range ± one standard deviation from the mean, that is, within the range 77 - 83.

Since the curve is symmetrical, 34% of the values must fall in the range 77 - 80 and 34% in the range 80 - 83.

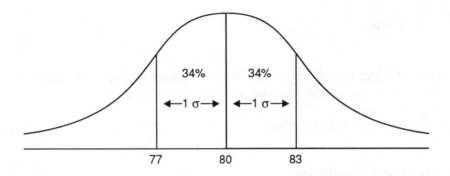

95% of the frequencies in a normal distribution occur in the range ± 1.96 standard deviations from the mean.

In our example, when $\mu = 80$, and $\sigma = 3$, 95% of the frequencies in the distribution would occur in the range

$80 \pm 1.96 \times 3$
$= \quad 80 \pm 5.88 \quad$ (the range 74.12 to 85.88)

$47\frac{1}{2}\%$ would be in the range 74.12 to 80 and $47\frac{1}{2}\%$ would be in the range 80 – 85.88.

99% of the frequencies occur in the range ± 2.58 standard deviations from the mean.

In our example, 99% of frequencies in a normal distribution with $\mu = 80$ and $\sigma = 3$ would lie in the range

$80 \pm 2.58 \times 3$
$= \quad 80 \pm 7.74$
$= \quad 72.26$ to 87.74.

Exercise 4

A normal distribution for the daily outputs (in units) of workers in a factory has a mean of 50 and a standard deviation of 10. Within what range from 50 upwards would $47\frac{1}{2}\%$ of the frequencies fall?

Normal distribution tables

Although there are an infinite number of normal distributions, depending on values of the mean μ and the standard deviation σ, the relative dispersion of frequencies around the mean, measured as proportions of the total population, is *exactly the same for all normal distributions*.

A normal distribution table, shown at the start of this text, gives the proportion of the total between the mean and a point above or below the mean for any multiple of the standard deviation.

Distances above or below the mean are expressed in numbers of standard deviations z.

BPP Publishing

$$z = \frac{x - \mu}{\sigma}$$

where z =   the number of standard deviations above or below the mean
       x =   the value of the variable under consideration
       μ =   the mean
       σ =   the standard deviation.

Example: the normal distribution

A frequency distribution is normal, with a mean of 100 and a standard deviation of 10.

What proportion of the total frequencies will be:

(a) above 90;
(b) above 115;
(c) below 95;
(d) below 108;
(e) in the range 80 - 110;
(f) in the range 90 - 95?

Solution

To calculate the proportion of frequencies *above* a certain value:

(a) if the value is below the mean, the total proportion is:

0.5 plus (proportion between the value and the mean):

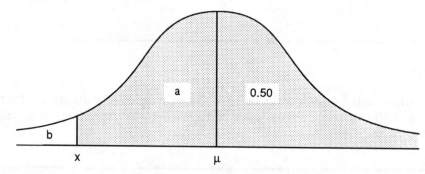

(b) if the value is above the mean, the proportion can be worked out as follows.

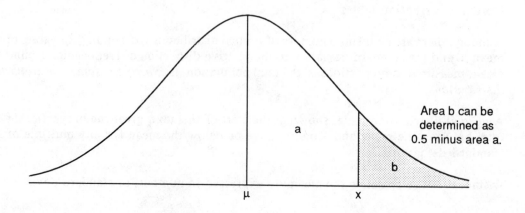

Area b can be determined as 0.5 minus area a.

To calculate the proportion of frequencies *below* a certain value:

(a) if the value is below the mean, the proportion required can be worked out as follows.

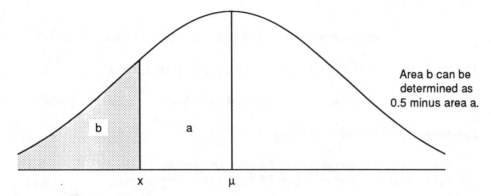

Area b can be determined as 0.5 minus area a.

(b) if the value is above the mean, the proportion required is 0.5 plus (the proportion between the value and the mean).

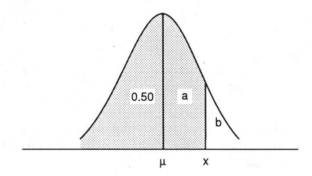

The solutions are therefore as follows.

(a) 90 is $\frac{100 - 90}{10}$ = 1 standard deviation below the mean. From the tables, when z = 1, the proportion is 0.3413.

The proportion of frequencies above 90 is 0.5 + 0.3413 = 0.8413.

(b) 115 is $\frac{115 - 100}{10}$ = 1.5 standard deviations above the mean. From the tables, where z = 1.5 the proportion is 0.4332.

The proportion of frequencies above 115 is therefore 0.5 - 0.4332 = 0.0668.

(c) 95 is $\frac{100 - 95}{10}$ = 0.5 standard deviations below the mean. When z = 0.5 the proportion from the tables is 0.1915. The proportion of frequencies below 95 is therefore 0.5 - 0.1915 = 0.3085.

(d) 108 is $\frac{108 - 100}{10}$ = 0.8 standard deviations above the mean. From the tables for z = 0.8 the proportion is 0.2881.

The proportion of frequencies below 108 is 0.5 + 0.2881 = 0.7881.

(e) The range 80 to 110 may be divided into two parts:

(i)   80 to 100 (the mean);
(ii) 100 to 110.

The proportion in the range 80 to 100 is (2 standard deviations) 0.4772

The proportion in the range 100 to 110 is (1 standard deviation) 0.3413

The proportion in the total range 80 to 110 is 0.4772 + 0.3413 = 0.8185.

(f) The range 90 to 95 may be analysed as:

(i)   the proportion above 90 (and below the mean)
(ii) minus the proportion above 95 (and below the mean).

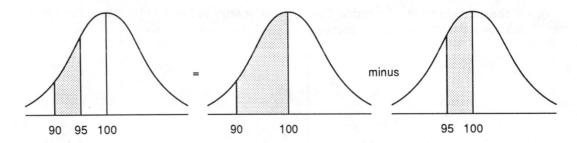

Proportion above 90 and below the mean (1 standard deviation)   0.3413
Proportion above 95 and below the mean (0.5 standard deviations)   0.1915
Proportion between 90 and 95   0.1498

Exercise 5

The salaries of employees in an industry are normally distributed, with a mean of £14,000 and a standard deviation of £2,700.

(a) What proportion of employees earn less than £12,000?
(b) What proportion of employees earn between £11,000 and £19,000?

The normal distribution and the binomial distribution

When n in a binomial distribution gets large, then so long as p is reasonably close to 0.5 (say 0.3 to 0.7) a binomial distribution approximates closely to a normal distribution. This can save a lot of work.

Example : the normal distribution as an approximation to the binomial distribution

The probability that an accountant will make a mistake filling in a VAT return is 0.3. What is the probability that fewer than 570 returns out of 2,000 will be in error?

Solution

Using a binomial distribution, we could make calculations as follows.

$$P(0) = \frac{2,000!}{0!2,000!} (0.7)^{2,000} (0.3)^0$$

$$P(1) = \frac{2,000!}{1!1,999!} (0.7)^{1,999} (0.3)^1$$

$$P(2) = \quad ...$$

This would be a laborious process.

Instead, we can assume that the binomial distribution approximates closely to a normal distribution, with:

(a) a mean of np = 2,000 × 0.3 = 600;

(b) a standard deviation of $\sqrt{npq} = \sqrt{2,000 \times 0.3 \times 0.7} = 20.49$.

We need a cut-off point for 'fewer than 570'. We will be as accurate as we can, and use 569.5. This gives z = (569.5 - 600)/20.49 = -1.49.

Normal distribution tables then give us the required probability, 0.5 - 0.4319 = 0.0681.

The continuity correction

When normal distributions are used for discrete variables rather than continuous variables, we should use a continuity correction when estimating probabilities. What this means is that if values can only be whole numbers: 0, 1, 2, 3 and so on, then in the normal distribution, the value 0 should be represented by - 0.5 to + 0.5, 1 should be represented by 0.5 to 1.5, 2 by 1.5 to 2.5 and 3 by 2.5 to 3.5 etc.

When the range of values of the discrete variable we are interested in is large, the continuity correction can be ignored because it will be insignificant. It ought to be used, however, when the range is small enough to make a difference of 0.5 potentially significant.

Example: the continuity correction

Suppose that we have a normal distribution for the number of players in a football team of 11 who have broken their leg at some time in the past, with a mean of 5.3 and a standard deviation of 1.2. Values are only whole numbers, since we cannot have a fraction of a player. What is the probability that in a particular football team, Mishap United, at least four players will have broken their leg at some time in the past?

Solution

We should apply the continuity correction, as follows.

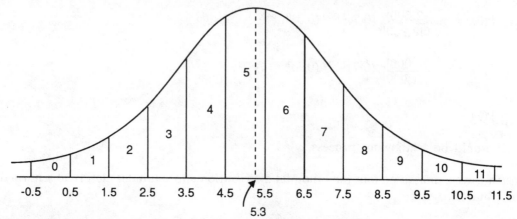

The possible number of players in the team who have suffered a broken leg will range between 0 and 11 and the values 0, 1, 2, 3, 4 and so on, are represented by the ranges shown in the diagram.

The probability of at least four is the probability of exceeding 3.5.
3.5 is (5.3 - 3.5)/1.2 = 1.5 standard deviations below the mean.

From the table, when z = 1.5, P = 0.4332, and so the probability of four or more players having broken a leg is 0.5 + 0.4332 = 0.9332.

Exercise 6

A coin is tossed 250 times. Applying the continuity correction, what is the approximate probability of getting 122, 123, 124 or 125 heads?

Chapter roundup

(a) A probability distribution summarises the probabilities of the various values which a variable may have.

(b) If we have to select x items from among n items, the number of possible ways of doing so is given by the formula for permutations (if the order of selection matters) or the formula for combinations (if the order does not matter).

(c) The binomial distribution applies when there are n trials and we want to know the probability of x successes, when we know the probability of a success on any one trial.

(d) The Poisson distribution applies when events occur randomly within an interval. It can also be used as an approximation to the binomial distribution when n is large and p is small.

(e) The normal distribution applies in many statistical situations. Probabilities can be found using normal distribution tables, which give values based on the number of standard deviations from the mean.

(f) The normal distribution can be used as an approximation to the binomial distribution when n is large and p is close to 0.5. The continuity correction may be needed.

Quick quiz

1 What is the difference between a combination of items and a permutation of items?

2 What is the formula for the binomial distribution?

3 What are the formulae for the mean and the standard deviation of a binomial distribution?

4 What is the formula for the Poisson distribution?

5 What is the value of e to use in the Poisson distribution formula?

6 What is the value of the standard deviation of a Poisson distribution?

7 When is the Poisson distribution a good approximation to the binomial distribution?

8 When is the normal distribution a good approximation to the binomial distribution?

9 Explain when the continuity correction should be used with the normal distribution.

Solutions to exercises

1   (a)   The number of different possible orderings of the whole class is

$$_{15}P_{15} = \frac{15!}{(15-15)!} = \frac{15!}{0!} = 15! = 1,307,674,368,000$$

(b)   The number of different possible results for the top three places is given by the number of permutations of three out of 15.

$$_{15}P_3 = \frac{15!}{(15-3)!} = \frac{15!}{12!} = 15 \times 14 \times 13 = 2,730$$

(c)   The number of ways of having three people taking the top three places is given by the number of combinations of three out of 15.

$$_{15}C_3 = \frac{15!}{(15-3)!3!} = \frac{15 \times 14 \times 13}{3 \times 2 \times 1} = 455$$

2   (a)   Let the probability of demand equalling or exceeding eight units be p, and the probability of demand being less than eight units be q.

$$p = 0.1, \quad q = 0.9$$

$$P(2) = \frac{6!}{2!4!} (0.1)^2 (0.9)^4 = 0.0984$$

(b) $$P(3) = \frac{6!}{3!3!} (0.1)^3 (0.9)^3 = 0.01456$$

3   Mean per two days = $2.6 \times 2 = 5.2$

$$P \text{ (7 over 2 days)} = \frac{5.2^7 \ e^{-5.2}}{7!} = 0.1125$$

4   Between 50 and $50 + 1.96 \times 10 = 69.6$. Thus $47\frac{1}{2}\%$ of workers would have daily outputs of between 50 and 69.6 units.

5   (a) $(12,000 - 14,000)/2,700 = -0.74$

From tables, the proportion of the normal distribution more than 0.74 standard deviations below the mean is $0.5 - 0.2704 = 0.2296$.

(b) $(11,000 - 14,000)/2,700 = -1.11$
$(19,000 - 14,000)/2,700 = 1.85$

The proportion with earnings between £11,000 and £14,000 is 0.3665.

The proportion with earnings between £14,000 and £19,000 is 0.4678.

The required proportion is $0.3665 + 0.4678 = 0.8343$.

6   The normal distribution is an appropriate approximation to the binomial distribution, as n is large and p is 0.5.

   n   =   250
   p   =   0.5
   μ =   np = 250 × 0.5 = 125

   σ = $\sqrt{npq}$ = $\sqrt{250 \times 0.5 \times 0.5}$ = 7.906

The range to consider is 121.5 to 125.5 successes.

121.5 successes is $\dfrac{125 - 121.5}{7.906}$ = 0.44 standard deviations below the mean.

125.5 successes is $\dfrac{125.5 - 125}{7.906}$ = 0.06 standard deviations above the mean.

P (between mean and 0.44 standard deviations below mean) = 0.1700
P (between mean and 0.06 standard deviations above mean) = 0.0239
Required probability   0.1939

8 ESTIMATION AND HYPOTHESIS TESTING

Signpost

We often need to rely on samples to get information about whole populations. In this chapter we will look at ways to squeeze as much information as we can out of a sample. Our methods are based on the concept of a sampling distribution, which shows the results we could have got from all possible samples, not just the sample we actually took. The standard deviation of a sampling distribution is its standard error, and we can use this to set limits (confidence limits) on how uncertain we are about our estimate of a population mean or proportion. We can use the same approach to test a theory (a hypothesis) which we might have about a population, such as a theory that the mean weight per brick of a large batch of bricks is 4kg.

Finally, we will look at a different type of test, called the chi-squared test, which can answer questions like: is whether or not a person drives connected with whether or not they have a credit card? (contingency tables); and does the distribution of wages in the population follow a normal distribution? (distribution fitting).

Your objectives

After completing this chapter you should:

(a) understand the concept of a sampling distribution;
(b) be able to compute standard errors and confidence limits;
(c) know the steps in hypothesis testing;
(d) be able to test hypotheses concerning means and proportions;
(e) be able to test hypotheses using small samples;
(f) be able to use the chi-squared test.

---

1   Populations and samples

We take a sample in order to estimate something about the population as a whole. For example, we might ask 1,000 people in Britain how much they earn, and work out the average for those 1,000 people. This would give us an idea of the average earnings of everyone in Britain. The sample average is likely to be close to the population average but not exactly the same.

This chapter is mainly concerned with the accuracy of the estimates of the *mean* of a population which are provided by the analysis of the *mean* of a sample. The theory discussed at the beginning of this chapter only holds if:

(a) the samples are taken at random;

(b)   the samples are fairly large (over 30).

Small samples need a slightly different treatment, which is discussed in the section below on the t distribution.

It is helpful to distinguish between the mean and standard deviation of a sample, and the mean and standard deviation of the population which the sample comes from. We shall therefore use the following symbols.

$\bar{x}$ is the mean of a sample
μ (mu) is the mean of the population
s is the standard deviation of a sample
σ (sigma) is the standard deviation of the population

Suppose that we wish to estimate the mean of a population, say the average weight of an item of product made in a factory. A sample of, say, 100 units of the product might be taken, and the mean weight per unit of the sample might be, say, 5.8 kg.

Another sample of 100 units might then be taken and the mean weight might be, say, 6.3 kg.

A large number of samples might be taken and the mean of each sample calculated. These means will not all be the same and they can be plotted as a frequency distribution. This distribution is called a 'sampling distribution of the mean'.

In our example, a frequency distribution of the mean weight per unit in each of 250 samples (of 100 units per sample) might be as follows.

Mean weight per unit $\bar{x}$		Mid-point of class interval	Frequency (No of samples)
at least	less than		
kg	kg	kg	
5.45	5.55	5.5	3
5.55	5.65	5.6	7
5.65	5.75	5.7	16
5.75	5.85	5.8	30
5.85	5.95	5.9	44
5.95	6.05	6.0	50
6.05	6.15	6.1	44
6.15	6.25	6.2	30
6.25	6.35	6.3	16
6.35	6.45	6.4	7
6.45	6.55	6.5	3
			250 samples

The mean weight per unit of 100 units in a sample might thus range from 5.45 to 6.55 kg. The true mean of the population, that is, the true mean weight of all units produced, presumably lies somewhere within this range. In this chapter we will see how to work out how close a sample mean is likely to be to the population mean.

2 The standard error and confidence limits

A sampling distribution of the mean has the following important properties.

(a) It is very close to being normally distributed. This is true even if the distribution of the population from which the samples are drawn is nowhere near normal. The larger the sample the more closely will the sampling distribution approximate to a normal distribution.

(b) The mean of the sampling distribution is the same as the population mean, μ.

(c) The sampling distribution has a standard deviation which is called the *standard error of the mean*.

In our example, the 250 samples give an estimate of the population mean. This distribution of sample means would be (approximately) normally distributed, with a mean of about 6 kg (weight per unit of product).

This mean of 6 kg would be the same as the population mean, μ.

The standard deviation of the sampling distribution (which could be calculated as 0.2 kg: workings not shown) is the standard error (se).

It can be shown that the standard error of the mean is

$$se = \sigma/\sqrt{n}$$

where n is the size of each sample and σ is the standard deviation of the population.

Estimating the standard error

The standard error is given by $\sigma/\sqrt{n}$, but σ is the standard deviation of the whole population and is normally not known. To overcome this problem the standard deviation of a sample, multiplied by *Bessel's correction*, is used. Bessel's correction is $\sqrt{[n/(n-1)]}$, so it makes our estimate of σ slightly larger than s.

Exercise 1

A sample of 50 items has a sample standard deviation of 2.7. Find the standard error of the mean.

The central limit theorem

The central limit theorem is the name given to the statistical rule that a sampling distribution of sample means is normally distributed. We can use this fact to get extra information from our sample results. Thus in the above example with a standard error of 0.2kg, someone might have taken a sample with a mean of 5.7 kg. Since nearly all of a normal distribution lies within three standard deviations of the mean, the person could be practically certain that the population mean is in the range 5.7 ± (3 × 0.2) = 5.7 ± 0.6 = 5.1 kg to 6.3 kg.

Confidence limits

From our knowledge of the properties of a normal distribution together with the rule that sample means are normally distributed around the true population mean with a standard deviation equal to the standard error, we can predict (using normal distribution tables) that:

(a) 68% of all sample means will be within one standard error of the population mean;
(b) 95% of all sample means will be within 1.96 standard errors of the population mean;
(c) 99% of all sample means will be within 2.58 standard errors of the population mean.

By looking at it the other way we can see that:

(a) with 68% probability, the population mean lies within the range: sample mean ± one standard error;

(b) with 95% probability, the population mean lies within the range: sample mean ± 1.96 standard errors;

(c) with 99% probability, the population mean lies within the range: sample mean ± 2.58 standard errors.

These degrees of certainty are known as *confidence levels*, and the ends of the ranges around the sample mean are called *confidence limits*. The ranges are called *confidence intervals*.

Example: confidence intervals

From a random sample of 576 of a company's 20,000 employees, it was found that the average number of days each person was absent from work due to illness was eight days a year, with a standard deviation (after Bessel's correction) of 3.6 days.

What are the confidence limits for the average number of days absence a year through sickness per employee for the company as a whole:

(a) at the 95% level of confidence;
(b) at the 99% level of confidence?

Solution

We must first calculate the standard error.

$$\text{se} = 3.6/\sqrt{576} = 0.15.$$

(a) At the 95% level of confidence, the true average number of days absence a year is in the range 8 ± (1.96 × 0.15)

= 8 ± 0.294
= 7.706 days to 8.294 days, say 7.7 days to 8.3 days.

(b) At the 99% level of confidence, the true average number of days absence a year is in the range 8 ± (2.58 × 0.15)

= 8 ± 0.387
= 7.613 days to 8.387 days, say 7.6 days to 8.4 days.

Why is it necessary to calculate confidence limits? If the sample mean was eight days would it not be sufficient to use eight days as a *point estimate* of the population mean?

In practice, a sample mean might indeed be used as a 'point estimate' of the population mean. However, we could not be sure how reliable the estimate might be, without first considering the size of the standard error. The sample mean might be above or below the true population mean, but we can say with 95% confidence that the sample mean is no more than 1.96 standard errors above or below the true population mean.

If the confidence limits cover a wide range of values, a point estimate of the population mean from the sample would not be reliable. On the other hand, if the confidence limits cover a narrow range of values, a point estimate of the population mean, using the sample mean, would be reliable.

Exercise 2

The cost of assembling an item of equipment has been estimated by obtaining a sample of 144 jobs. The average cost of assembly derived from the sample was £4,000 with a standard deviation (after Bessel's correction) of £1,500.

Estimate confidence limits for the true average cost of assembly. Use the 95% level of confidence.

The standard error of a proportion

The arithmetic mean is a very important statistic, and sampling is often concerned with estimating the mean of a population. Many surveys, however, attempt to estimate a *proportion* rather than a mean. Examples include surveys concerned with:

(a) attitudes or opinions about an issue;

(b) the percentage of times an event occurs (for example, the proportion of faulty items out of the total number of items produced in a manufacturing department).

Suppose for example, that we wished to know what proportion of an electorate intends to vote for the Jacobin party at the forthcoming general election. Several samples might be obtained, and the proportion of Jacobin voters in a sample might vary, say from 37% to 45%. The proportion of Jacobin voters in each sample could be arranged into a sampling distribution which:

(a) is normally distributed;

(b) has a mean equal to the proportion of pro-Jacobin voters in the population;

(c) has a standard deviation equal to the standard error of a proportion.

The formula for the standard error of a proportion is $\sqrt{[pq/n]}$

where p is the proportion in the population
q is 1 - p
n is the size of the sample.

We use the sample proportion p as an estimate of the population proportion. Just as we use μ for a population mean, we can use π for a population proportion (but we must not confuse this with the constant $\pi = 3.14159$).

Example: a confidence interval for a proportion

In a random sample of 500 out of 100,000 employees, 320 were members of a trade union. Estimate the proportion of trade union members in the entire organisation at the 95% confidence level.

Solution

The sample proportion is 320/500 = 0.64.

$$\text{Standard error} = \sqrt{\frac{0.64 \times (1 - 0.64)}{500}} = \sqrt{\frac{0.64 \times 0.36}{500}} = 0.0215$$

An estimate of the population proportion at the 95% confidence level is the sample proportion ± 1.96 standard errors.

The population proportion is $0.64 \pm (1.96 \times 0.0215) = 0.64 \pm 0.04$. The percentage of employees who are trade union members is between 60% and 68% at the 95% level of confidence.

Exercise 3

A researcher wishes to know the proportion of people who regularly travel by train. Of a sample of 400 people, 285 said they did so. Estimate the population proportion with 99% confidence.

3   The principles of hypothesis testing

Hypothesis testing is the process of establishing the significance of the results of sample data for beliefs (hypotheses) about the population.

The procedure for hypothesis testing is as follows.

Notes

(a) We establish a hypothesis, for example that the mean value of all of a company's invoices is £200. This is the *null hypothesis* (H_0). We also state an *alternative hypothesis* (H_1). For example that the mean value is not £200.

(b) We test the hypothesis. Are the sample results near enough what we would expect to get if the null hypothesis were true? To test the null hypothesis, we must select a *significance level*. This is the chance we take of wrongly rejecting the null hypothesis.

(c) Having tested the hypothesis, we draw a conclusion.

Example: hypothesis testing (1)

A company's management accountant has estimated that the average cost of providing a certain service to a customer is £40.

A sample has been taken, consisting of 150 service provisions, and the mean cost for the sample was £45 with a standard deviation (after Bessel's correction) of £10.

Is the sample consistent with the estimate of an average cost of £40?

Solution

To apply a hypothesis test, we begin by stating an initial view, called the null hypothesis, that the average direct cost per unit of service is £40. The alternative hypothesis will be that it is *not* £40.

Next, we select a significance level, which indicates how severely we are testing the null hypothesis. Here, we will use 5%. 5% is a common choice. The lower the significance level, the lower the probability of wrongly rejecting the null hypothesis, but the higher the probability of wrongly accepting it.

Our choice of 5% means that we shall assume that the sample mean (£45) is consistent with our estimated population mean (£40) provided that the sample mean is within what would be a 100% – 5% = 95% confidence interval around a sample mean equal to the mean given by the null hypothesis.

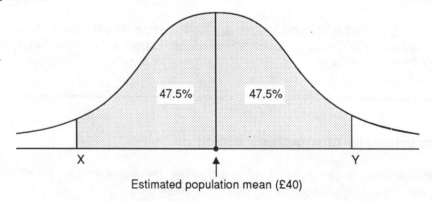

You may prefer to think of this in terms of the diagram above. If the sample mean of £45 is within the range from X to Y, we will conclude that our null hypothesis is acceptable.

X and Y are each 1.96 standard errors from the mean. From our sample, we can calculate the standard error as $10/\sqrt{150} = 0.816$.

We can now test the hypothesis. The sample mean is £5 higher than our hypothesised population mean, and this is $5/0.816 = 6.1$ standard errors above the mean.

At the 5% level of significance we would expect the sample mean to be within 1.96 standard errors of the hypothesised mean. It is not, and so at this level of significance, we reject the null hypothesis.

Conclusion

The average cost per unit of service is not £40, and the management accountant is wrong.

Note that if we had got a sample mean within 1.96 standard errors of the hypothesised mean, this would not have proved that the null hypothesis was true. It would only have shown that we did not have enough evidence to reject the null hypothesis.

Exercise 4

It is thought that the mean number of times a person uses a credit card in a year is 180, neither more nor less. To test this hypothesis, a sample of 55 people is taken. The sample mean is 192 uses and the sample standard deviation (after Bessel's correction) is 50 uses. What conclusion should be reached at 5% significance?

Example: hypothesis testing (2)

In a manufacturing operation, the standard level of scrapped units is 8% of input.

During one week, 18,400 units were input to the operation of which 1,580 were scrapped.

Does the level of rejects appear to exceed the expected level? Test at the 5% level of significance.

Solution

We begin by establishing a null hypothesis (H_0) that there is no difference between the actual level of scrapped items and the expected level of 8%.

We also need an alternative hypothesis (H_1) so that if the null hypothesis is rejected, we will accept the alternative hypothesis instead. In this example, H_1 will be that the level of scrapped units is *over* 8%.

If we expect 8% of units to be scrapped, the mean number of rejects in a batch of 18,400 units should be 8% of $18,400 = 1,472$ units.

The standard deviation is $\sqrt{(npq)} = \sqrt{[18,400 \times 0.08 \times 0.92]} = 36.8$ units.

This is the formula for the standard deviation of a binomial distribution.

We must establish a limit for the number of units scrapped, so as to ensure that there is only a 5% probability of the number of rejects in the sample exceeding the limit, if the average rejection rate for the population is in fact 8%. This may be shown in a diagram as follows.

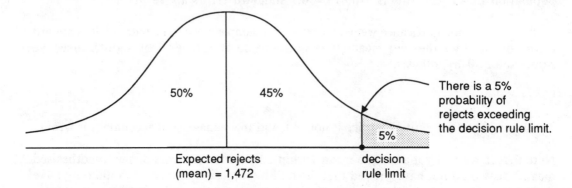

95% of the frequency distribution must lie to the left hand side of the limit. From normal distribution tables, 0.05 of the distribution lies more than 1.65 standard deviations above the mean.

The number of units scrapped was 1,580 which is 108 units more than the expected number. This represents 108/36.8 = 2.93 standard errors.

(a) We therefore reject H_0, that the level of scrap for the population is 8%.
(b) We accept H_1, that the level of scrap is now over 8%.

Another way of making the test would be as follows.

(a) Null hypothesis: the true level of rejects is 8% or 0.08.

(b) The actual level of rejects is 1,580/18,400 = 0.08587.

(c) The standard error of the proportion, calculated from the proportion in the null hypothesis, is $\sqrt{[pq/n]} = \sqrt{[0.08 \times 0.92/18,400]} = 0.002$.

(d) The actual level of rejects is 0.00587 above the expected level, which is 0.00587/0.002 = 2.93 standard errors.

This is exactly the same finding we came to earlier. Our conclusion is the same: since the actual level of rejects is more than 1.65 standard errors above the assumed mean, we reject the null hypothesis and conclude that the level of rejects is higher than 8% (at the 5% level of significance).

One-tail tests and two-tail tests

There are two different types of significance test, known as one-tail (one-sided) or two-tail (two-sided) tests.

The first example above (the cost of a service) was of a two-tail test, because the alternative hypothesis was of the form '... *does not equal* ...'. In the diagram we wanted 5% of the area in both tails taken together, hence our limits of ± 1.96 standard errors. For 1% significance, we would have used ± 2.58 standard errors.

The second example (scrapped units) was of a one-tail test, because the alternative hypothesis was of the form '... *is greater than* ...'. Where the alternative hypothesis is of the form
'... *is less than* ...' we also have a one-tail test. In the diagram, we wanted 5% of the area in one tail only, hence our use of 1.65 (2.33 for 1% significance).

Exercise 5

It is thought that the mean net weight of bags of sugar produced by a machine is at least 1.03 kg. A sample of 230 bags had a mean net weight of 1.02 kg, with a standard deviation of weights of 0.02 kg. Test the hypothesis that the population mean is at least 1.03 kg at the 1% significance level.

---

4 Differences between means

We may compare the means of two different samples. In such a comparison, we might want to learn whether the mean of one population equals that of the other, or whether there appears to be a difference between them. Hypothesis tests can be made in such cases.

Example: the difference between two means

Sample I is a sample of the productivity of 60 employees at Factory A on day 1, which shows that the mean output per employee is 106 units with a standard deviation of 8.067 units (after Bessel's correction). Sample II is a sample of 50 employees at Factory A on day 2 which shows a mean output per employee of 103 units with a standard deviation of 6.0605 units (after Bessel's correction).

Is it probable that there has been a change in the productivity at Factory A between day 1 and day 2?

Solution

The standard error of the difference between the two sample means would be calculated as follows.

Sample I Standard deviation $\quad s_1 = 8.067$
$\quad\quad\quad$ Estimate of population variance $\sigma_1^2 = 8.067^2 = 65.08$

Sample II Standard deviation $\quad s_2 = 6.0605$
$\quad\quad\quad$ Estimate of population variance $\sigma_2^2 = 6.0605^2 = 36.73$

The standard error of the difference between two means is given by the formula

$$\sqrt{\frac{\sigma_1^2}{n_1} + \frac{\sigma_2^2}{n_2}}$$

where $\sigma_1{}^2$ is the population variance estimated from the first sample

n_1 is the size of the first sample

$\sigma_2{}^2$ is the population variance estimated from the second sample

n_2 is the size of the second sample.

Standard error of the difference between the means $= \sqrt{\dfrac{65.08}{60} + \dfrac{36.73}{50}}$

$$= \sqrt{(1.0847 + 0.7346)}$$

$$= 1.35$$

The mean output per employee on day 1 was 106 units and on day 2 it was 103 units. The difference between the means was 3. A difference of 3 is $3/1.35 = 2.22$ standard errors.

The null hypothesis is that there is no difference between the two population means. The alternative hypothesis is that there is a difference.

We will test the null hypothesis with a two-tail test at the 5% level of significance. The null hypothesis would be accepted if the actual difference between the sample means did not exceed 1.96 standard errors. However, because the difference is 2.22 standard errors, the null hypothesis would be rejected at the 5% level of significance, and management would assume that average productivity on day 2 was different from that on day 1, because 2.22 standard errors is over 1.96. (The null hypothesis would not be rejected, however, at the 1% level of significance because the difference between the sample means is not more than 2.58 standard errors).

Exercise 6

The analysis of average annual sales per customer for two sales areas for 19X6 based on random samples was as follows.

	Midland	South
Sample size	100	100
Sample mean	£93.30	£57.70
Sample variance (after Bessel's correction)	5,398.60	791.10

Test the hypothesis that there is no difference in the average annual sales per customer between the two areas. Use the 1% significance level.

---

5 Differences between proportions

We can test whether the proportions in two populations are the same, on the basis of two samples.

Example: the difference between two proportions.

In a test of the hypothesis that the proportion of homes with central heating is not more than the proportion of homes with two or more televisions, 60% of a sample of 90 homes were found to have central heating and 55% of a sample of 80 homes were found to have two or more televisions. What conclusion should be reached at the 5% significance level?

Solution

Let p_1 be the sample proportion of homes with central heating (0.6) and let p_2 be the sample proportion of homes with two or more televisions (0.55).

$H_0 : \pi_1 = \pi_2$ (the null hypothesis is that the two population proportions are equal)

$H_1 : \pi_1 > \pi_2$ (the alternative hypothesis is that the proportion of homes with central heating exceeds the proportion of homes with two or more televisions)

This is a one-tail test, with a critical level (at 5% significance) of 1.65.

The standard error of the difference between two sample proportions is:

$$\sqrt{p(1-p)\ \frac{1}{n_1} + \frac{1}{n_2}}$$

where $p = \dfrac{p_1 n_1 + p_2 n_2}{n_1 + n_2}$

       n_1 is the size of the first sample
       p_1 is the proportion in the first sample
       n_2 is the size of the second sample
       p_2 is the proportion in the second sample

$p = (0.6 \times 90 + 0.55 \times 80)/(90 + 80) = 0.576$

Standard error $= \sqrt{0.576(1-0.576)\left(\dfrac{1}{90} + \dfrac{1}{80}\right)} = 0.0759$

$(0.6 - 0.55)/0.0759 = 0.66$

0.66 is less than 1.65, so the null hypothesis may be accepted.

6   Small samples and the t distribution

The sampling and hypothesis testing theory described so far only holds good for fairly large samples ($n > 30$). For small samples, the Central Limit Theorem (that sample means are *normally* distributed around the population mean) is not valid. The means of small samples are distributed around the population mean in a manner similar to, but not exactly a normal distribution. The distribution of small sample means is a *t distribution* (sometimes referred to as a 'Student's t distribution'.)

The techniques for small samples are similar to those for large samples, but the t distribution replaces the normal distribution. In using the t distribution, we must assume that the population is approximately normally distributed.

For small samples, factors such as 1.65 and 1.96 derived from normal distribution tables must be replaced by a factor t. t varies with the *degrees of freedom*. The number of degrees of freedom is ($n - 1$) for a sample of size n.

There is a separate t distribution for each number of degrees of freedom. t distribution tables for selected t scores (numbers of standard errors) for various degrees of freedom are given in a table at the start of this text.

Note that the t tables are based on the areas in one tail. The column headed 1 tail: 5% is therefore used for a one-tail test at 5% significance, or a two-tail test at 10% significance. This is confirmed by the bottom row, where the familiar normal distribution figures (1.65, 1.96, 2.33 and 2.58) are shown.

The rows of the table are for degrees of freedom (df) from 1 upwards.

For example, in a one-tail test using a sample of ten items (df = 10 - 1 = 9) at the 5% level of significance H_0 would be rejected if the sample mean was more than 1.83 standard errors from the population mean (1.83 is in the column for 5% in a one-tail test, and the row df = 9).

Similarly, in a two-tail test using a sample of 16 items (df = 15) at 1% significance, the limit is 2.95 standard errors from the hypothesised mean (2.95 is in the column for 1%, two-tail test). The same factor (2.95) would be used to establish a 99% confidence interval.

Example: the t distribution

In a quality control check, nine ball point pens were used until they stopped writing. The times taken (in hours) were 220, 250, 240, 290, 200, 300, 230, 210, 220.

Find a 99% confidence interval for the population mean life, given that the sample mean is 240 hours.

Solution

Life		
x	$x - \bar{x}$	$(x - \bar{x})^2$
220	-20	400
250	+10	100
240	0	0
290	+50	2,500
200	-40	1,600
300	+60	3,600
230	-10	100
210	-30	900
220	-20	400
2,160		9,600

Sample standard deviation = $\sqrt{(9,600/9)}$ = 32.66

Estimate of population standard deviation, $\sigma = 32.66 \times \sqrt{(9/8)} = 34.64$

Standard error = $34.64/\sqrt{9}$ = 11.55.

The sample size is nine so there are eight degrees of freedom. The value of t for eight degrees of freedom at the 99% confidence level is 3.36 (from the t distribution table, df = 8 and Pr = 1% for two tails).

Population mean = 240 ± 3.36 × 11.55
= 240 ± 38.81

The mean time to failure is about 240 ± 39 hours at the 99% confidence level, that is, 201 to 279 hours.

Exercise 7

The labour cost for making a unit of product T should be £20. The management accountant has taken a sample of 12 units, and found that the sample had a mean labour cost of £23 per unit, with a standard deviation (after Bessel's correction) of £2.089.

Test, at the 5% level of significance, whether the sample indicates that the labour cost per unit exceeds £20.

t tests and the difference between two means

We can also use a t test to test the significance of the difference between the means of two small samples. We use a slightly different formula from that described in Section 4 of this chapter, and apply t distribution tables, with $(n_1 + n_2 - 2)$ degrees of freedom, where n_1 and n_2 are the two sample sizes. We must also make the assumption that the two populations are approximately normally distributed with approximately equal standard deviations.

Example: the difference between two means

The following figures were calculated from two series of tests on two batches of the same product, liquid D. Do the figures support the assertion that the mean strengths of the two batches are the same?

	Batch 1	Batch 2
Number of tests	6	8
Mean strength (parts per hundred)	4.26	4.35
Sample standard deviation (after Bessel's correction)	0.0548	0.0424

Solution

	Batch 1	Batch 2
Sample standard deviation	0.0548	0.0424
Sample variance	0.0030	0.0018

$$\text{Pooled estimated } \hat{\sigma} = \sqrt{\frac{(n_1-1)\sigma_1^2 + (n_2-1)\sigma_2^2}{n_1 + n_2 - 2}} = \sqrt{\frac{5 \times 0.0030 + 7 \times 0.0018}{6 + 8 - 2}}$$

$$= 0.048$$

The standard error of the difference between the two sample means is

$$\hat{\sigma} \sqrt{\frac{1}{n_1} + \frac{1}{n_2}} = 0.048 \times \sqrt{\frac{1}{6} + \frac{1}{8}}$$

$$= 0.026$$

The difference between the two sample means is 4.35 - 4.26 = 0.09, which is 0.09/0.026 = 3.46 standard errors.

There are $(6 + 8 - 2) = 12$ degrees of freedom.

The significance test is a two-tail test, and if we test at the 5% level of significance, the t statistic is 2.18.

Since the actual difference between the sample means represents 3.46 standard errors, we reject the null hypothesis, and conclude instead that the mean strengths of the two batches differ.

Exercise 8

It is hypothesised that the average amount of cash carried by women is the same as that carried by men, neither more nor less. Samples are taken, with the following results.

	Women	Men
Number in sample	10	12
Sample mean	£35	£32
Sample standard deviation (after Bessel's correction)	£2.40	£1.30

What conclusion may be reached at the 5% significance level?

---

7 Nonparametric tests

The hypothesis tests we have looked at so far are all *parametric tests*. This means that they make an assumption about the distribution of the population we are sampling from: our tests assume it is approximately normal. With large samples, the assumption can generally be ignored, as its falsity would have very little effect. However, with small samples it becomes very important.

Nonparametric tests (also called *distribution-free tests*) are available, which do not make any such assumption. We will not go into details about such tests here, but you should be aware that they exist.

Advantages of nonparametric tests

(a) No assumptions about the underlying populations need be made. Thus we are not in danger of making a false assumption that a population is normally distributed.

(b) The mathematical concepts are simpler.

(c) They can be used on very small samples.

Disadvantages of nonparametric tests

(a) The tests are more prone to error (wrongly accepting H_0, or wrongly rejecting H_0) than parametric tests where the assumptions made by the parametric tests are justified. That is, nonparametric tests are *less powerful* than parametric tests.

(b) The arithmetic often takes a long time.

8 The chi-squared test

In sampling and in hypothesis testing of sample results, we often use the normal distribution, and with small samples a t distribution is used. Whether a normal distribution is used for large samples, or a t distribution for small samples, hypothesis testing concentrates on the *mean* of the population. We could not, for example, use such methods to test whether people's heights were associated with their interest in sport.

To make such tests, we use the chi-squared distribution. Chi-squared is pronounced 'Ki squared' after the Greek letter 'chi'. You will often find chi-squared referred to by the Greek letter itself, as χ^2.

Contingency tables

We perform our test of whether the values of two variables are associated by setting up a *contingency table* (so called because it sets out all the possibilities, or contingencies). The table has rows for values of one variable and columns for values of the other.

We have observed values, O, which are the numbers of instances we observed for each cell of the table (for example the number observed at height over 170cm and interest in sport high).

We need an expected value, E, based on a null hypothesis that the values of the variables are not associated, to go with each observed value.

For each cell,

$$E = \frac{\Sigma O \text{ for the row} \times \Sigma O \text{ for the column}}{\Sigma O \text{ for the whole table}}$$

Exercise 9

Here is a contingency table, with observed frequencies (numbers of people).

		Up to 170 cm	Height Over 170 cm	Total
Interest in sport	Low	70	20	90
	High	38	57	95
	Total	108	77	185

For the top left cell (height up to 170cm, low interest in sport), work out E using the formula given above. Then work out the overall proportion of the 185 people who have low interest in sport, and take that proportion of the 108 people with heights up to 170cm. Then explain why the formula given above for E is correct.

Example: chi-squared tests

An investigation is being carried out into delays in the payment of invoices by the customers of a company. Details of the current debtors are as follows.

| | Status as a debtor | | | |
Type of customer	Slow payer (> 3 months)	Average payer (1 and <3 months)	Prompt payer (< 1 month)	Total
Large private companies	8	17	6	31
Small private companies	20	25	22	67
Quoted companies	11	16	9	36
Local authorities	6	8	2	16
	45	66	39	150

Determine whether there is any relationship between the type of customer and its status as a payer. Use the 5% level of significance.

Solution

The problem is to decide whether different types of customer have different payment habits, or whether all customers are much the same in the time they take to pay their debts. The null hypothesis is that there is no association between the type of customer and the customer's payment habits. The alternative hypothesis is that there is such an association.

A contingency table can be drawn up as follows.

		Status as a debtor					
		Slow		Average		Prompt	
Type of customer	Total	Observed	Expected	Observed	Expected	Observed	Expected
Large private companies	31	8	9.3	17	13.6	6	8.1
Small private companies	67	20	20.1	25	29.5	22	17.4
Quoted companies	36	11	10.8	16	15.8	9	9.4
Local authorities	16	6	4.8	8	7.0	2	4.2
	150	45	45.0	66	66.0	39	39.0

For example, the expected frequency for slow paying large private companies is

$$\frac{\text{Row total} \times \text{Column total}}{\text{Table total}} = \frac{31 \times 45}{150} = 9.3$$

The overall proportion of slow payers is $45/150 = 0.3$, so if the null hypothesis is true we would expect $0.3 \times 31 = 9.3$ large private companies to be slow payers.

There are 12 pairs of observed and expected frequencies in this 4×3 table.

A chi-squared statistic $(\chi)^2$ is calculated by taking the difference between each observed result and the corresponding expected result, squaring the difference, and dividing this square by the expected result. All the figures found are then added up.

$$\chi^2 = \sum \frac{(O - E)^2}{E}$$

where O is the observed frequency and E is the expected frequency of each item in the sample.

	O	E	(O-E)	(O-E)²	$\frac{(O-E)^2}{E}$
Slow payers					
Large private companies	8	9.3	-1.3	1.69	0.18
Small private companies	20	20.1	-0.1	0.01	0.00
Quoted companies	11	10.8	+0.2	0.04	0.00
Local authorities	6	4.8	+1.2	1.44	0.30
Average payers					
Large private companies	17	13.6	+3.4	11.56	0.85
Small private companies	25	29.5	-4.5	20.25	0.69
Quoted companies	16	15.8	+0.2	0.04	0.00
Local authorities	8	7.0	+1.0	1.00	0.14
Prompt payers					
Large private companies	6	8.1	-2.1	4.41	0.54
Small private companies	22	17.4	+4.6	21.16	1.22
Quoted companies	9	9.4	-0.4	0.16	0.02
Local authorities	2	4.2	-2.2	4.84	1.15
				$\chi^2 =$	5.09

Chi-squared distribution tables

A chi-squared distribution table is shown at the start of this text.

(a) The table has a column for each significance level that we might decide to test at.

(b) There is a row for each number of degrees of freedom. This is the number of expected values which could vary freely while still allowing us to keep the row and column totals the same. For an $m \times n$ table it is $(m - 1) \times (n - 1)$.

(c) For each significance level and number of degrees of freedom, the table gives us a critical value. There is no distinction between one-tail and two-tail tests.

Our value for χ^2 is 5.09. We must now determine whether 5.09 is below the critical value in the χ^2 distribution at the 5% level of significance.

The contingency table has four rows and three columns. The degrees of freedom are therefore $(4-1)(3-1) = 3 \times 2 = 6$.

From the χ^2 table, the critical value at the 5% level of significance when there are six degrees of freedom is 12.6.

The value of χ^2 in our test is 5.09, well below the critical value.

We therefore accept the null hypothesis that there is no difference between the payment patterns of different types of customer.

Exercise 10

Here is a contingency table showing the results of tests of the effects of three fertilisers A, B and C on plant growth. Each fertiliser was tried on several different plots of land. Each figure is a number of plots of land.

		Fertiliser			
		A	*B*	*C*	*Total*
Growth	Strong	47	62	22	131
	Weak	25	48	19	92
Total		72	110	41	223

Test at the 1% level for an association between the choice of fertiliser and plant growth.

Yates's correction

In calculating χ^2 for a 2×2 contingency table (when there is *only one degree of freedom*) you should deduct 0.5 from the absolute value (the value ignoring any minus sign) of (O-E) for each item. This adjustment is called Yates's correction.

Example: Yates's correction

In a market survey carried out on behalf of Waring Titfer Ltd, a hat manufacturer, the following results were obtained.

	Men	*Women*
Never wear hats	82	65
Sometimes wear hats	24	25

The marketing manager wants to know whether the survey reveals any difference between the hat-wearing habits of men and women. Advise him, using the 5% level of significance.

Solution

The null hypothesis is that there is no difference in the hat-wearing habits of men and women.

The contingency table is as follows.

Attribute	Total	Men Observed	Men Expected	Women Observed	Women Expected
Never wear hats	147	82	79.5	65	67.5
Sometimes wear hats	49	24	26.5	25	22.5
	196	106	106.0	90	90.0

Because we have a 2 × 2 contingency table, we apply Yates's correction, and calculate, not (O-E), but (|O-E| - 0.5). The bars in |O-E| mean that we ignore any minus sign.

Observed	Expected	(O-E)	(|O-E| - 0.5)	(|O-E| - 0.5)²	$\frac{(|O-E| - 0.5)^2}{E}$
82	79.5	+2.5	2	4	0.05
24	26.5	-2.5	2	4	0.15
65	67.5	-2.5	2	4	0.06
25	22.5	+2.5	2	4	0.18
				χ^2 =	0.44

There is only one degree of freedom, since $(2-1)(2-1) = 1$

At the 5% level of significance, the critical value in the χ^2 distribution with one degree of freedom is 3.84. Since the value of χ^2 in the test is 0.44 and below the critical value, we accept the null hypothesis that there is no difference between the hat wearing habits of men and women.

You may have noticed in the above example that all the values of |O-E| are the same. This is always true for 2 × 2 contingency tables, and can save you time. However, it does *not* work for other sizes of table.

Low expected frequencies

There is one more correction to bear in mind. χ^2 tests becomes unreliable if any expected frequency E is less than 5. If this happens, you should combine a row or a column with an adjacent row or column to get rid of the low frequency. It does not matter whether you combine rows or columns, but if one alternative would eliminate the problem with less combining of figures than the other, you should choose that first alternative.

For example, the following contingency table has an expected frequency of 4.67 at the top left.

O	E	O	E	O	E
2	4.67	50	31.08	20	36.25
10	7.77	60	51.80	50	60.43
15	14.56	70	97.12	140	113.32

Quantitative methods

Notes

It could be amended to the following table. A χ^2 test with $(3-1)(2-1) = 2$ degrees of freedom could then be performed.

O	E	O	E
52	35.75	20	36.25
70	59.57	50	60.43
85	111.68	140	113.32

Distribution fitting

Chi-squared tests can also be used to test a hypothesis that some data fit a given distribution. This is called *distribution fitting*, or sometimes *curve fitting*. The value of χ^2 is computed using the same formula as for contingency tables, but the degrees of freedom are computed differently. They are as follows, where n is the number of observed frequencies.

Distribution	Degrees of freedom
No specific distribution (just a list of proportions in each class)	n – 1
Poisson with specified mean	n – 2
Binomial, with specified probability and total number	n – 2
Normal, with specified mean and standard deviation	n – 3

Example: Poisson distribution

In a traffic survey the numbers of cars passing a given point in 100 five minute periods were as follows.

Number of cars	Frequency
0	10
1	25
2	40
3	20
4	3
5 or more	2
	100

The mean number of cars is 1.87 if the final two observations are each taken to be five cars. Test the hypothesis that the number of cars per five minutes follows a Poisson distribution.

Solution

The Poisson probabilities for m = 1.87 are as follows.

$P(0) = 0.1541$
$P(1) = 0.2882$
$P(2) = 0.2695$
$P(3) = 0.1680$
$P(4) = 0.0785$
$P(5 \text{ or more}) = 1 - [P(0) + P(1) + P(2) + P(3) + P(4)] = 0.0417$

BPP Publishing   158

Multiply by 100 to obtain the expected frequencies.

No of cars (x)	Observed frequency O	Expected frequency E	$\frac{(O-E)^2}{E}$
0	10	15.41	1.8993
1	25	28.82	0.5063
2	40	26.95	6.3192
3	20	16.80	0.6095
4	3	7.85	2.9965
5+	2	4.17	1.1292
		$\chi^2 =$	13.4600

At 5% significance level and 6−2 = 4 degrees of freedom, the critical value of χ^2 is 9.49.

The value of χ^2 in this case exceeds the critical value and hence the observed frequencies differ significantly from the expected ones. At 5% significance we cannot therefore accept that the traffic flow follows a Poisson distribution.

Exercise 11

It is thought that a certain variable fits a normal distribution, with a mean of 0 and standard deviation of 1. Results from 1,000 observations were as follows.

Value	Proportion of cases
Below −2	0.04
At least −2 but below −1	0.15
At least −1 but below 0	0.30
At least 0 but below 1	0.35
At least 1 but below 2	0.10
At least 2	0.06

What conclusion should be reached at 1% significance?

Chapter roundup

(a) If we take many samples (of the same size) from a population, and compute each sample's mean, the resulting list of means is a sampling distribution of the mean. Its standard deviation is the standard error, and its mean is the same as the population mean.

(b) We can use the standard error to compute confidence intervals, because the sampling distribution is normally distributed. We can also compute confidence intervals for proportions, using the formula for the standard error of a proportion.

(c) We can test a null hypothesis, of the form that a mean or a proportion equals a certain value, or that two means or two proportions are equal, against an alternative hypothesis. The test may be one-tail or two-tail, depending on the form of the alternative hypothesis.

(d) A hypothesis test is made by comparing the result from a sample with what we would expect if the null hypothesis were true. If the gap between the reality and the expectation is too wide, we reject the null hypothesis.

(e) With small samples ($n < 30$), we must use the t distribution with $n - 1$ degrees of freedom instead of the normal distribution.

(f) Nonparametric tests do not make assumptions about the population, but they are less powerful than parametric tests.

(g) A chi-squared test can test the hypothesis that two variables are unconnected. Expected frequencies are computed, and are then compared with observed frequencies.

(h) A chi-squared test can also be used to test whether observed data fit a given distribution. Again, expected frequencies are computed and compared with observed frequencies.

Quick quiz

1 What are the conditions for the distribution of sample means to be able to be approximated by a normal distribution?

2 Define the standard error of the mean.

3 What is the formula for the standard error of the mean?

4 What is the formula for the standard error of a proportion?

5 What is a null hypothesis?

6 What is the formula for the standard error of the difference between two sample means?

7 Below what sample size should the t distribution be used rather than the normal distribution?

8 For a sample of size n, how many degrees of freedom should be used when carrying out a t test?

9 What are the advantages and disadvantages of nonparametric tests?

10 What is the formula to calculate the value of χ^2 from some data?

11 How many degrees of freedom should be used in a χ^2 test with an m × n contingency table?

12 Explain Yates's correction.

Solutions to exercises

1 $s = 2.7$
σ is estimated as $2.7 \times \sqrt{(50/49)} = 2.7 \times 1.01 = 2.727$
$se = 2.727/\sqrt{50} = 0.386$

2 The standard error is estimated as $1,500/\sqrt{144} = £125$.

At the 95% level of confidence, the population mean is in the range $£(4,000 \pm (1.96 \times 125)) = £(4,000 \pm 245)$, that is, £3,755 to £4,245.

3 The sample proportion is $285/400 = 0.7125$.

The standard error is $\sqrt{\dfrac{0.7125 \times (1-0.7125)}{400}} = 0.0226$

The 99% confidence interval for the population proportion is

$$0.7125 \pm (2.58 \times 0.0226)$$
$$= \quad 0.7125 \pm 0.0583$$
$$= \quad 0.6542 \text{ to } 0.7708$$

4   H_0 is that $\mu = 180$, and H_1 is that $\mu \neq 180$.

The standard error is $50/\sqrt{55} = 6.74$

The sample mean is $192 - 180 = 12$ higher than the hypothesised mean, and is $12/6.74 = 1.78$ standard errors above that mean.

As this is within 1.96 standard errors, the null hypothesis (that the population mean is 180 uses) cannot be rejected.

5   H_0: $\mu \geqslant 1.03$ kg.
    H_1: $\mu < 1.03$ kg.

This is a one-tail test, so the critical value for 1% significance is –2.33. (The minus sign is put in because we will reject H_0 if the sample mean is more than 2.33 standard errors *below* the hypothesised mean.)

Standard error $= 0.02/\sqrt{230} = 0.00132$

$(1.02 - 1.03)/0.00132 = -7.58$.

H_0 should be rejected. There is clear evidence that the population mean weight is below 1.03 kg.

6   The null hypothesis H_0 is that there is no difference between the means of the two areas.

The alternative hypothesis H_1 is that there is a difference.

The standard error of the difference between the two means is

$$\sqrt{\frac{5{,}398.6}{100} + \frac{791.1}{100}} = 7.87$$

The actual difference between the sample means is $93.3 - 57.7 = 35.6$

This is $35.6/7.87 = 4.5$ standard errors.

The difference is significant at the 1% level of significance, and so the null hypothesis is rejected, and it may be concluded that the average annual sales per customer differs between the two areas.

7   The standard error of the mean is $2.089/\sqrt{12} = 0.60$.

The difference between the standard cost of £20 and the actual cost of £23 is £3. This is $3/0.6 = 5$ standard errors.

Referring to t distribution tables, at the 5% level of significance (one-tail test, 5%) with $12 - 1 = 11$ degrees of freedom, the t statistic is 1.80.

Since the actual difference is well in excess of 1.80, we reject the null hypothesis that the actual average cost does not exceed £20. The actual average cost is greater than £20.

8    $H_0 : \mu_1 = \mu_2$
    $H_1 : \mu_1 \neq \mu_2$

This is a two-tail test at 5% significance with $10 + 12 - 2 = 20$ degrees of freedom, giving a critical value of 2.09.

$$\hat{\sigma} = \sqrt{\frac{9 \times 5.76 + 11 \times 1.69}{10 + 12 - 2}} = 1.88$$

$$\text{Standard error} = 1.88 \times \sqrt{\frac{1}{10} + \frac{1}{12}} = 0.80$$

Difference between means $= (35 - 32)/0.80 = 3.75$ standard errors.

As 3.75 exceeds 2.09, the null hypothesis should be rejected. The conclusion is that the average amounts of cash carried by men and women differ.

9    $\dfrac{\text{Row total} \times \text{Column total}}{\text{Table total}} = \dfrac{90 \times 108}{185} = 52.54$

Proportion with low interest in sport $= 90/185 = 0.4865$.

$108 \times 0.4865 = 52.54$

We have effectively done the same computation in two different ways. The expected values are computed on the basis that height and interest in sport are unconnected, so they should be found by distributing people in any one height class over the interest classes in the same proportion as the population as a whole is distributed over the interest classes.

    BPP Publishing

Quantitative methods

10   The value of χ^2 is computed as follows.

Growth	Fertiliser	O	E	$(O - E)^2/E$
Strong	A	47	42.3	0.52
	B	62	64.6	0.10
	C	22	24.1	0.18
Weak	A	25	29.7	0.74
	B	48	45.4	0.15
	C	19	16.9	0.26
				1.95

The critical value at 1% for (3-1)(2-1) = 2 degrees of freedom is 9.21.

1.95 is less than 9.21, so there is no evidence of an association between the choice of fertiliser and the strength of plant growth.

11   The expected proportions are derived from normal distribution tables. Thus the expected proportion for the range from 1 to 2 standard deviations below the mean is 0.1587 – 0.02275 = 0.13595 (rounded to 0.1359 because we have rounded 0.02275 to 0.0228 for the first class). Each proportion is then multiplied by 1,000.

O	E	O – E	$(O - E)^2/E$
40	22.8	17.2	12.98
150	135.9	14.1	1.46
300	341.3	–41.3	5.00
350	341.3	8.7	0.22
100	135.9	–35.9	9.48
60	22.8	37.2	60.69
			89.83

The critical level for 6 – 3 = 3 degrees of freedom and 1% significance is 11.3. The hypothesis should therefore be rejected at this level of significance.

9 CORRELATION AND REGRESSION

Signpost

We often expect the values of two variables to increase or decrease together: for example, the length of a journey and the time taken to make it. When variables move in step like this, or when one goes up as the other goes down (for example sales of coats and the temperature), they are said to be correlated. In this chapter we will look at two different measures of the strength of any correlation, the Pearsonian correlation coefficient and Spearman's rank correlation coefficient. We will also see that the coefficient of determination answers the question: How much of the variation in one variable is explained by variation in the other variable?

If the values of two variables are linked, the link between them (such as: one is about twice as big as the other) can be represented by a line on a graph (with one variable on each axis). This is the line of best fit, because it fits the data we have better than any other line. We will see how to find it using linear regression. Finally, we will look at the approach to problems when one variable is influenced by several others (multiple regression).

Objectives

After completing this chapter you should:

(a)   understand the concept of correlation between two variables;

(b)   be able to compute and interpret the Pearsonian correlation coefficient, the coefficient of determination and Spearman's rank correlation coefficient;

(c)   understand the concept of a line of best fit;

(d)   be able to compute a line of best fit using linear regression and use it to make predictions;

(e)   understand the concept of multiple regression.

---

1   Correlation

When the value of one variable is related to the value of another, they are said to be correlated. Correlation therefore means an inter-relationship or correspondence. Examples of variables which might be correlated are:

(a)   a person's height and weight;
(b)   output from a factory and electricity consumed in it.

One way of showing the correlation between two related variables is on a *scattergraph* or *scatter diagram*, plotting a number of pairs of data on the graph. For example, a scattergraph showing monthly selling costs against the volume of sales for a 12 month period might be as follows.

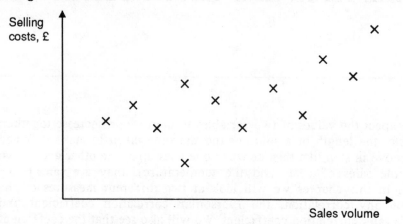

This scattergraph suggests that there is some correlation between selling costs and sales volume, so that as sales volume rises, selling costs tend to rise as well.

Degrees of correlation

Two variables might be perfectly correlated, partly correlated or uncorrelated. These differing degrees of correlation can be illustrated by scatter diagrams.

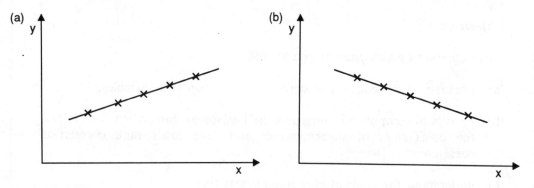

All the pairs of values lie on a straight line. An exact linear relationship exists between the two variables.

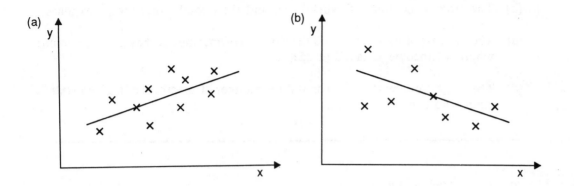

In (a), although there is no exact relationship, low values of x tend to be associated with low values of y, and high values of x with high values of y.

In (b) again, there is no exact relationship, but low values of x tend to be associated with high values of y and vice versa.

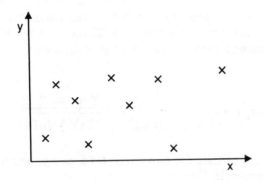

The values of these two variables are not correlated with each other.

Positive correlation and negative correlation

Correlation, whether perfect or partial, can be positive or negative. Positive correlation means that low values of one variable are associated with low values of the other, and high values of one variable are associated with high values of the other. Thus we might expect positive correlation between the output of a factory and the electricity consumed in it. Negative correlation means that low values of one variable are associated with high values of the other, and high values of one variable with low values of the other. Thus we might expect negative correlation between the number of quality controls applied to a factory's output and the number of defective units which leave the factory.

Exercise 1

What sorts of correlation (perfect or partial, positive or negative) would you expect to find between the following pairs of variables?

(a) People's heights and their weights

(b)   The sizes of companies' workforces and their total annual wage expenses

(c)   The incomes of individuals and the amounts of income tax they pay, in a country where all income is taxed at 25%

(d)   The heights of a high jump bar and the number of members of a given athletics team who can clear the bar

The correlation coefficient

The degree of correlation between two variables can be measured, and we can decide, using actual results in the form of pairs of data, whether two variables are perfectly or partially correlated, and if they are partially correlated, whether there is a high or low degree of partial correlation.

This degree of correlation is measured by the *Pearsonian correlation coefficient* (also called the product moment correlation coefficient). There are several formulae for the correlation coefficient, although each formula will give the same value. We will use the following one.

$$\text{Correlation coefficient, } r = \frac{n\Sigma xy - \Sigma x\Sigma y}{\sqrt{[n\Sigma x^2 - (\Sigma x)^2][n\Sigma y^2 - (\Sigma y)^2]}}$$

where x and y represent pairs of data for two variables x and y, and n is the number of pairs of data used in the analysis.

r must always fall between -1 and $+1$. If you get a value outside this range you have made a mistake.

r = +1   means that the variables are *perfectly positively correlated*
r = -1   means that the variables are *perfectly negatively correlated*
r = 0   means that the variables are *uncorrelated*.

Example: the correlation coefficient

The cost of output at a factory is thought to depend on the number of units produced. Data have been collected for the number of units produced each month in the last 6 months, and the associated costs, as follows.

Month	Output in '000s of units	Cost (£'000)
	x	y
1	2	9
2	3	10
3	1	7
4	4	13
5	3	12
6	5	15

Is there any correlation between output and cost?

Solution

$$r = \frac{n\Sigma xy - \Sigma x \Sigma y}{\sqrt{[n\Sigma x^2 - (\Sigma x)^2]\,[n\Sigma y^2 - (\Sigma y)^2]}}$$

We need to find the values for:

(a) Σxy Multiply each value of x by its corresponding y value, so that there are six values for xy. Add up the six values to get the total;

(b) Σx Add up the six values of x to get a total. $(\Sigma x)^2$ will be the square of this total;

(c) Σy Add up the six values of y to get a total. $(\Sigma y)^2$ will be the square of this total;

(d) Σx^2 Find the square of each value of x, so that there are six values for x^2. Add up these values to get a total;

(e) Σy^2 Find the square of each value of y, so that there are six values for y^2. Add up these values to get a total.

Workings

x	y	xy	x^2	y^2
2	9	18	4	81
3	10	30	9	100
1	7	7	1	49
4	13	52	16	169
3	12	36	9	144
5	15	75	25	225
$\Sigma x = 18$	$\Sigma y = 66$	$\Sigma xy = 218$	$\Sigma x^2 = 64$	$\Sigma y^2 = 768$

$(\Sigma x)^2 = 18^2 = 324$ $(\Sigma y)^2 = 66^2 = 4,356$

$n = 6$

$$r = \frac{(6 \times 218) - (18 \times 66)}{\sqrt{(384 - 324) \times (4,608 - 4,356)}}$$

$$= \frac{1,308 - 1,188}{\sqrt{(384 - 324) \times (4,608 - 4,356)}}$$

$$= \frac{120}{\sqrt{60 \times 252}} = \frac{120}{\sqrt{15,120}} = \frac{120}{123} = 0.98$$

There is very high partial perfect positive correlation between the volume of output at the factory and costs.

Correlation in a time series

Correlation exists in a time series (a series of values over time, such as sales figures each year) if there is a relationship between the period of time and the recorded value for that period of time. The correlation coefficient is calculated with time as the x variable although it is convenient to use simplified values for x instead of year numbers. For example, instead of having a series of years from 1988 to 1992, we could have values for x from 0 (1988) to 4 (1992).

Exercise 2

Sales of product A between 1988 and 1992 were as follows.

Year	Units sold ('000s)
1988	20
1989	18
1990	15
1991	14
1992	11

Is there a trend in sales? In other words, is there any correlation between the year and the number of units sold?

The coefficient of determination, r^2

Unless the correlation coefficient r is exactly or very nearly +1, -1 or 0, its meaning or significance is a little unclear. For example, if the correlation coefficient between advertising expenditure and sales revenue is +0.8, this would tell us that the two amounts are positively correlated, but the correlation is not perfect. It would not really tell us much else. A more meaningful analysis is available from the square of the correlation coefficient, r^2, which is called the *coefficient of determination*.

r^2 measures the proportion of the total variation in the value of one variable that can be explained by variations in the value of the other variable. If, in the example of advertising expenditure and sales revenue, r = 0.8, r^2 = 0.64. This means that 64% of variations in sales revenue can be explained by variations in advertising expenditure, leaving 36% of variations to be explained by other factors.

Note, however, that if r^2 = 0.64, we would say that 64% of the variations in sales revenue can be *explained* by variations in advertising expenditure. We do not necessarily conclude that 64% of variations in sales revenue are *caused* by variations in advertising expenditure. It might be that high advertising expenditure happened to coincide with a general economic boom, which was the real cause of both the increase in advertising expenditure and the increase in sales. We must beware of reading too much significance into our statistical analysis.

Non-linear relationships

The formulae used above for r and r^2 only work for linear or near linear relationships. All the points on a scatter diagram might lie on a smooth curve as follows.

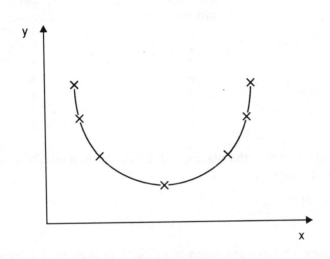

If the formula for r were used in this case, a low value of r would be obtained, suggesting that very little correlation exists, whereas in fact the two sets of variables are perfectly correlated by a non-linear relationship.

Spearman's rank correlation coefficient

In the examples considered above, the data were given in terms of the values of the relevant variables, such as the number of hours. Sometimes however, they are given in terms of order or ranks rather than actual values. When this occurs, a correlation coefficient known as Spearman's rank correlation coefficient, r_s, should be calculated using the following formula.

$$\text{Coefficient of rank correlation} = 1 - \frac{6 \, \Sigma \, d^2}{n(n^2 - 1)}$$

where   n = number of pairs of data
            d = the difference between the rankings in each set of data.

The coefficient of rank correlation can be interpreted in exactly the same way as the ordinary correlation coefficient. Its value can range from -1 to +1.

Example: the rank correlation coefficient

The examination placings of seven students were as follows.

Student	Statistics placing	Economics placing
A	2	1
B	1	3
C	4	7
D	6	5
E	5	6
F	3	2
G	7	4

You are asked to judge whether the placings of the students in Statistics correlate with their placings in Economics.

Solution

Correlation must be measured by Spearman's coefficient, because we are given the placings of students, and not their actual marks.

$$r_s = 1 - \frac{6 \sum d^2}{n(n^2 - 1)}$$

where d is the difference between the rank in statistics and the rank in economics for each student.

Student	Rank Statistics	Rank Economics	d	d^2
A	2	1	1	1
B	1	3	2	4
C	4	7	3	9
D	6	5	1	1
E	5	6	1	1
F	3	2	1	1
G	7	4	3	9
			$\sum d^2 =$	26

$$r_s = 1 - \frac{6 \times 26}{7 \times (49 - 1)} = 1 - \frac{156}{336} = 0.536$$

The correlation is positive, 0.536, but the correlation is not strong.

Tied ranks

If in a problem some of the items tie for a particular ranking, these must be given an average place before the coefficient of rank correlation is calculated. Here is an example.

Position of students in examination				Express as
A	1 =	average of 1 and 2		1.5
B	1 =			1.5
C	3			3
D	4			4
E	5 =			6
F	5 =	average of 5, 6 and 7		6
G	5 =			6
H	8			8

Exercise 3

Five different cameras were placed in order of merit by two different judges working for a consumer's organisation as follows.

Camera	Judge P Rank	Judge Q Rank
A	1	4 =
B	2 =	1
C	4	3
D	5	2
E	2 =	4 =

How are the two sets of rankings correlated?

2 Regression

The correlation coefficient measures the degree of correlation between two variables, but it does not tell us how to predict values for one variable (y) given values for the other variable (x). To do that, we need to find a line which is a good fit for the points on a scattergraph, and then use that line to find the value of y corresponding to each given value of x.

Linear regression (also known as the *least squares method*) is a statistical technique for calculating a line of best fit with the equation y = a + bx.

The formulae for a and b in y = a + bx are as follows.

$$b = \frac{n\Sigma xy - \Sigma x\Sigma y}{n\Sigma x^2 - (\Sigma x)^2}$$

$$a = \bar{y} - b\bar{x}$$

where   n   is the number of pairs of data
         $\bar{x}$ is the average x value of all the pairs of data
         $\bar{y}$ is the average y value of all the pairs of data.

BPP Publishing

Quantitative methods

There are some points to note about these formulae.

(a) The line of best fit that is derived represents the *regression of y upon x*.

A different line of best fit could be obtained by interchanging x and y in the formulae. This would then represent the *regression of x upon y* (x = a + by) and it would have a slightly different slope. You will usually want to find the regression of y upon x, where x is the independent variable (the one which influences y), and y is the dependent variable (the one influenced by x) whose value we wish to forecast for given values of x. In a time series, x will represent time.

(b) Since a = $\bar{y}$ - b$\bar{x}$, it follows that the line of best fit must *always* pass through the point ($\bar{x}$, $\bar{y}$).

(c) If you look at the formula for b and compare it with the formula we gave for the Pearsonian correlation coefficient you should see some similarities between the two formulae.

Example: the least squares method

You are given the following data for output at a factory and costs of production over the past five months.

Month	Output '000 units	Costs £'000
	x	y
1	20	82
2	16	70
3	24	90
4	22	85
5	18	73

There is a high degree of correlation between output and costs, and so it is decided to calculate fixed costs and the variable cost per unit of output using the least squares method.

(a) Find an equation to determine the expected level of costs, for any given volume of output.

(b) Estimate total costs if output is 22,000 units.

(c) Confirm that the degree of correlation between output and costs is high by calculating the correlation coefficient.

Solution

(a) *Workings*

x	y	xy	x^2	y^2
20	82	1,640	400	6,724
16	70	1,120	256	4,900
24	90	2,160	576	8,100
22	85	1,870	484	7,225
18	73	1,314	324	5,329
$\Sigma x = 100$	$\Sigma y = 400$	$\Sigma xy = 8,104$	$\Sigma x^2 = 2,040$	$\Sigma y^2 = 32,278$

$n = 5$ (There are five pairs of data for x and y values)

$$b = \frac{n\Sigma xy - \Sigma x \Sigma y}{n\Sigma x^2 - (\Sigma x)^2}$$

$$= \frac{(5 \times 8,104) - (100 \times 400)}{(5 \times 2,040) - 100^2}$$

$$= \frac{40,520 - 40,000}{10,200 - 10,000} = \frac{520}{200}$$

$$= 2.6$$

$$a = \bar{y} - b\bar{x}$$

$$= \frac{400}{5} - 2.6 \times \left(\frac{100}{5}\right)$$

$$= 28$$

$y = 28 + 2.6x$
where y = total cost, in thousands of pounds
       x = output, in thousands of units.

(b) If the output is 22,000 units, we would expect costs to be

$28 + 2.6 \times 22$

$= 85.2 = £85,200.$

(c) $r = \dfrac{520}{\sqrt{200 \times (5 \times 32,278 - 400^2)}}$

$= \dfrac{520}{\sqrt{200 \times 1,390}} = \dfrac{520}{527.3} = +0.99$

Regression lines and time series

The same technique can be applied to calculate a regression line (a trend line) for a time series. This is particularly useful for purposes of forecasting. As with correlation, years can be numbered from 0 upwards.

Exercise 4

Sales of product B over the seven year period from 1987 to 1993 were as follows.

Year	Sales of B '000 units
1987	22
1988	25
1989	24
1990	26
1991	29
1992	28
1993	30

There is high correlation between time and the volume of sales. Calculate the trend line of sales, and forecast sales in 1994 and 1995.

Multiple regression analysis

In the techniques so far described, there is an assumed relationship between one dependent variable, y, and one independent variable, x. Multiple regression analysis, in contrast, involves three or more variables. There is still a dependent variable, y, but now there are two or more independent (or explaining) variables. For example, wage rates might depend on both the general rate of price inflation and the number of school leavers.

(a) As with linear regression, the function for y is derived from an analysis of historical data.

(b) The function for y is described by the formula

$$y = a + bx_1 + cx_2 + dx_3 + \dots + hx_n$$

where $x_1, x_2, x_3, \dots x_n$ are the various factors which affect the value of y;

a = a constant value;

b, c, d and so on reflect the impact on y of each particular factor.

(c) The function for y cannot be drawn on a two-dimensional graph, because there are three or more variables in the equation.

The aim of multiple regression analysis is to improve predictions of the value of y by recognising that *several* different explaining factors might be involved. For example, we might try to forecast the demand for steel from the demand for cars and the demand for canned food. Multiple regression is particularly likely to be useful when there is fairly high correlation between the x variables and the y variable, but low correlation between pairs of the x variables.

The disadvantage of multiple regression analysis is its relative complexity. A computer program is normally used to derive the function for y.

Exercise 5

It is thought that the heating and lighting costs per month in the head offices of Thermostat Ltd vary with the number of working days in the month, the average daily (midday) temperature outside the building during the month and the number of employees. Using multiple regression analysis, the following formula for estimating these costs per month has been derived.

$$y = 3,000 + 95x_1 - 220x_2 + 1.5x_3$$

where x_1 is the number of working days in the month
        x_2 is the average daily temperature (°C)
        x_3 is the number of employees

The actual costs of heating and lighting in June 1993 were £2,000. During the month, there were 22 working days, the average daily temperature was 18 °C and there were 500 employees.

What is the difference between actual costs and the costs that would have been expected?

Notes

Chapter roundup

(a) The relationship, if any, between the values of two variables can be measured by their correlation.

(b) Correlation may be perfect or partial, and it may be positive or negative. Zero correlation is also possible.

(c) The Pearsonian correlation coefficient, r, is computed using values of the two variables, x and y, collected as pairs of data. Spearman's rank correlation coefficient, r_s, is computed using ranks (first, second and so on) rather than actual values.

(d) Both correlation coefficients can take values between +1 and -1 inclusive.

(e) The coefficient of determination, r^2, shows the extent to which variations in the value of one variable are explained by variations in the value of the other variable.

(f) The actual relationship between two variables may be estimated using linear regression. The equation of a line of best fit $y = a + bx$ is computed from observed pairs of values of x and y.

(g) Once a regression line has been computed, it may be used to compute values of y corresponding to unobserved values of x. However, such predictions are prone to errors.

(h) Multiple regression can be used to take account of the effect on a dependent variable of several other variables.

Quick quiz

1   Give some examples of pairs of variables which you would expect to be correlated.

2   Give a formula for the Pearsonian correlation coefficient.

3   Compute both the Pearsonian correlation coefficient and Spearman's rank correlation coefficient for the following data.

x	1	2	3	4	6	9
y	52	47	42	48	35	35

4   How should the coefficient of determination be interpreted?

5   40 pairs of values of variables x and y have been collected. $\Sigma x = 820$ and $\Sigma y = 1,320$. The regression line passes through the point x = 100, y = 165. What is the equation of the line?

6   When is multiple regression most likely to be useful?

Solutions to exercises

1   (a)   Partial positive correlation
    (b)   Partial positive correlation
    (c)   Perfect positive correlation
    (d)   Partial negative correlation

2   Let 1988 to 1992 be years 0 to 4.

x	y	xy	x^2	y^2
0	20	0	0	400
1	18	18	1	324
2	15	30	4	225
3	14	42	9	196
4	11	44	16	121
$\Sigma x = 10$	$\Sigma y = 78$	$\Sigma xy = 134$	$\Sigma x^2 = 30$	$\Sigma y^2 = 1{,}266$

$(\Sigma x)^2 = 100$ $(\Sigma y)^2 = 6{,}084$

$n = 5$

$$r = \frac{(5 \times 134) - (10 \times 78)}{\sqrt{(5 \times 30 - 100) \times (5 \times 1{,}266 - 6{,}084)}}$$

$$= \frac{670 - 780}{\sqrt{(150 - 100) \times (6{,}330 - 6{,}084)}} = \frac{-110}{\sqrt{50 \times 246}}$$

$$= \frac{-110}{\sqrt{12{,}300}} = \frac{-110}{110.90536} = -0.992$$

There is partial negative correlation between the year of sale and units sold. The value of r is close to –1, therefore a high degree of correlation exists, although it is not quite perfect correlation. This means that there is a clear downward trend in sales.

3

	Judge P Rank	Judge Q Rank	d	d^2
A	1.0	4.5	-3.5	12.25
B	2.5	1.0	1.5	2.25
C	4.0	3.0	1.0	1.00
D	5.0	2.0	3.0	9.00
E	2.5	4.5	-2.0	4.00
				28.50

$$r_s = 1 - \frac{6 \times 28.5}{5 \times (25-1)} = -0.425$$

There is a slight negative correlation between the rankings.

         BPP Publishing

4

Year	x	y	xy	x^2
1987	0	22	0	0
1988	1	25	25	1
1989	2	24	48	4
1990	3	26	78	9
1991	4	29	116	16
1992	5	28	140	25
1993	6	30	180	36
	$\Sigma x = 21$	$\Sigma y = 184$	$\Sigma xy = 587$	$\Sigma x^2 = 91$

$n = 7$

Where $y = a + bx$

$$b = \frac{(7 \times 587) - (21 \times 184)}{(7 \times 91) - (21 \times 21)}$$

$$= \frac{245}{196}$$

$$= 1.25$$

$$a = \frac{184}{7} - \frac{1.25 \times 21}{7}$$

$$= 22.5357, \text{ say } 22.5$$

$y = 22.5 + 1.25x$ where $x = 0$ in 1987, $x = 1$ in 1988 and so on.

Using this trend line, predicted sales in 1994 (year 7) would be

$22.5 + 1.25 \times 7 = 31.25 = 31,250$ units.

Similarly, for 1995 (year 8) predicted sales would be

$22.5 + 1.25 \times 8 = 32.50 = 32,500$ units.

5 *Expected costs*

$y = 3,000 + (95 \times 22) - (220 \times 18) + (1.5 \times 500)$
$= £1,880$

The expenditure difference is £2,000 - £1,880 = £120.

Solutions to quick quiz

3

x	y	x^2	y^2	xy	Rank (x)	Rank (y)	d^2
1	52	1	2,704	52	6	1.0	25.00
2	47	4	2,209	94	5	3.0	4.00
3	42	9	1,764	126	4	4.0	0.00
4	48	16	2,304	192	3	2.0	1.00
6	35	36	1,225	210	2	5.5	12.25
9	35	81	1,225	315	1	5.5	20.25
25	259	147	11,431	989			62.50

$$r = \frac{6 \times 989 - 25 \times 259}{\sqrt{(6 \times 147 - 25^2) \times (6 \times 11,431 - 259^2)}}$$

$$= \frac{5,934 - 6,475}{\sqrt{(257 \times 1,505)}} = -541/621.92 = -0.87$$

$$r_s = 1 - [(6 \times 62.50)/(6 \times (6^2 - 1))]$$

$$= 1 - 375/210 = 1 - 1.79 = -0.79$$

5   The line must pass through ($\bar{x}$, $\bar{y}$) as well as through (100, 165).

$\bar{x}$ = 820/40 = 20.5 $\bar{y}$ = 1,320/40 = 33

Let y = a + bx

b = (165 - 33)/(100 - 20.5) = 1.66

165 = a + (1.66 × 100)

165 = a + 166

a = -1

The equation of the regression line is y = -1 + 1.66x.

10 TIME SERIES

Signpost

A company may well collect data over time, for example on sales. Such a series of figures is a time series, and it can be analysed into components which combine to give the actual data. In particular, there is likely to be an underlying trend (such as an increase in sales of 2% a year), and seasonal variations (such as sales being higher in summer than in winter). Once we have found out how big the seasonal variations are, we can use them to remove seasonal effects from data: thus if sales are high in summer, we can reduce a summer figure to get an idea of how the trend is progressing. We can also make forecasts, by assuming that a trend will continue to be followed and then incorporating seasonal variations. Finally, we can use another method of forecasting, exponential smoothing, which continually adjusts an original forecast to take account of actual results.

Your objectives

After completing this chapter you should:

(a) know the four components of a time series;

(b) be able to find a trend using moving averages;

(c) be able to compute and average the seasonal variations from a trend;

(d) be able to remove seasonal effects from data;

(e) be able to make forecasts by extrapolating a trend and applying average seasonal variations;

(f) know and be able to use the exponential smoothing formula.

---

1 The analysis of time series

A time series is a series of figures or values recorded over time. Examples of time series are:

(a) output at a factory each day for the last month;
(b) monthly sales over the last two years;
(c) total annual costs for the last ten years;
(d) the Retail Prices Index each month for the last ten years;
(e) the number of people employed by a company each year for the last 20 years.

A graph of a time series is called a *time series plot*. For example, consider the following time series.

Year	Sales £'000
19X0	20
19X1	21
19X2	24
19X3	23
19X4	27
19X5	30
19X6	28

The time series plot is as follows.

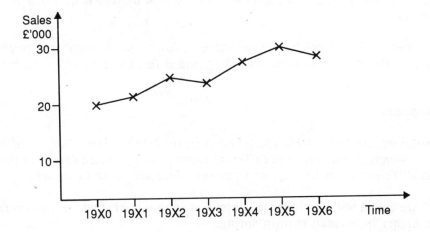

The horizontal axis is always chosen to represent time, and the vertical axis represents the values of the data recorded.

There are several features of a time series which it may be necessary to identify. These are:

(a)   a trend;

(b)   seasonal variations or fluctuations;

(c)   cycles, or cyclical variations;

(d)   non-recurring, random variations; these may be caused by unforeseen circumstances, such as a change in the government of the country, a war, the collapse of a company, technological change or a fire.

The trend

The trend is the underlying long-term movement over time in the values of the data recorded. In the following examples of time series, there are three types of trend.

	Output per labour hour Units	Cost per unit £	Number of employees
19X4	30	1.00	100
19X5	24	1.08	103
19X6	26	1.20	96
19X7	22	1.15	102
19X8	21	1.18	103
19X9	17	1.25	98
	(A)	(B)	(C)

(a) In time series (A) there is a *downward* trend in the output per labour hour. Output per labour hour did not fall every year, because it went up between 19X5 and 19X6, but the long-term movement is clearly a downward one.

(b) In time series (B) there is an *upward* trend in the cost per unit. Although unit costs went down in 19X7 from a higher level in 19X6, the basic movement over time is one of rising costs.

(c) In time series (C) there is no clear movement up or down, and the number of employees remained fairly constant around 100. The trend is therefore a *static*, or level one.

Seasonal variations

Seasonal variations are short-term fluctuations in recorded values, due to different circumstances which affect results at different times of the year, on different days of the week, at different times of day, or whatever. Here are some examples.

(a) Sales of ice cream will be higher in summer than in winter, and sales of overcoats will be higher in autumn than in spring.

(b) Shops might expect higher sales shortly before Christmas, or in their winter and summer sales.

(c) Sales might be higher on Friday and Saturday than on Monday.

(d) The telephone network may be heavily used at certain times of the day (such as mid-morning and mid-afternoon) and much less used at other times (such as in the middle of the night).

'Seasonal' is a term which may appear to refer to the seasons of the year, but its meaning in time series analysis is somewhat broader, as the examples given above show.

Example: a trend and seasonal variations

The number of customers served by a company of travel agents over a period of four years is shown in the following time series plot.

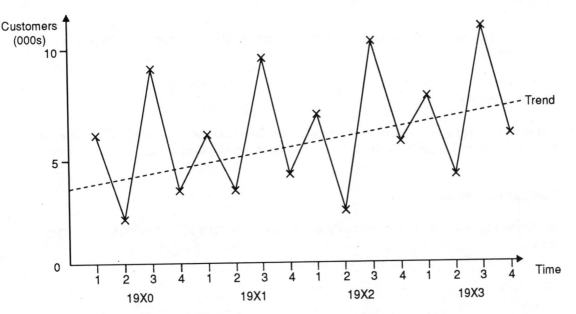

In this example, there would appear to be large seasonal fluctuations in demand, but there is also a basic upward trend.

Exercise 1

What seasonal variations would you expect to see in sales of video recorders?

Cyclical variations

Cyclical variations are medium term changes in results caused by circumstances which repeat in cycles. In business, cyclical variations are commonly associated with economic cycles, successive booms and slumps in the economy. Economic cycles may last a few years. Cyclical variations are longer term than seasonal variations.

2 Finding the trend and seasonal variations

The main problem we are concerned with in time series analysis is how to identify the trend, seasonal variations, cyclical variations and random variations in a set of results over a period of time. You need to be aware of cyclical and random variations, but time series analysis problems are usually about a trend and seasonal variations.

There are two principal methods of finding a trend and seasonal variations.

(a) *Regression analysis by the least squares method.* This is a technique to calculate the 'line of best fit'. This method, described in Chapter 9, makes the assumption that the trend line, whether up or down, is a straight line. Periods of time (such as quarters for which sales figures are given) are numbered, commonly from 0, and the regression line of the data on those period numbers is found. That line is then taken to be the trend.

(b) *Moving averages.* This method attempts to remove seasonal variations by a process of averaging.

Moving averages

A moving average is an average of the results of a fixed number of periods. Since it is an average of several time periods, it is related to the mid-point of the overall period.

Example: moving averages

The following table shows a company's annual sales, in units of its product, over seven years.

Year	Sales Units
19X0	390
19X1	380
19X2	460
19X3	450
19X4	470
19X5	440
19X6	500

Take a moving average of the annual sales over a period of three years.

Solution

(a) Average sales in the three year period 19X0 - 19X2 were

$$\left(\frac{390 + 380 + 460}{3} \right) = \frac{1,230}{3} = 410$$

This average relates to the middle year of the period, 19X1.

(b) Similarly, average sales in the three year period 19X1 - 19X3 were

$$\left(\frac{380 + 460 + 450}{3} \right) = \frac{1,290}{3} = 430$$

This average relates to the middle year of the period, 19X2.

(c) The average sales can also be found for the periods 19X2 - 19X4, 19X3 - 19X5 and 19X4 - 19X6, to give the following.

Year	Sales	Moving total of 3 years sales	Moving average of 3 years sales (÷ 3)
19X0	390		
19X1	380	1,230	410
19X2	460	1,290	430
19X3	450	1,380	460
19X4	470	1,360	453
19X5	440	1,410	470
19X6	500		

Note the following points.

(i) The moving average series has five figures relating to the years from 19X1 to 19X5. The original series had seven figures for the years from 19X0 to 19X6.

(ii) There is an upward trend in sales, which is more noticeable from the series of moving averages than from the original series of *actual* sales each year.

The above example averaged over a three year period. Over what period should a moving average be taken? The answer to this question is that the moving average which is most appropriate will depend on the circumstances and the nature of the time series. Note the following points.

(a) A moving average which takes an average of the results in many time periods will represent results over a longer term than a moving average of two or three periods.

(b) On the other hand, with a moving average of results in many time periods, the last figure in the series will be out of date by several periods. In our example, the most recent average related to 19X5. With a moving average of five years' results, the final figure in the series would relate to 19X4 (the average for 19X2, 19X3, 19X4, 19X5 and 19X6).

(c) When there is a known cycle over which seasonal variations occur, such as all the days in the week or all the seasons in the year, the most suitable moving average would be one which covers one full cycle.

Exercise 2

Using the following data, what is the three month moving average for April?

Month	Number of new houses finished
January	500
February	450
March	700
April	900
May	1,250
June	1,000

Moving averages of an even number of results

In the previous example, moving averages were taken of the results in an *odd* number of time periods, and the average then related to the mid-point of the overall period.

If a moving average were taken of results in an *even* number of time periods, the basic technique would be the same, but the mid-point of the overall period would not relate to a single period. For example, if an average were taken of the following four results:

Spring	120	
Summer	90	
Autumn	180	average 115
Winter	70	

the average would relate to the mid-point of the period, between summer and autumn.

The trend line average figures need to relate to particular time periods; otherwise, seasonal variations cannot be calculated. To overcome this difficulty, we take a moving average of the moving average. An example will illustrate this technique.

Example: moving averages over an even number of periods

Calculate a moving average trend line of the following results.

Year	Quarter	Volume of sales '000 units
19X5	1	600
	2	840
	3	420
	4	720
19X6	1	640
	2	860
	3	420
	4	740
19X7	1	670
	2	900
	3	430
	4	760

Solution

A moving average of four will be used, since the volume of sales would appear to depend on the season of the year, and each year has four quarterly results.

The moving average of four does not relate to any specific period of time; therefore a second moving average of two will be calculated on the first moving average trend line.

Year	Quarter	Actual volume of sales '000 units (A)	Moving total of 4 quarters' sales '000 units (B)	Moving average of 4 quarters' sales '000 units (B ÷ 4)	Mid-point of 2 moving averages TREND LINE (C)
19X5	1	600			
	2	840			
	3	420	2,580	645.0	650.00
	4	720	2,620	655.0	657.50
19X6	1	640	2,640	660.0	660.00
	2	860	2,640	660.0	662.50
	3	420	2,660	665.0	668.75
	4	740	2,690	672.5	677.50
19X7	1	670	2,730	682.5	683.75
	2	900	2,740	685.0	687.50
	3	430	2,760	690.0	
	4	760			

By taking a mid point (a moving average of two) of the original moving averages, we can relate the results to specific quarters (from the third quarter of 19X5 to the second quarter of 19X7).

Exercise 3

What is the four quarter moving average centred on year 1, quarter 4 for the following data?

Year	Quarter	Data
1	1	52
	2	54
	3	56
	4	55
2	1	57
	2	60
	3	59
	4	62

Seasonal variations

Once a trend has been established, by whatever method, we can find the seasonal variations. An example will show how this is done.

Example: the trend and seasonal variations

Output at a factory appears to vary with the day of the week. Output over the last three weeks has been as follows.

BPP Publishing

		Week 1 '000 units	Week 2 '000 units	Week 3 '000 units
	Monday	80	82	84
	Tuesday	104	110	116
	Wednesday	94	97	100
	Thursday	120	125	130
	Friday	62	64	66

With the days numbered from 0 to 14, a trend line has been found using regression analysis. It is $y = 0.42x + 92.7$.

Find the seasonal variation for each of the 15 days, and the average seasonal variation for each day of the week.

Solution

The difference between the actual result on any one day and the trend figure for that day will be the seasonal variation for the day. The trend figures themselves are found simply by putting the day numbers (0 to 14) as values of x in the equation $y = 0.42x + 92.7$.

The seasonal variations for the 15 days are as follows.

		Actual	Trend	Seasonal variation
Week 1	Monday	80	92.70	– 12.70
	Tuesday	104	93.12	+ 10.88
	Wednesday	94	93.54	+ 0.46
	Thursday	120	93.96	+ 26.04
	Friday	62	94.38	– 32.38
Week 2	Monday	82	94.80	– 12.80
	Tuesday	110	95.22	+ 14.78
	Wednesday	97	95.64	+ 1.36
	Thursday	125	96.06	+ 28.94
	Friday	64	96.48	– 32.48
Week 3	Monday	84	96.90	– 12.90
	Tuesday	116	97.32	+ 18.68
	Wednesday	100	97.74	+ 2.26
	Thursday	130	98.16	+ 31.84
	Friday	66	98.58	– 32.58

	Monday	Tuesday	Wednesday	Thursday	Friday
Week 1	– 12.70	+ 10.88	+ 0.46	+ 26.04	– 32.38
Week 2	– 12.80	+ 14.78	+ 1.36	+ 28.94	– 32.48
Week 3	– 12.90	+ 18.68	+ 2.26	+ 31.84	– 32.58
Average	– 12.80	+ 14.78	+ 1.36	+ 28.94	– 32.48

The variation between the actual results on any one particular day and the trend line average is not the same from week to week, but an average of these variations can be taken.

Our estimate of the 'seasonal' or daily variation is almost complete, but there is one more important step to take. Variations around the basic trend line should cancel each other out, and add up to 0. At the moment, they do not.

	Monday	Tuesday	Wednesday	Thursday	Friday	Total
Estimated daily variation	- 12.80	+ 14.78	+ 1.36	+ 28.94	- 32.48	- 0.2
Adjustment to reduce total variation to 0	+ 0.04	+ 0.04	+ 0.04	+ 0.04	+ 0.04	+ 0.2
Final estimate of daily variation	- 12.76	+ 14.82	+ 1.40	+ 28.98	- 32.44	0

These might be rounded up or down as follows.
Monday -13; Tuesday +15; Wednesday +1; Thursday +29; Friday -32; Total 0.

Exercise 4

The following sales figures are to be analysed into a trend and seasonal variations, assuming that the seasonal variations have a period of three months (that is, they follow a pattern of rises and falls which lasts three months). What is the seasonal variation for April?

Month	Sales £'000
March	8
April	13
May	16
June	11

Seasonal variations using the multiplicative model

The method of estimating the seasonal variations in the above example was to use the differences between the trend and actual data. This is called the *additive model*. The alternative is to use the *multiplicative model* whereby each actual figure is expressed as a percentage of the trend. Sometimes this method is called the *proportional model*. The above example of output at a factory can be reworked on this alternative basis.

		Actual	Trend	Seasonal percentage
Week 1	Monday	80	92.70	86.3
	Tuesday	104	93.12	111.7
	Wednesday	94	93.54	100.5
	Thursday	120	93.96	127.7
	Friday	62	94.38	65.7

		Actual	Trend	Seasonal percentage
Week 2	Monday	82	94.80	86.5
	Tuesday	110	95.22	115.5
	Wednesday	97	95.64	101.4
	Thursday	125	96.06	130.1
	Friday	64	96.48	66.3
Week 3	Monday	84	96.90	86.7
	Tuesday	116	97.32	119.2
	Wednesday	100	97.74	102.3
	Thursday	130	98.16	132.4
	Friday	66	98.58	67.0

The summary of the seasonal variations expressed in percentage terms is as follows.

	Monday %	Tuesday %	Wednesday %	Thursday %	Friday %
Week 1	86.3	111.7	100.5	127.7	65.7
Week 2	86.5	115.5	101.4	130.1	66.3
Week 3	86.7	119.2	102.3	132.4	67.0
Average	86.5	115.5	101.4	130.1	66.3

Instead of adding up to zero, as with the additive model, these should add up (in this case) to 500 (an average of 100%).

They actually add up to 499.8 so 0.04% has to be added to each one. This is too small to make a difference to figures rounded to one decimal place, so we should add 0.1% to each of two seasonal variations. We could arbitrarily increase Monday's variation to 86.6% and Tuesday's to 115.6%.

The multiplicative model is better than the additive model where the trend is increasing or decreasing over time. In this case, the actual variations will tend to increase (or decrease) so absolute seasonal adjustments will become out of date, unlike percentage adjustments.

Exercise 5

A company's quarterly sales figures have been analysed into a trend and seasonal variations using moving averages. Here is an extract from the analysis.

Year	Quarter	Actual £'000	Trend £'000
1991	1	350	366
	2	380	370
	3	400	380
	4	360	394
1992	1	410	406
	2	430	414
	3	450	418
	4	370	423

Find the average seasonal variation for each quarter, using the multiplicative model.

Deseasonalisation

Economic statistics, such as unemployment figures, are often in 'seasonally adjusted' or 'deseasonalised' terms. All this means is that seasonal variations have been taken out, to leave a figure should indicate the trend.

Example: deseasonalisation

Actual sales figures for four quarters, together with appropriate seasonal adjustment factors derived from previous data, are as follows.

		Seasonal adjustments	
	Actual	Additive	Multiplicative
Quarter	sales	model	model
	£'000	£'000	%
1	150	+3	102
2	160	+4	105
3	164	-2	98
4	170	-5	95

Deseasonalise these data.

Solution

We are reversing the normal process of applying seasonal variations to trend figures, so with the additive model we *subtract* positive seasonal variations (and add negative ones), and with the multiplicative model we *divide* by the seasonal variation factors (expressed as proportions).

		Deseasonalised sales	
	Actual	Additive	Multiplicative
Quarter	sales	model	model
	£'000	£'000	£'000
1	150	147	147
2	160	156	152
3	164	166	167
4	170	175	179

3 Forecasting

Forecasting is an essential, but difficult task of management. Sales, costs, needs for labour and materials and profits all need to be forecast. Many forecasts are made by guessing, but they are unlikely to be reliable.

BPP Publishing

There are several mathematical techniques of forecasting which could be used. These techniques will not necessarily provide accurate forecasts, but on the whole, they are likely to provide more reliable estimates than guesswork. Techniques cannot eliminate uncertainty about the future, but they can help to ensure that managers take account of all known facts in the preparation of their forecasts.

The technique which we will look at here is extrapolating a trend and then adjusting for seasonal variations.

Forecasts of future values should be made by:

(a)   calculating a trend line;

(b)   using the trend line to forecast future trend line values;

(c)   adjusting these values by the average seasonal variation applicable to the future period, to determine the forecast for that period. With the additive model, add (or subtract for negative variations) the variation. With the multiplicative model, multiply the trend value by the variation (expressed as a proportion).

Extending a trend line outside the range of known data, in this case forecasting the future from a trend line based on data about the past, is known as *extrapolation*.

Example: forecasting

Sales of product X each quarter for the last three years have been as follows (in thousands of units). Trend values, found by a moving averages method, are shown in brackets.

Year	1st quarter	2nd quarter	3rd quarter	4th quarter
1	18	30	20 (18.75)	6 (19.375)
2	20 (20)	33 (20.5)	22 (21)	8 (21.5)
3	22 (22.125)	35 (22.75)	25	10

Average seasonal variations for quarters 1 to 4 are –0.1, +12.4, +1.1 and –13.4 respectively.

Use the trend line and estimates of seasonal variations to forecast sales in each quarter of year 4.

Solution

The trend line indicates an increase of about 0.6 per quarter. This can be confirmed by calculating the average quarterly increase in trend line values between the third quarter of year 1 (18.75) and the second quarter of year 2 (22.75). The average rise is

$$\frac{22.75 - 18.75}{7} = \frac{4}{7} = 0.57, \text{ say } 0.6.$$

Taking 0.6 as the quarterly increase in the trend, the forecast of sales for year 4, *before* seasonal adjustments (the trend line forecast) would be as follows.

Year	Quarter		Trend line
3	*2nd (actual trend)	22.75, say	22.8
	3rd		23.4
	4th		24.0
4	1st		24.6
	2nd		25.2
	3rd		25.8
	4th		26.4

* last known trend line value.

Seasonal variations should now be incorporated to obtain the final forecast.

	Quarter	Trend line forecast '000 units	Average seasonal variation '000 units	Forecast of actual sales '000 units
Year 4	1st	24.6	– 0.1	24.5
	2nd	25.2	+12.4	37.6
	3rd	25.8	+ 1.1	26.9
	4th	26.4	–13.4	13.0

If we had been using the multiplicative model, with an average variation for (for example) quarter 3 of 105.7%, our prediction for the third quarter of year 4 would have been 25.8 × 105.7% = 27.3.

Note that if the trend had been given as a regression line, trend values could have been obtained simply by inserting the numbers for the quarters as values of x in the regression line equation.

Exercise 6

A company's sales figures for January 1992 (month 0) to December 1993 (month 23) have been analysed into a trend and percentage seasonal variations using regression analysis.

The regression line is y = 780 + 4x, where x is the month number and y is sales in thousands of pounds.

The average seasonal variation for March is 106%.

Forecast the sales for March 1994.

Residuals

A *residual* is the difference between the results which would have been predicted (for a past period for which we already have data) by the trend line adjusted for the average seasonal variation and the actual results.

The residual is therefore the difference which is not explained by the trend line and the average seasonal variation. The residual gives some indication of how much actual results were affected by other factors. Large residuals suggest that any forecast is likely to be unreliable.

In the above example of sales of product X, the 'prediction' for the third quarter of year 1 would have been 18.75 + 1.1 = 19.85. As the actual value was 20, the residual was only 20 - 19.85 = 0.15. The residual for the fourth quarter of year 2 was 8 - (21.5 - 13.4) = 8 - 8.1 = -0.1.

Exponential smoothing

Another forecasting technique is exponential smoothing. It differs from the methods considered so far in that, rather than working out a trend and average seasonal variations and then applying them to several forecasts, it continually takes account of the accuracy of recent forecasts and tries to move closer to accurate forecasts.

By this method, a forecast for a period's results is obtained by the following formula.

Forecast = forecast for preceding period + α (actual outcome for preceding period - forecast for preceding period)

where α is the *smoothing factor* or *smoothing constant*.

α will be in the range 0 to 1, but its actual value is chosen depending on which value would have been most suitable in the past.

Example: exponential smoothing (1)

Smooth Ltd uses the following formula to estimate future sales demand.

Demand in period t + 1 = forecast of demand in period t + 0.2 (actual demand in period t - forecast of demand in period t)

The forecast of demand in 19X3 was 20,000 units, but actual demand was 21,500 units. What will be the forecast of demand for 19X4?

Solution

Forecast of demand in 19X4 = forecast for 19X3 + 0.2 × (difference between forecast and actual results)

= 20,000 + 0.2 (21,500 - 20,000)
= 20,300 units.

An important drawback to exponential smoothing is that if there is an upward or downward trend in the time series, forecasts using exponential smoothing will lag behind the trend.

(a) If α = 0, every forecast will be the same.

(b) If α = 1, each forecast will be the actual results in the period just ended.

(c)   The closer α is to 1, the greater will be the emphasis on recent results in preparing a forecast; whereas the closer α is to 0, the greater will be the emphasis on previous forecasts.

Exercise 7

A company forecasts the number of employees absent each day by exponential smoothing using a smoothing constant of 0.3. The forecast number of absentees for Wednesday was 470, and the actual number was 520. What is the forecast number of absentees for Thursday?

Chapter roundup

(a)   A time series is a series of values over time. It may be analysed into a trend, cyclical variations, seasonal variations and random variations, although a time series is often analysed into just a trend and seasonal variations.

(b)   A trend may be found using regression analysis or moving averages. If a moving average of an even number of periods is taken, a second stage of averaging is needed to give trend figures which relate to actual periods.

(c)   Seasonal variations may be computed using the additive model (actual–trend) or the multiplicative model (actual/trend). Seasonal variations should be averaged and then adjusted so that their net effect is zero.

(d)   Data may be deseasonalised by applying seasonal variations in reverse.

(e)   Forecasts may be made by extrapolating a trend and then applying average seasonal variations. The size of residuals is a guide to the likely reliability of a forecast.

(f)   Exponential smoothing is another forecasting technique. It takes account of both the most recent forecast and the most recent observation.

Quick quiz

1 What is the definition of a time series?

2 What are the four components that combine to form a time series?

3 How can trend lines be found?

4 Distinguish between the additive model and the multiplicative model of time series.

5 What is deseasonalisation?

6 Describe how the additive model may be used in forecasting.

7 What is the formula for exponential smoothing?

Solutions to exercises

1 Sales of video recorders might peak at Christmas, and also before major sporting events such as the FA Cup Final and Wimbledon.

2 Three month moving average for April = average of March, April and May data

$$= \frac{700 + 900 + 1,250}{3} = 950 \text{ houses}$$

3

Year	Quarter	Data	4-quarter total	4-quarter average	Mid-point of averages
1	2	54			
	3	56			
			222	55.5	
	4	55			56.25
			228	57.0	
2	1	57			
	2	60			

The required average is 56.25.

4

Month	Data	3-month total	3-month average (trend)	Seasonal variation
March	8			
April	13	37	12.33	+0.67
May	16			

The required variation is +0.67.

---

5   *Quarter*

	1	2	3	4
	%	%	%	%
Variation, 1991	95.6	102.7	105.3	91.4
Variation, 1992	101.0	103.9	107.7	87.5
Average variation	98.3	103.3	106.5	89.5
Adjustment	0.6	0.6	0.6	0.6
Adjusted average variation	98.9	103.9	107.1	90.1

6   $x = 26$

Forecast $= 1.06 \times [780 + (4 \times 26)] = 937.04 = £937,040$ or about £937,000.

7   Forecast absentees for Thursday $= 470 + 0.3 \times (520 - 470) = 485$

11 LINEAR PROGRAMMING

Signpost

In this chapter we will see how to solve problems like: How many tables and how many desks should a company make next week in order to maximise its profits, given that it has only 1,000 kg of timber and 120 kg of steel available? The best solution might be to make only tables, only desks or some mix of the two. It depends on the profit per table, the profit per desk and the amounts of timber and steel used in each. Linear programming is a way of solving such problems: a graph can be used when there are only two products, but the simplex method is used when there are more than two products. We can extend the linear programming method to answer questions like: what difference would it make if the profit per desk increased by £10 (a change in the objective function); and what would happen if the amount of timber available increased to 1,400 kg? (a change in a constraint).

Your objectives

After completing this chapter you should:

(a) understand the uses of linear programming;

(b) be able to formulate linear programming problems;

(c) be able to solve linear programming problems using the graphical method;

(d) be able to compute what changes in an objective function will change the optimum;

(e) be able to compute the effects of changes in constraints;

(f) have a basic understanding of the simplex method.

1   The basic ideas of linear programming

Among the most important decisions which face managers are those relating to the use of limited resources. In most businesses, there are insufficient resources available to do as many things as management would wish, and the problem is to decide how the resources should be allocated to obtain the best results. In other words, management will be faced with numerous problems that involve allocating labour, materials and capital in a way that will maximise profit or minimise costs. *Linear programming* is a technique for solving problems of this type.

A linear programming model can be constructed and solved, to determine the best course of action within the restrictions or constraints that exist, and the model will consist of:

(a) an objective function, showing management's goal;
(b) certain constraints.

The objective function

Every linear programming model must have an objective function. This is a quantified statement of what is being aimed for.

The objective will be either:

(a) to maximise a value (such as profit); or
(b) to minimise a value (such as costs).

The objective function is expressed in terms of the *decision variables* in the model, which are the things under management's control. For example, if a company makes three products X, Y and Z, and it wishes to maximise profit, the objective function will be expressed in terms of the quantities of X, Y and Z that are made and sold. So if the profits per unit from X, Y and Z are £5, £4 and £3 respectively, the objective would be to maximise $5x + 4y + 3z$, where x, y and z are the decision variables, the quantities of the products that should be made and sold.

Constraints

Since resources are scarce, there are limitations on what can be achieved. For example, if materials and machine time are in short supply, output will be limited by the availability of these resources. In a linear programming model, these restrictions are a set of conditions which any solution must satisfy, and they are known as *constraints*.

Example: constraints

Suppose that a company wishes to plan its production budget for the next month. It makes three products, X, Y and Z, which require 2 hours, 5 hours and 1.5 hours of machine time per unit respectively, on the same type of machine. In the next month, machine capacity will be restricted to 400 hours. The company is committed to supplying one particular customer with *at least* 50 units in total of X and Y, although the customer will accept any combination of X and Y in this total order. What are the constraints?

Solution

The problem facing management is to decide how many units of X, Y and Z to make in the next month. There are two constraints. These relate to machine capacity and sales orders.

If x = the number of units of X to be made;
    y = the number of units of Y to be made;
    z = the number of units of Z to be made;

then the constraints could be written as follows.

$$2x + 5y + 1.5z \leq 400 \text{ (machine hours)}$$
$$x + y \geq 50 \text{ (sales order)}$$

Non-negativity constraints

The variables in linear programming models should usually be non-negative in value. You cannot make -200 units of a product. Additional constraints in the example above would therefore be as follows.

$x \geqslant 0; y \geqslant 0; z \geqslant 0$

You should not omit these when formulating a linear programming problem.

We must identify the decision variables, the objective function and the constraints. Depending on the nature of the problem, you are likely to find one of these items easier to identify than the others. Start with what you can identify first, and build up the model from there.

Exercise 1

Maxim Wise Ltd makes three products, A, B and C. Each product is made by the same grades of labour, and the time required to make one unit of each product is as follows.

	A	*B*	*C*
Skilled labour	3 hours	4 hours	1 hour
Unskilled labour	2.5 hours	2 hours	6 hours

The costs per unit of A, B and C are £28, £30 and £26 respectively. The products sell for £40, £40 and £34 respectively.

In March the company expects to have only 600 hours of skilled labour and 2,000 hours of unskilled labour available. There is a minimum requirement for 40 units of B and 120 units of C in the month. The company's objective is to maximise profit.

Formulate a linear programming problem.

---

2 The graphical method

We have looked at how to formulate a problem. Now we must think about solving a problem. There are two main ways of solving linear programming problems:

(a) the graphical method;
(b) the simplex method.

In this section of the chapter, we shall look at the graphical method. The simplex method is described in Section 4 of this chapter.

A graphical solution is only possible when there are two decision variables in the problem. One variable is represented by the x axis and one by the y axis of the graph.

If the problem included a constraint that y could not exceed 6 (because, say, no more than 6 tonnes of product Y could be sold), the *inequality* y ≤ 6 would be represented by the shaded area of the graph below.

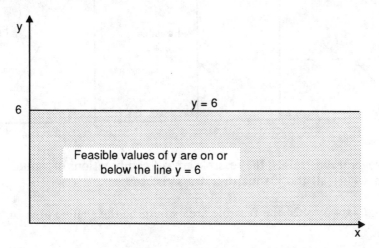

We might have a constraint 4x + 3y ≤ 24, if (say) each tonne of product X required 4 labour hours, each tonne of product Y required 3 labour hours and only 24 labour hours were available in total. Any combined value of x and y within the shaded area below (on or below the line) would satisfy the constraint.

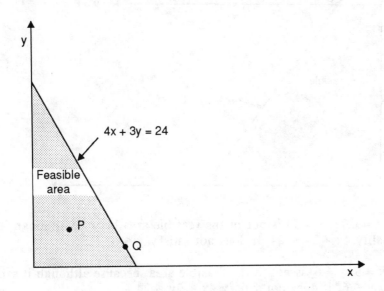

For example, at point P where x = 2, y = 2, we have 4x + 3y = 14 which is less than 24; and at point Q where x = 5.5, y = 2/3, we have 4x + 3y = 24. Both P and Q lie within the *feasible area* (the area where the inequality is satisfied, also called the *feasible region*). A feasible area enclosed on all sides may also be called a *feasible polygon*.

The inequalities y ≥ 6, x ≥ 6 and 4x + 3y ≥ 24, would be shown graphically as follows.

BPP Publishing

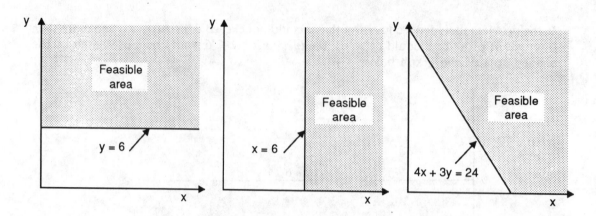

When there are several constraints, the feasible area of combinations of values of x and y must be an area where all the inequalities are satisfied.

Thus, if y ≤ 6 *and* 4x + 3y ≤ 24 the feasible area would be the shaded area in the graph below.

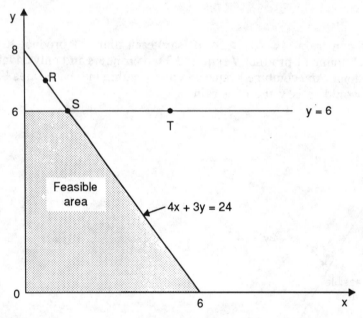

(a) Point R (x = 0.75, y = 7) is not in the feasible area because although it satisfies the inequality 4x + 3y ≤ 24, it does not satisfy y ≤ 6.

(b) Point T (x = 5, y = 6) is not in the feasible area, because although it satisfies the inequality y ≤ 6, it does not satisfy 4x + 3y ≤ 24.

(c) Point S (x = 1.5, y = 6) satisfies both inequalities and lies just on the boundary of the feasible area since y = 6 exactly, and 4x + 3y = 24. Point S is thus at the intersection of the two lines.

Exercise 2

Draw the feasible area for the following inequalities.

$$2x + 3y \leqslant 12$$
$$y \geqslant 2x$$
$$x \geqslant 0, y \geqslant 0$$

Iso-profit lines

The previous paragraphs have illustrated a technique by which constraints in a linear programming problem can be shown on a graph, and feasible values for the two decision variables can be shown.

One further aspect to consider is the use of iso-profit lines. ('Iso' just means equal.)

Suppose that one tonne of a product X earns a profit of £5 and one tonne of product Y earns a profit of £10.

To earn a total profit of £1,500 from the sale of both products, we could sell:

(a)   300 tonnes of X and 0 tonnes of Y;

(b)   0 tonnes of X and 150 tonnes of Y;

(c)   a proportionate 'mix' of X and Y, such as 20 tonnes of X and 140 tonnes of Y, or 100 tonnes of X and 100 tonnes of Y.

The possible combinations of X and Y required to earn a total profit of £1,500 could be shown by the straight line on a graph, $5x + 10y = 1,500$.

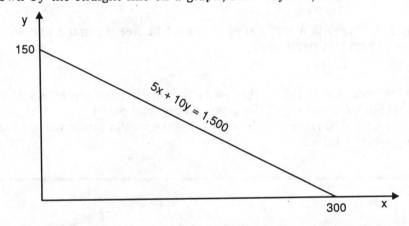

For a total profit of £2,000, a similar line $5x + 10y = 2,000$ could be drawn, to show the various combinations of X and Y which would achieve the total of £2,000.

Similarly, a line $5x + 10y = 2,500$ would show the various combinations of X and Y which would earn a total profit of £2,500.

BPP Publishing

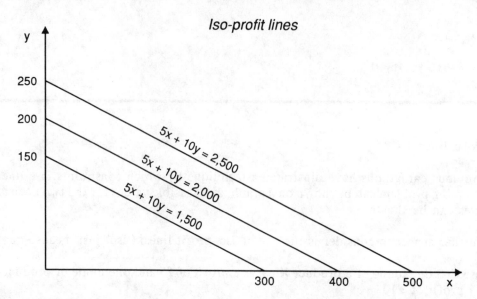

Iso-profit lines

The profit lines are parallel to each other. A similar line drawn for any other total profit would also be parallel to the three lines shown here. This means that if we wish to know the *slope* or *gradient* of the profit line, for any value of total profit, we can simply draw one line for any convenient value of profit, and we will know that all the other lines will be parallel to the one drawn: they will have the same gradient.

The gradient of a straight line can be found by putting its equation into the form $y = a + bx$. The gradient is b. It will be negative for a line sloping downwards from left to right. Here is an example, for one of the lines above, $5x + 10y = 2,500$.

$$5x + 10y = \quad 2,500$$
$$10y = \quad 2,500 - 5x$$
$$y = \quad 250 - 0.5x$$

The gradient is -0.5. A line with a gradient of -1 would be steeper, and a line with a gradient of -0.3 would be less steep.

One further point to note is that the further away the line is from the *origin* of the graph (the corner where $x = 0$ and $y = 0$) the greater is the total profit. Thus $5x + 10y = 2,500$ is further away from the origin than $5x + 10y = 2,000$ which in turn is further from the origin than $5x + 10y = 1,500$.

Exercise 3

The objective of a linear programming problem is to maximise profit $= 12x + 47y$. What is the gradient of each iso-profit line?

We have now covered enough ground to be able to follow an example of the graphical method.

Example: a maximisation problem

Brunel Ltd manufactures plastic-covered steel fencing in two qualities, standard and heavy gauge. Both products pass through the same processes, involving steel-forming and plastic bonding.

Standard gauge fencing sells at £18 a roll and heavy gauge fencing at £24 a roll. Variable costs per roll are £16 and £21 respectively. There is an unlimited market for the standard gauge, but demand for the heavy gauge is limited to 1,300 rolls a year. Factory operations are limited to 2,400 hours a year in each of the two production processes.

	Processing hours per roll	
Gauge	*Steel-forming*	*Plastic-bonding*
Standard	0.6	0.4
Heavy	0.8	1.2

What is the production mix which will maximise total profit and what would be the total profit?

Solution

Let S be the number of standard gauge rolls per year.
Let H be the number of heavy gauge rolls per year.

The objective is to maximise $2S + 3H$ (profit) subject to the following constraints.

$$0.6S + 0.8H \leqslant 2,400 \text{ (steel-forming hours)}$$
$$0.4S + 1.2H \leqslant 2,400 \text{ (plastic-bonding hours)}$$
$$H \leqslant 1,300 \text{ (sales demand)}$$
$$S, H \geqslant 0$$

Note that the constraints are *inequalities*, and are not equations. There is no requirement to use up the total hours available in each process, nor to satisfy all the demand for heavy gauge rolls.

If we take the production constraint of 2,400 hours in the steel-forming process

$$0.6S + 0.8H \leqslant 2,400$$

it means that since there are only 2,400 hours available in the process, output must be limited to a maximum of:

(a) $\dfrac{2,400}{0.6}$ = 4,000 rolls of standard gauge;

(b) $\dfrac{2,400}{0.8}$ = 3,000 rolls of heavy gauge; or

(c) a proportionate combination of each.

This maximum output represents the boundary line of the constraint, where the inequality becomes the equation

$$0.6S + 0.8H = 2,400.$$

The line for this equation may be drawn on a graph by joining up two points on the line (such as S = 0, H = 3,000; H = 0, S = 4,000).

The other constraints may be drawn in a similar way with lines for the following equations.

$$0.4S + 1.2H = 2,400 \text{ (plastic bonding)}$$
$$H = 1,300 \text{ (sales demand)}$$

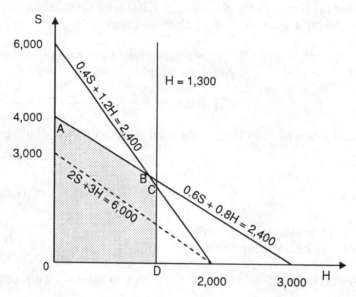

To satisfy all the constraints simultaneously, the values of S and H must lie on or below each constraint line. The outer limits of the feasible polygon are the lines which have been shaded on the above graph.

The next step is to find the optimal solution, which maximises the objective function. The solution to the problem is found by:

(a) establishing the slope of the iso-profit lines, by drawing a line for any one level of profit. In our solution, a line 2S + 3H = 6,000 has been drawn. (6,000 was chosen as a convenient multiple of 2 and 3). This line has no significance except to indicate the gradient of every iso-profit line for 2S + 3H;

(b) using a ruler to judge at which corner of the feasible polygon we can draw an iso-profit line which is as far to the right as possible, (away from the origin) but which still touches the feasible polygon. We want to go as far to the right as we can, because iso-profit lines further to the right represent higher total profits.

This occurs at corner B where the constraint line 0.4S + 1.2H = 2,400 crosses with the constraint line 0.6S + 0.8H = 2,400. At this point, there are simultaneous equations, from which the exact values of S and H may be calculated.

$$
\begin{array}{lll}
0.4S + 1.2H & = 2,400 & (1) \\
0.6S + 0.8H & = 2,400 & (2) \\
1.2S + 3.6H & = 7,200 & (3) \; ((1) \times 3) \\
1.2S + 1.6H & = 4,800 & (4) \; ((2) \times 2) \\
2H & = 2,400 & (5) \; ((3) - (4)) \\
H & = 1,200 & (6)
\end{array}
$$

Substituting 1,200 for H in either equation, we can calculate that S = 2,400.

The profit is maximised where H = 1,200, and S = 2,400.

	Units	Profit per unit £	Total profit £
Standard gauge	2,400	2	4,800
Heavy gauge	1,200	3	3,600
			8,400

Exercise 4

The Dervish Chemical Company operates a small plant. Operating the plant requires two raw materials, A and B, which cost £5 and £8 per litre respectively. The maximum available supply per week is 2,700 litres of A and 2,000 litres of B.

The plant can operate using either of two processes, which have differing profits and raw material requirements, as follows.

Process	Raw materials consumed (litres per processing hour)		Profit per hour £
	A	B	
1	20	10	70
2	30	20	60

The plant can run for 120 hours a week in total, but for safety reasons, process 2 cannot be operated for more than 80 hours a week.

Formulate a linear programming model, and then solve it, to determine how many hours process 1 should be operated each week and how many hours process 2 should be operated each week.

Minimisation problems in linear programming

Although linear programming problems usually involve the maximisation of profit, there may be a requirement to minimise costs. A graphical solution, involving two variables, is very similar to that for a maximisation problem, with the exception that instead of finding a profit line touching the feasible area as far away from the origin as possible, we look for a total cost line touching the feasible area as close to the origin as possible.

Example: a minimisation problem

Bilton Sandys Ltd has undertaken a contract to supply a customer with at least 260 units in total of two products, X and Y, during the next month. At least 50% of the total output must be units of X. The products are each made by two grades of labour, as follows.

	X Hours	Y Hours
Grade A labour	4	6
Grade B labour	4	2
Total	8	8

Although additional labour can be made available at short notice, the company wishes to make use of 1,200 hours of Grade A labour and 800 hours of Grade B labour which has already been assigned to working on the contract next month. The total variable cost per unit is £120 for X and £100 for Y.

Bilton Sandys Ltd wishes to minimise expenditure on the contract next month. How much of X and Y should be supplied in order to meet the terms of the contract?

Solution

Let the number of units of X supplied be x, and the number of units of Y supplied be y. The objective is to minimise $120x + 100y$ (costs), subject to the following constraints.

$$
\begin{aligned}
x + y &\geqslant 260 \quad &\text{(supply total)} \\
x &\geqslant 0.5\,(x + y) \quad &\text{(proportion of x in total)} \\
4x + 6y &\geqslant 1,200 \quad &\text{(Grade A labour)} \\
4x + 2y &\geqslant 800 \quad &\text{(Grade B labour)} \\
x, y &\geqslant 0
\end{aligned}
$$

The constraint $x \geqslant 0.5\,(x + y)$ needs simplifying further.

$$
\begin{aligned}
x &\geqslant 0.5\,(x + y) \\
2x &\geqslant x + y \\
x &\geqslant y
\end{aligned}
$$

In a graphical solution, the line will be $x = y$. Check this carefully in the following diagram.

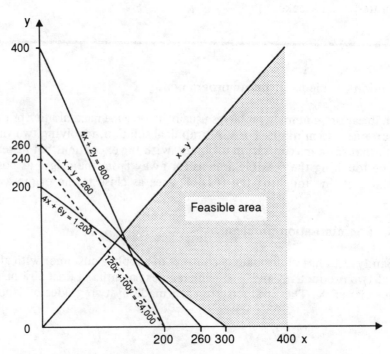

The cost line $120x + 100y = 24,000$ has been drawn to show the slope of every cost line. Costs are minimised where a cost line touches the feasible area as close as possible to the origin of the graph. This occurs where the constraint line $4x + 2y = 800$ crosses the constraint line $x + y = 260$. This point is found as follows.

$x + y$	$=$	260	(1)
$4x + 2y$	$=$	800	(2)
$2x + y$	$=$	400	(3) ((2) ÷ 2)
x	$=$	140	(4) ((3) – (1))
y	$=$	120	(5)

Costs will be minimised by supplying the following.

	Unit cost £	Total cost £
140 units of X	120	16,800
120 units of Y	100	12,000
		28,800

The proportion of units of X in the total would exceed 50%, and demand for Grade A labour would exceed the 1,200 hours minimum.

Exercise 5

A marketing manager may use large posters and/or small posters to advertise a new product. There must be at least half as many large posters as small posters and at least 50 large posters. There must be at least 100 posters in total, and not more than 150 small posters. Each large poster costs £4 and each small poster costs £2. What is the minimum total cost?

3 Sensitivity analysis and dual prices

Once a graphical solution has been given to a linear programming problem, we can get further information by seeing what would happen if certain values in the model were to change. We could ask questions like the following.

(a) What would happen if the profit per unit from product A were £1 lower than expected?
(b) What would happen if the selling price of product B were raised by £2?
(c) What would happen if we had an extra 100kg of materials?

A new example will be introduced.

Example: sensitivity analysis

Dual Ltd makes two products, X and Y which have the following selling prices and costs.

Notes

	X		Y	
	£	£	£	£
Unit selling price		14		15
Costs				
Materials (at £1 per kg)	3		2	
Labour (at £3 per hr)	6		9	
		9		11
Unit profit		5		4

What production plan would maximise profit in the next period, given that the supply of materials will be restricted to 600 kg, only 450 labour hours will be available, and a minimum demand for 150 units of product X must be met?

How would changes in the selling prices affect the solution?

Solution

The problem could be solved graphically, as follows.

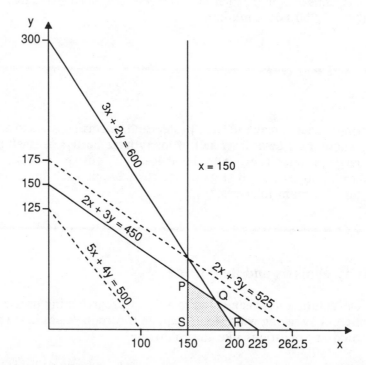

The feasible polygon is PQRS, and profit would be maximised at point Q, where

$$3x + 2y = 600$$
$$2x + 3y = 450$$

Therefore x = 180, y = 30, and total profit is £1,020.

The optimum will shift to point R (x = 200, y = 0) if X becomes sufficiently more profitable. It will shift when the iso-profit line becomes steeper than the line $3x + 2y = 600$. That line's gradient is -1.5, and the iso-profit line's gradient is

$$\frac{-\text{ unit profit from X}}{\text{unit profit from Y}}$$

Thus the optimum will shift to R if the unit profit from Y remains at £4 but the unit profit from X increases to more than £6, corresponding to an increase in the unit selling price of more than £1 to more than £15.

Exercise 6

In the above example, if the unit profit from X remains at £5, what would the unit profit from Y have to increase to in order to shift the optimum to point P? What unit selling price of Y does this new profit correspond to?

The point of sensitivity analysis is that it indicates the risk of our selecting the wrong solution. If small changes in prices would lead to a different optimum applying, there is a high risk of our selecting the wrong solution. If, on the other hand, large changes in prices would leave the optimum unchanged, errors in predicting prices are unlikely to lead to our selecting the wrong solution.

Dual prices

The *dual price* (also called the shadow price) of a resource which is fully used at the optimum is the amount by which:

(a)   total profit would fall if the company were deprived of one unit of the resource;

(b)   total profit would rise if the company were able to obtain one extra unit of the scarce resource, *provided that* the resource remains an effective constraint on production and *provided also* that the extra unit of the resource can be obtained at its normal unit cost. The dual price is therefore the maximum amount which should be paid *in excess of the normal rate* for each extra unit of the resource.

The dual price is calculated on the assumption that there is a change in the availability of one resource, but with the availability of other resources being held constant.

In the above example (Dual Ltd), both materials and labour hours are used up fully in the planned production mix. Let us therefore calculate the effect on total profit if the company were deprived of one unit of materials, so that only 599 kg were available (but labour hours available remain at 450).

The new optimal production mix would be at the intersection point of the two constraint lines:

$$3x + 2y = 599$$
$$2x + 3y = 450$$

Solving the simultaneous equations, $x = 179.4$ units and $y = 30.4$ units.

Product	Units	Profit
		£
X	179.4 (× £5)	897.00
Y	30.4 (× £4)	121.60
		1,018.60
Profit in original problem		1,020.00
Reduction in profit from loss of 1 kg of materials		1.40

The dual price of materials is therefore £1.40 per kg.

Suppose that materials available are 600 kg, but that the labour supply is reduced by 20 hours to 430 hours. The optimal production mix occurs at the intersection of the two constraints:

$$2x + 3y = 430;$$
$$3x + 2y = 600.$$

Solving the simultaneous equations, x = 188 units and y = 18 units.

Product	Units	Profit
		£
X	188 (× £5)	940
Y	18 (× £4)	72
		1,012
Profit in original problem		1,020
Reduction in profit from loss of 20 labour hours		8

The dual price of labour is therefore 8/20 = £0.40 an hour.

The dual price of a resource also shows by how much profit would increase if an additional unit of the resource were made available. In our example, if the materials available were 600 kg but the labour supply were raised to 451 hours, the optimum production mix would be 179.6 units of X and 30.6 units of Y.

Product	Units	Profit
		£
X	179.6 (× £5)	898.00
Y	30.6 (× £4)	122.40
		1,020.40
Profit in original problem		1,020.00
Increase in profit from one extra unit of labour		0.40

Once again, the dual price of labour is £0.40 an hour.

The increase in contribution of £0.40 per extra labour hour is calculated on the assumption that the extra labour hour would be paid for at the normal variable cost, which is £3 an hour in the problem.

(a) The management of the company should be prepared to pay up to £0.40 extra per extra hour of labour in order to obtain more labour hours (perhaps through overtime working: the maximum value of overtime premium would then be £0.40 per hour). We assume that the existing 450 hours of labour are still paid only £3 an hour.

(b) This value of labour only applies as long as labour remains fully used. If more and more labour hours are made available, there will eventually be so much labour that it is no longer a scarce resource. In our problem, this will occur when the third constraint, $x \geqslant 150$, prevents a further reduction in the output of X in order to increase output of Y.

We can calculate how many hours must be available before labour ceases to be fully used. This will happen when the new labour constraint passes through the intersection of $x = 150$ and $y = 75$, so that the constraint for labour $2x + 3y$ would be

$$2x + 3y = ?$$

If $x = 150$ and $y = 75$ $2x + 3y = (2 \times 150) + (3 \times 75) = 525$

This is shown as the upper right dotted line on the graph above.

The dual price of labour is £0.40 per hour in the initial problem, but only up to a maximum supply of 525 labour hours (75 hours more than the original 450 hours). Extra labour above 525 hours would not have any use, and the two limiting factors would now be materials and the minimum demand for x. Beyond 525 hours, labour would have a dual price of zero. Once the labour constraint ceases to matter in this way, it becomes an *ineffective, non-binding* or *non-critical* constraint.

Any resource which is not fully used has a dual price of zero: losing one unit will not matter, and there is no point in paying over the normal rate for extra units.

Exercise 7

A linear programming problem is as follows.

Maximise profit, $4x + 2y$, subject to the following constraints.

$$3x + 6y \leqslant 12,000 \quad \text{(hours of labour)}$$
$$5x + 2y \leqslant 10,000 \quad \text{(hours of machine time)}$$
$$x,y \geqslant 0$$

The optimum is at the intersection of the labour constraint and the machine time constraint. What is the dual price per hour of machine time?

---

4   The simplex method

The linear programming problems solved so far have included only two decision variables. In practice, few problems will be this simple. For example, a company may have ten products to set production levels for. One method of solving linear programming problems with any number of decision variables is the simplex method.

The simplex method involves testing one feasible solution after another, in a succession of tables, until the optimal solution is found. It can be used for problems with any number of decision variables.

 BPP Publishing

In addition to the decision variables, the method introduces additional variables, known as 'slack variables'. There will be one slack variable for each constraint in the problem (excluding non-negativity constraints). They are put in so as to turn constraints into equations: thus a materials constraint $5x + 2y \leqslant 3,000$ would become $5x + 2y + a = 3,000$, with a representing the unused materials.

For example, if a linear programming problem has three decision variables and four constraints, there will be four slack variables in the problem, so that with the three decision variables, there will be a total of seven variables and four constraints in the problem.

The simplex technique tests a number of feasible solutions to the problem until the optimum solution is found.

The technique is a repetitive, step-by-step process. At each step:

(a) we establish a feasible solution and the value of the objective function for that solution;

(b) we establish whether that particular solution is the one that optimises the value of the objective function.

Each feasible solution is tested by drawing up a table with:

(a) one row for each constraint, and a solution row;

(b) one column for each decision variable and one for each slack variable, and a solution column.

Example: the simplex method

Shore Toffer Lott Ltd produces and sells two products, X and Y. Products X and Y require the following resources.

	Materials Units	Labour Hours	Machine time Hours	Profit per unit £
X, per unit	5	1	3	20
Y, per unit	2	3	2	16
Slack variable	a	b	c	

| Total available, each week | 3,000 units | 1,750 hours | 2,100 hours |

Intepret the following simplex table, which shows the optimal solution.

	x	y	a	b	c	Solution
Variable in solution						
x	1	0	0	-0.2857	0.4286	400
a	0	0	1	0.5714	-1.8571	100
y	0	1	0	0.4286	-0.1429	450
Solution	0	0	0	1.1428	6.2858	15,200

Solution

The 'variable in solution' column and the 'solution' column show that the optimal solution is to make and sell 400 units of X and 450 units of Y, to earn a profit of £15,200. The solution will leave 100 units of materials unused (slack variable a, second row, right hand column), but will use up all available labour and machine time.

The dual price of labour time (b) is £1.1428 an hour (bottom of column b), which indicates the amount by which profit could be increased if more labour time could be made available at its normal variable cost.

The dual price of machine time (c) is £6.2858 an hour (bottom of column c), which indicates the amount by which profit could be increased if more machine time could be made available at its normal variable cost.

The dual price of materials is zero (bottom of column a), because there are 100 units of unused materials in the solution.

The figures in column b in the final table tell us how the solution would change if more labour hours (variable b) were available. For each extra labour hour that is available:

(a)   the profit would increase by £1.1428;
(b)   the value of x would fall by 0.2857 units;
(c)   the value of a (unused materials) would increase by 0.5714 units;
(d)   the value of y would increase by 0.4286 units.

In other words, we would make 0.4286 extra units of Y, to earn profit of ($\times$ £16) £6.8576, but we would make 0.2857 units less of X and so lose profit of ($\times$ £20) £5.714, leaving a net increase in profit of £(6.8576 - 5.714) = £1.1436. Allowing for rounding errors of £0.0008, this is the figure given above.

Since x = 400 in the optimal table, and extra labour hours would lead to a reduction in x of 0.2857 units, there is a limit to the number of extra labour hours that would earn an extra £1.1428. This limit is

$$\frac{400}{0.2857} = 1,400 \text{ extra labour hours.}$$

In other words, the dual price of £1.1428 per hour for labour is only valid for 1,400 extra labour hours on top of the given constraint in the initial problem, which was 1,750 hours: that is, up to a total of 3,150 hours.

If there were *fewer* labour hours available, the same sort of analysis would apply, but in reverse.

(a)   The profit would fall by £1.1428 per hour unavailable.
(b)   The value of x would increase by 0.2857 units.
(c)   The value of a would fall by 0.5714 units.
(d)   The value of y would fall by 0.4286 units.

Exercise 8

Look at the optimal solution table again. How would the optimal solution change if more *machine hours* were available (variable c) and what is the maximum number of extra machine hours for which your analysis applies?

5 The limitations of linear programming

Linear programming is a powerful technique, but it has its limitations. Here are some which you should bear in mind.

(a) In all practical situations there are likely to be substantial problems involved in estimating the total quantities of resources available. Furthermore, the final estimates used may well be wrong. It is possible to study the effects of errors using sensitivity analysis.

(b) There is an assumption of linearity. Each extra unit of a given product is supposed to change the profit by the same amount and use the same resources. In practice, this assumption may be invalid except over small ranges. For example, in a profit maximisation problem, it may well be found that there are substantial changes in unit variable costs arising from increasing or decreasing returns to scale.

(c) The linear programming model is essentially static and is therefore not really suitable for analysing in detail the effects of changes over time.

(d) In some circumstances, a solution derived from a linear programming model may be of limited use when, for example, the variables may only take on integer values. Thus the solution might be to build 12.7 houses and 2.4 blocks of flats, whereas in practice only complete houses or blocks of flats can be built. A solution can be found by a combination of rounding up or down and trial and error, but this sort of approach is not really suitable for large-scale practical problems.

Chapter roundup

(a) Linear programming is a technique for finding the most profitable (or least costly) mix of products when output is subject to constraints.

(b) A problem is formulated in terms of an objective function and the constraints, using decision variables (usually, the quantities of the various products).

(c) If there are only two decision variables, the problem can be solved graphically. The constraints are drawn on a graph to find the feasible area, and a line for any convenient value of the objective function is drawn. The solution is found by finding the line parallel to this objective line which touches the feasible area but which is as far as possible from the origin (maximisation problems) or as close as possible to the origin (minimisation problems).

(d) It is possible to test the effect of changes in the objective function by comparing its gradient with the gradients of constraints.

(e) Dual prices show the effect of changing the constraints.

(f) The simplex method is used when there are more than two decision variables.

Quick quiz

1   What is an objective function?

2   What would the inequality $4x + 3y \leqslant 24$ look like when drawn on a graph?

3   What is an iso-profit line?

4   How does the graphical solution of minimisation problems differ from that of maximisation problems?

5   Define the dual price of a resource.

6   What is the role of slack variables in the simplex method?

7   How do you interpret the final simplex table for a problem?

Solutions to exercises

1   The decision variables are the products A, B and C. We want to decide how many of each to produce in the month.

Let the number of units of product A made be a.
Let the number of units of product B made be b.
Let the number of units of product C made be c.

The objective is to maximise the monthly profit. The profit per unit is £12 for A, £10 for B and £8 for C. The objective is therefore to maximise $12a + 10b + 8c$ (profit).

There are constraints relating to the availability of skilled labour and unskilled labour, and the minimum requirements for B and C. In addition, there are the constraints that A, B and C cannot have negative values, but since B and C must exceed 40 and 120 respectively, the non-negativity constraints are redundant for these two variables.

The programme may therefore be formulated as follows.

Objective: maximise $12a + 10b + 8c$ (profit)
subject to the constraints:

$3a + 4b + c$	$\leqslant$	600	(skilled labour)
$2.5a + 2b + 6c$	$\leqslant$	2,000	(unskilled labour)
b	$\geqslant$	40	(requirement for B)
c	$\geqslant$	120	(requirement for C)
a	$\geqslant$	0	

2

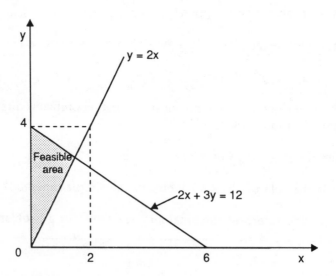

3   Take any value of profit, say 1,000

$$
\begin{aligned}
12x + 47y &= 1,000 \\
47y &= 1,000 - 12x \\
y &= 1,000/47 - (12/47)x
\end{aligned}
$$

The gradient is $-12/47 = -0.2553$.

4   The decision variables are processing hours in each process. If we let the processing hours per week for process 1 be P_1 and the processing hours per week for process 2 be P_2 we can formulate an objective and constraints as follows.

The objective is to maximise $70P_1 + 60P_2$, subject to the following constraints.

$$20P_1 + 30P_2 \leqslant 2{,}700 \text{ (material A supply)}$$
$$10P_1 + 20P_2 \leqslant 2{,}000 \text{ (material B supply)}$$
$$P_2 \leqslant 80 \text{ (maximum time for } P_2 \text{)}$$
$$P_1 + P_2 \leqslant 120 \text{ (total maximum time)}$$
$$P_1, P_2 \geqslant 0$$

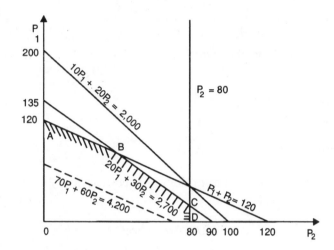

The feasible area is ABCDO.

The optimal solution, found by moving the iso-profit line outwards, is at point A, where $P_1 = 120$ and $P_2 = 0$.

Total profit would be $120 \times 70 = £8{,}400$ a week.

5   We must formulate the constraints and the objective function, draw a sketch graph, identify the optimum point and find the total cost at this point.

Let L = number of large posters
      S = number of small posters

The constraints are:

$$L \geqslant 0.5S$$
$$L \geqslant 50$$
$$L + S \geqslant 100$$
$$S \leqslant 150$$

The objective is to minimise $4L + 2S$.

A sketch graph follows. A trial objective ($4L + 2S = 400$) has been included.

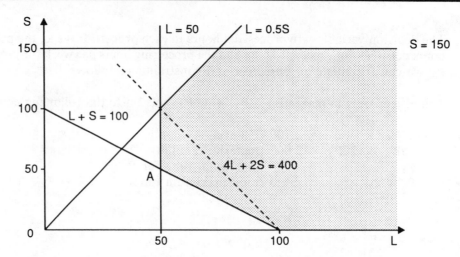

The optimum is at point A, at the intersection of the lines L = 50 and L + S = 100.

At this point,

L	=	50
L + S	=	100
50 + S	=	100
S	=	50

The cost at this point, which is the minimum total cost, is 50 × £4 + 50 × £2 = £300.

6   The gradient of 2x + 3y = 450 is - 2/3. We therefore need:

    5/Unit profit from Y < 2/3
    Unit profit from Y > £7.50
    Unit selling price of Y > £18.50

7   The optimum is at the following point.

3x + 6y	=	12,000
5x + 2y	=	10,000
15x + 6y	=	30,000
12x	=	18,000
x	=	1,500
y	=	1,250

Profit = (1,500 × 4) + (1,250 × 2) = £8,500.

With one extra machine hour, the optimum would be as follows.

3x + 6y	=	12,000
5x + 2y	=	10,001
15x + 6y	=	30,003
12x	=	18,003
x	=	1,500.25
y	=	1,249.875

Profit = (1,500.25 × 4) + (1,249.875 × 2) = £8,500.75.

The dual price per machine hour is £(8,500.75 - 8,500.00) = £0.75.

8   For each extra machine hour available:

(a)   the value of x would increase by 0.4286 units;
(b)   the value of a (unused materials) would fall by 1.8571 units;
(c)   the value of y would fall by 0.1429 units;
(d)   profit would increase by £6.2858.

This analysis only applies until either a or y falls to 0 in value, whichever happens first.

$$\frac{a}{}\qquad\qquad\qquad \frac{y}{}$$

$$\frac{100}{1.8571} = 53.8 \text{ units*} \qquad \frac{450}{0.1429} = 3{,}149 \text{ units}$$

* lowest positive value

Extra machine hours will no longer earn extra profit of £6.2858 an hour after about 54 extra machine hours have been obtained.

   BPP Publishing

12 DIFFERENTIAL CALCULUS

Signpost

Differential calculus is about rates of change. We might, for example, want to know how fast profit rises as sales rise. If we have an equation giving profit in terms of sales, we can differentiate it to get the answer. If we differentiate expressions for total cost and total revenue, to find how fast they change with quantity produced and sold, we get marginal cost and marginal revenue, which we can use to find the quantity which will maximise profit. Finally, we can use differentiation to find maximum and minimum values for any expression, not just one for profit, by working out where the peaks and troughs on a graph must be.

Your objectives

After completing this chapter you should:

(a)   understand the role of differential calculus;

(b)   be able to differentiate;

(c)   be able to use differential calculus to find marginal cost and marginal revenue, and hence find the profit-maximising level of output;

(d)   be able to use differentiation to find maximum and minimum points;

(e)   be able to use the second derivative to distinguish between maximum and minimum points.

---

1   Introduction to differential calculus

Differential calculus is a branch of mathematics which is concerned with the way one variable changes in relationship to another. For example, we may wish to know:

(a)   how sales revenue changes with the volume of units sold;
(b)   how costs change with the volume of units produced;
(c)   how demand for a product varies with its price.

The value of differential calculus in business mathematics is twofold.

(a)   Since it is concerned with the way in which one variable changes in relationship to another, it enables us to identify *the rate of change* at any particular point. For example, we can find:

(i)   the rate at which revenue is changing at a particular volume of sales; this gives us the marginal revenue from extra sales;

(ii) the rate at which costs are changing at a particular volume of sales; this gives us the marginal cost of extra sales;

(b)   It can also identify when one variable reaches a maximum or a minimum point. For example, profits may rise as output and sales increase, but only up to a certain volume of sales, after which falling prices or rising costs will result in a decline in profits. Similarly, we can identify at what level of activity costs would be minimised.

2   The gradient of a curve

Suppose, for example, that the number of hours a year (y) which a bank manager spends on a business customer is related to the customer's account balance in thousands of pounds (x) by the equation $y = x^2$. Thus a customer who has a lot of money (high positive x), or one who is heavily overdrawn (high negative x) gets a lot of attention. We could draw a curve of $y = x^2$.

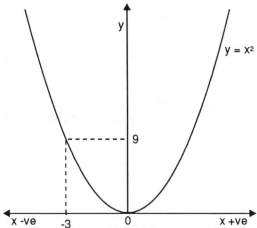

The rate of change in y at any point on the curve is shown by the gradient or slope of the curve at that point. This gradient is equal to twice the value of x at that point. (In the next section you will see how to find this out.) Thus when x = -3, y = +9, the rate of change in y at that point is twice the value of x, 2 × (-3) = -6, and the gradient of the curve is -6. (The fact that it is negative shows that the curve slopes downwards from left to right at that point.) The straight line y = -6x - 9 would touch the curve $y = x^2$ at the point x = -3, y = +9.

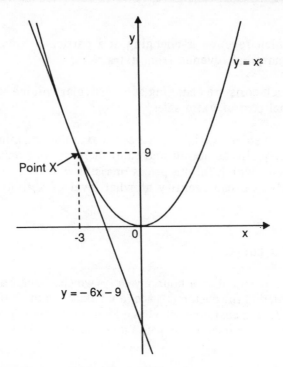

At point X, the gradients of the straight line and the curve are exactly the same.

3   Differentiation

The rate of change in one variable as another variable changes can be found by means of *differentiation*. We said above that if $y = x^2$, the rate of change of y as x changes is 2x. That is, we *differentiate* x^2 and get 2x.

If we have a function

$y = ax^n$

where x is the independent variable and y is the dependent variable, we can find the rate of change in y as x changes by differentiating y with respect to x to get dy/dx.

When $y = ax^n$, $\dfrac{dy}{dx} = nax^{n-1}$

dy/dx, the result of differentiating, is called the *first derivative* of y with respect to x. It is pronounced 'dee - y by dee - x'. It gives the rate of change of y as x changes for any given value of x, and we can say that we have differentiated y *with respect to x*.

Here are two examples.

(a)   The heat energy lost each hour through a factory's ventilation system, y, rises rapidly with the difference, x, between the temperature inside the factory and the external air temperature. The relevant equation is $y = 3x^4$.

If $y = 3x^4$, $\dfrac{dy}{dx} = 4 \times 3 \times x^{4-1} = 12x^3$.

So when x = 1 (when the temperature inside the factory is 1°C higher than outside), y rises $12 \times 1^3 = 12$ times as fast as x; when x = 2, y rises $12 \times 2^3 = 96$ times as fast as x, and so on.

(b) The price (p) which a company must pay for each kg of a rare material rises with the quantity (x) it buys each week.

$$\text{If } p = 5q^2, \frac{dp}{dq} = 2 \times 5 \times q^{2-1} = 10q.$$

The following points should be noted.

(a) On differentiation, any constant disappears. For example, if $y = 3x^2 + 8$, the constant, 8, disappears on differentiation, and

$$\frac{dy}{dx} = 2 \times 3 \times x^{2-1} = 6x$$

(b) If after differentiation we have x^0, remember that $x^0 = 1$. Thus, if $y = 7x$

$$\frac{dy}{dx} = 1 \times 7 \times x^{1-1} = 7x^0 = 7 \times 1 = 7$$

(c) If there are several expressions in the function, each element in the function may be differentiated separately. For example, if $y = 3x^4 - 2x^3 + 6x^2 - 8x + 24$

$$\frac{dy}{dx} = 4 \times 3 \times x^3 - 3 \times 2 \times x^2 + 2 \times 6 \times x - 8$$

$$= 12x^3 - 6x^2 + 12x - 8$$

(d) The rule also applies when negative powers are involved. For example, if $y = 3/x^2 = 3x^{-2}$,

$$\frac{dy}{dx} = -2 \times 3 \times x^{-2-1}$$

$$= -6x^{-3}$$

$$= \frac{-6}{x^3}$$

Exercise 1

(a) Differentiate $y = 6x + 9$ with respect to x.

(b) Total production costs are fixed costs of £30,000 and variable costs of £5 a unit. Express total costs (C) as a function of output (x) and use differential calculus to find the marginal cost (the charge in total costs per extra unit made).

(c) Differentiate the following with respect to x.

   (i) $y = x^3 + 2x$

   (iii) $2y = 5x^2 - 4x + 7$

   (ii) $y = 3x^3 + 4x^2 - 2x + 5$

   (iv) $y = \dfrac{1}{x^2} - \dfrac{3}{2x^3} + \dfrac{5}{4x^4}$

(d) The volume of demand for a product is $1,000 + 20p - 3p^2$ where p is the unit price in pounds. Formulate an expression for total revenue (price times quantity) in terms of the unit price and calculate the rate at which total revenue changes with the unit price.

The following example illustrates a practical use of differential calculus, the maximisation of profits.

Example: profit maximisation

Sloth Ltd has estimated that the demand curve for its product is $P = 10 - 0.003Q$ where P is the unit price in pounds and Q is the quantity of sales.

The total cost function is (in pounds) $C = 1,000 + 3Q + 0.004Q^2$.

(a) Calculate the level of output and the unit price at which profit will be maximised.
(b) Calculate the amount of profit at this level.

Solution

If $P = 10 - 0.003Q$, then total revenue R is

   $R = PQ = (10 - 0.003Q)Q = 10Q - 0.003Q^2$

and the marginal revenue function (the rate of change of total revenue with quantity) is found by differentiating R with respect to Q.

   $\dfrac{dR}{dQ} = MR = 10 - 0.006Q$

Since $C = 1,000 + 3Q + 0.004Q^2$ the marginal cost function (the rate of change of total cost with quantity) is

   $\dfrac{dC}{dQ} = MC = 3 + 0.008Q$

Profit is maximised where MC = MR, as above that point each additional unit will increase total costs by more than total revenue.

   $3 + 0.008 Q = 10 - 0.006Q$

   $0.014Q = 7$

   $Q = 500$

The unit price is P $\quad = 10 - 0.003Q$
$\qquad = 10 - 0.003(500)$
$\qquad = 8.50$

	£
Revenue (500 × 8.50)	4,250
Less costs $(1,000 + 3(500) + 0.004(500)^2)$	3,500
Profit	750

Exercise 2

A company has estimated that the demand curve for its product is $P = 8 - 0.05Q$, where P is the unit price and Q is the quantity of sales, in thousands. The total cost function is $C = 400 + 5Q + 0.1Q^2$. (C is in thousand of pounds.) What value of Q will maximise profits?

4   Maximum and minimum points

The first derivative of a function (dy/dx) indicates the gradient of the graph of the function. For example, if the total revenue from a product is $R = 5Q - 0.001Q^2$ the marginal revenue (MR) will be $dR/dQ = 5 - 0.002Q$. If Q = 1,000 units, MR = 5 - 2 = 3 which is positive. This means that at output and sales of 1,000 units, total revenue is still increasing as more units are sold, and the gradient of the total revenue curve is positive. However, if Q = 3,000 units, MR = 5 - 6 = -1, which is negative. This means that at output and sales of 3,000 units, total revenue is declining as more units are sold, and the gradient of the total revenue curve is negative. Clearly total revenue must reach a maximum point somewhere between 1,000 units and 3,000 units.

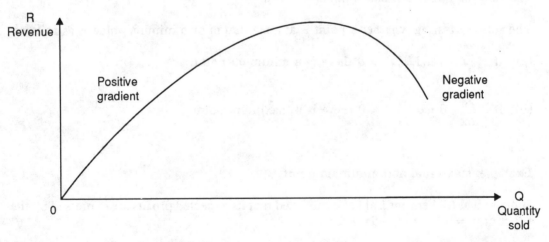

At a maximum or minimum point, the gradient is zero, because at the top or bottom of a curve you are going neither up nor down.

BPP Publishing

In the example of revenue above, $R = 5Q - 0.001Q^2$, and since $dR/dQ = 5 - 0.002Q$, the maximum point occurs where dy/dx (the gradient) $= 0 = 5 - 0.002Q$, that is, where $Q = 2,500$.

Total revenue would then be $5 \times 2,500 - 0.001 \times 2,500^2 = £6,250$.

We can see from the graph that this is a maximum point and not a minimum, but it is useful to be able to tell maxima from minima without drawing a graph. To do this, we need to compute the second derivative of a function.

The second derivative

The first derivative of a function, $\dfrac{dy}{dx}$, can be used to calculate the gradient of the curve on a graph for any given value of x.

The *second derivative* of a function is the derivative of $\dfrac{dy}{dx}$, and it is written as $\dfrac{d^2y}{dx^2}$ (pronounced 'd – two – y – by – d – x – squared'). For example,

if $\quad y \quad = \quad 3x^3 - 2x^2 + 4x - 20$

then $\dfrac{dy}{dx} = \quad 9x^2 - 4x + 4$

and $\dfrac{d^2y}{dx^2} = \quad 18x - 4$

The second derivative may be used to calculate the rate at which the gradient of the curve is increasing or decreasing.

The rule for maximum and minimum points

The rule for testing whether a point is at a maximum or minimum value is as follows.

(a) If $\quad \dfrac{dy}{dx} = 0$ and $\dfrac{d^2y}{dx^2} > 0$ there is a minimum point.

(b) If $\quad \dfrac{dy}{dx} = 0$ and $\dfrac{d^2y}{dx^2} < 0$ there is a maximum point.

Example: maximum and minimum points

Suppose that Makermint Ltd has established that its expected profits are expressed by the function $y = x^3 - 6x^2 + 9x + 4$ where

$\quad\quad y \quad = \quad$ profit, in thousands of pounds
$\quad\quad x \quad = \quad$ output, in units

We could draw the profit curve as follows.

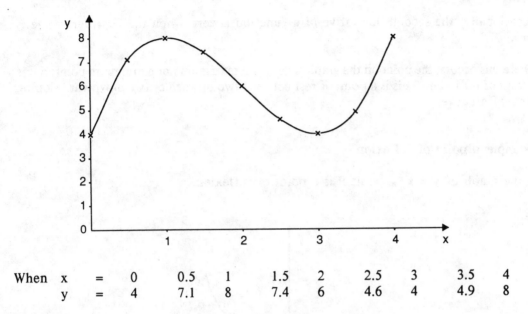

When	x	=	0	0.5	1	1.5	2	2.5	3	3.5	4
	y	=	4	7.1	8	7.4	6	4.6	4	4.9	8

The profit curve has a maximum point and a minimum point, at both of which the gradient $dy/dx = 0$.

Use the second derivative to identify which point is a maximum and which point is a minimum, without reference to the graph.

Solution

(a) $y = x^3 - 6x^2 + 9x + 4$

(b) $\dfrac{dy}{dx} = 3x^2 - 12x + 9$, which equals 0 when $x = 1$ and when $x = 3$.

(c) $\dfrac{d^2y}{dx^2} = 6x - 12$

(d) When $x = 1, \dfrac{d^2y}{dx^2} = 6 - 12 = -6$

This is negative, therefore we have a maximum point when $x = 1$.

(e) When $x = 3, \dfrac{d^2y}{dx^2} = 18 - 12 = +6$

This is positive, therefore we have a minimum point when $x = 3$.

Exercise 3

If a company produces and sells x units in a year, its profit in pounds is $-x^3 + 294x^2 + 2,400x - 100,000$. Find the maximum profit.

Points of inflexion

Occasionally, the second derivative of a function is zero when the first derivative is zero.

Where this occurs, the point on the graph is neither a maximum nor a minimum point, but is a point of inflexion. This is a point of rest between two upward or two downward sloping parts of a curve.

Example: a point of inflexion

In the graph of $y = x^3$, point P is a point of inflexion.

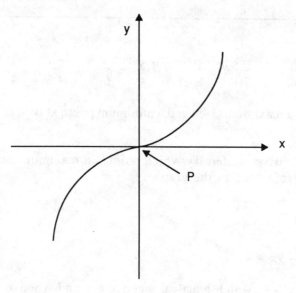

$\dfrac{dy}{dx} = 3x^2$. This is zero when x = 0.

$\dfrac{d^2y}{dx^2} = 6x$. When x = 0, this also equals 0.

Chapter roundup

(a) Differential calculus enables us to establish the rate at which one variable changes as another variable changes.

(b) If a function is differentiated, the resulting expression gives the gradient of the graph of the original function.

(c) If ax^n is differentiated, the result is nax^{n-1}.

(d) Differentiating total cost and total revenue with respect to quantity gives functions for marginal cost (MC) and marginal revenue (MR), and profit is maximised where MC = MR.

(e) At a maximum or a minimum, the first derivative is zero. At a maximum, the second derivative is negative and at a minimum the second derivative is positive. If the second derivative is also zero, we have a point of inflexion.

Quick quiz

1   Does a positive first derivative at a point indicate that a graph is upwards sloping or downwards sloping (from left to right) at that point?

2   If we have $y = ax^n$, what is the formula for the first derivative of y with respect to x?

3   What is the significance of a point at which $\frac{dy}{dx} = 0$?

4   How can the second derivative be used to distinguish a maximum from a minimum?

5   What is a point of inflexion?

Solutions to exercises

1   (a) $\frac{dy}{dx} = 6$

(b) $C = 30{,}000 + 5x$

$\frac{dC}{dx} = 5$ so the marginal cost is £5 per unit at all levels of output.

(c)   (i) $\frac{dy}{dx} = 3x^2 + 2$

(ii) $\dfrac{dy}{dx} = 9x^2 + 8x - 2$

(iii) $y = \dfrac{5x^2}{2} - 2x + \dfrac{7}{2}$

$\dfrac{dy}{dx} = 5x - 2$

(iv) $y = x^{-2} - \dfrac{3x^{-3}}{2} + \dfrac{5x^{-4}}{4}$

$\dfrac{dy}{dx} = -2x^{-3} \dfrac{+9x^{-4}}{2} - 5x^{-5}$

$= \dfrac{-2}{x^3} + \dfrac{9}{2x^4} - \dfrac{5}{x^5}$

(d) Demand, d $= 1,000 + 20p - 3p^2$

Price $= p$

Total revenue, r $= p(1,000 + 20p - 3p^2)$

r $= 1,000p + 20p^2 - 3p^3$

$\dfrac{dr}{dp}$ $= 1,000 + 40p - 9p^2$

2   P $= 8 - 0.05Q$

Total revenue,   R $=$ Quantity $\times$ Price $= Q \times P$

$= Q(8 - 0.05Q)$

$= 8Q - 0.05Q^2$

Marginal revenue, $\dfrac{dR}{dQ}$ $= 8 - 0.1Q$

Total cost,   C $= 400 + 5Q + 0.1Q^2$

Marginal cost, $\dfrac{dC}{dQ}$ $= 5 + 0.2Q$

To maximise profit, marginal cost $=$ marginal revenue

$5 + 0.2Q = 8 - 0.1Q$

$0.3Q = 3$

$Q = 10$

The value of Q to maximise profit is therefore 10, that is 10,000 units.

3    $y = -x^3 + 294x^2 + 2,400x - 100,000$

$\dfrac{dy}{dx} = -3x^2 + 588x + 2,400$

$\dfrac{d^2y}{dx^2} = -6x + 588$

Let $-3x^2 + 588x + 2,400 = 0$

$x = \dfrac{-588 \pm \sqrt{[588^2 - 4 \times (-3) \times 2,400]}}{2 \times (-3)}$

    $= 200$ or -4

Production needs to be positive, so $x = 200$.

If $x = 200$, $\dfrac{d^2y}{dx^2} = -6 \times 200 + 588 = -612 < 0$, so we have a maximum.

Maximum profit $= -200^3 + 294 \times 200^2 + 2,400 \times 200 - 100,000 = £4,140,000$

13 BREAKEVEN ANALYSIS

Signpost

The management of an organisation usually wish to know not only the profit likely to be made if the aimed-for production and sales for the year are achieved, but also the point at which neither profit nor loss occurs (the breakeven point) and the amount by which budgeted sales can fall before a loss is made (the margin of safety). Breakeven analysis assists them in doing this. Breakeven analysis uses marginal costing, which focuses on the difference each extra unit will make to revenue, cost and profit: the impact of each extra unit on profit is called the contribution per unit.

Breakeven analysis uses charts in various forms or arithmetic using the contribution/sales ratio, which is simply the contribution per pound of revenue. It can also be used to find the sales needed to make any given profit (target profit).

Your objectives

After completing this chapter you should:

(a)   understand the concepts of marginal costing, contribution, the breakeven point and the margin of safety;

(b)   be able to draw breakeven charts in two different forms and identify the breakeven point;

(c)   be able to show the effects of changes in selling prices and costs on breakeven charts;

(d)   be able to draw profit-volume charts;

(e)   be able to compute the required sales to achieve a given profit;

(f)   be able to compute and use the contribution/sales ratio;

(g)   know the limitations of breakeven analysis.

---

1   An introduction to breakeven analysis

Managers like to be able to assess and plan their future profits, so they need to be able to forecast future costs and revenues. One way of presenting information about expected future costs and revenues is *breakeven analysis*. Breakeven analysis is sometimes called CVP or Cost-Volume-Profit analysis. It uses *marginal costing*.

The basic idea of marginal costing is that if one extra unit is produced, then the costs which vary with production, such as materials costs, will all go up slightly. It therefore makes sense to identify those costs as the costs of production, the *marginal costs*. On the other hand, overheads such as rent, rates and heating will remain the same even if an extra unit is produced. They are *fixed* costs, and are not linked directly to the level of production.

Contribution

Contribution is the difference between sales value and the marginal cost of sales.

For instance, if an item has a marginal cost of £10 a unit, and is sold for £12 a unit, each sale generates a contribution of £2. This contribution will go towards covering the fixed overheads of the business (such as rent and managers' pay), and once these have been covered, the excess is profit. If the business has fixed overheads of £8,000 a year, the first 4,000 units sold will generate enough contribution to pay the fixed overheads of the year, and any further sales will contribute £2 a unit clear profit. In any business, the total contribution from all sales during a period can be compared with the fixed costs for that period; contribution - fixed costs = profit, or fixed costs - contribution = loss.

The breakeven point

The management of an organisation usually wishes to know not only the profit likely to be made if the production and sales aimed for are achieved, but also the point at which neither profit nor loss occurs (the breakeven point), and the amount by which actual sales can fall below anticipated sales without a loss being incurred.

The breakeven point can be calculated arithmetically. The number of units which must be sold in order to break even will be the total fixed costs divided by the contribution per unit. This is because the contribution required to break even must be an amount which exactly equals the amount of fixed costs.

Example: the breakeven point

Expected sales	10,000 units at £12 = £120,000
Variable cost	£10 a unit
Fixed costs	£8,000

Compute the breakeven point.

Solution

The contribution per unit is £ (12 - 10)	= £2
Breakeven point (BEP)	= £8,000 ÷ £2
	= 4,000 units
In revenue, BEP	= 4,000 × £12 = £48,000

Sales above £48,000 will result in profit of £2 for each unit of additional sales and sales below £48,000 will mean a loss of (4,000 units - actual units sold) × £2.

BPP Publishing

	Sales	
	4,000 units	*4,001 units*
	£	£
Revenue	48,000	48,012
Less variable costs	40,000	40,010
Contribution	8,000	8,002
Less fixed costs	8,000	8,000
Profit	0	2

The margin of safety

The *margin of safety* is the difference in units between budgeted sales volume and breakeven sales volume, and it is sometimes expressed as a percentage of the budgeted sales volume. It may also be expressed as the difference between the budgeted sales revenue and breakeven sales revenue, expressed as a percentage of the budgeted sales revenue.

Exercise 1
A product sells for £15 a unit and has a variable cost of £11 a unit. If the breakeven point is annual sales of 38,000 units, what are the annual fixed costs?

2 Breakeven and P/V charts

Breakeven charts

The breakeven point can be determined graphically. A breakeven chart is prepared showing sales (in units) on the horizontal axis and values for sales and costs on the vertical axis.

Example: breakeven charts

The budgeted annual output of a factory is 120,000 units. The fixed overheads amount to £40,000 and the variable costs are 50p a unit. The selling price is £1 a unit.

Construct a breakeven chart showing the breakeven point and the profit earned at budgeted output.

Solution

Budget	£
Sales (120,000 units)	120,000
Less variable costs	60,000
Contribution	60,000
Less fixed costs	40,000
Profit	20,000

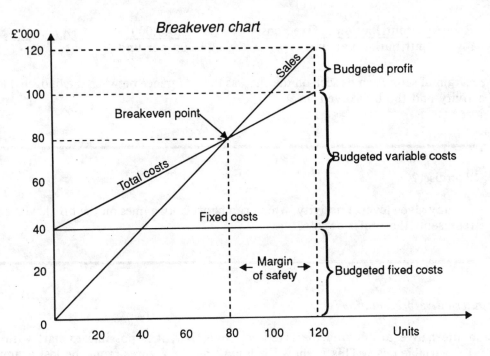

The chart is drawn as follows.

(a) The vertical axis represents money: costs and revenues, and the horizontal axis represents the level of activity: production and sales.

(b) The fixed costs are represented by a horizontal line (in our example, at £40,000).

(c) The variable costs are added to fixed costs to give total costs.

To draw the straight line of total costs, only two points need to be plotted and joined up. Perhaps the two most convenient points to plot are total costs at zero output, and total costs at the budgeted output and sales.

(i) At zero output, costs are equal to the fixed costs, £40,000, since there are no variable costs.

(ii) At the budgeted output of 120,000 units costs are as follows.

	£
Fixed costs	40,000
Variable costs (120,000 × 50p)	60,000
Total costs	100,000

Therefore the total costs line can be drawn by joining up the points (0, 40,000) and (120,000, 100,000)

(d) The revenue line is also drawn by plotting two points and joining them up.

(i) At zero sales, revenue is zero.
(ii) At the budgeted output and sales of 120,000 units, revenue is £120,000.

The breakeven point is where total costs are matched exactly by total revenue. From the chart, this can be seen to occur at output and sales of 80,000 units, when revenue and costs are both £80,000. This breakeven point can be proved mathematically as follows.

Notes

$$\frac{\text{Required contribution} = \text{fixed costs}}{\text{Contribution per unit}} = \frac{£40,000}{50\text{p per unit}} = 80,000 \text{ units}$$

The margin of safety can be seen on the chart as the difference between the budgeted level of activity and the breakeven level.

Exercise 2

For any given level of activity, which gap between two lines on the breakeven chart represents the profit or loss?

An alternative presentation

As an alternative to drawing the fixed cost line first, it is possible to start with the line for variable costs. This is shown below using the figures from the last example.

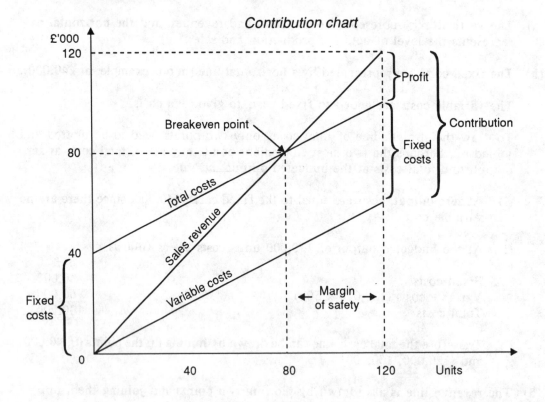

Contribution chart

One of the advantages of this presentation is that it shows clearly the contribution for different levels of production (indicated here at 120,000 units, the budgeted level of output), as the wedge shape between the sales revenue line and the variable costs line.

Variations in prices and costs

Breakeven charts can be used to show variations in the possible sales price, variable costs or fixed costs.

Example: variations in price

A company sells a product which has a variable cost of £2 a unit. Fixed costs are £15,000. It has been estimated that if the price is set at £4.40 a unit, the sales volume will be 7,500 units; whereas if the price is £4 a unit, the sales volume will be 10,000 units.

Draw a breakeven chart covering each of the possible sales prices, and state the budgeted profits, the breakeven points and the margins of safety.

Solution

Budgeted outcome	Price £4.40 a unit £		Price £4 a unit £
Fixed costs	15,000		15,000
Variable costs			
7,500 × £2	15,000	10,000 × £2	20,000
Total costs	30,000		35,000
Budgeted revenue			
7,500 × £4.40	33,000	10,000 × £4	40,000
Budgeted profit	3,000		5,000

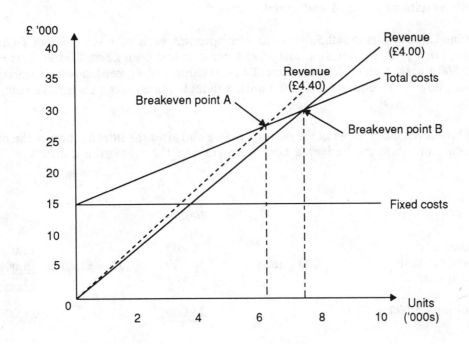

(a) Breakeven point A is the breakeven point at a price of £4.40 a unit, which is 6,250 units or £27,500 in costs and revenues.

$$\frac{\text{Required contribution to break even}}{\text{Contribution per unit}} \quad = \quad \frac{£15,000}{£2.40 \text{ a unit}} \quad = \quad 6,250 \text{ units.}$$

The margin of safety is 7,500 units – 6,250 units = 1,250 units or 16.7% of expected sales.

(b) Breakeven point B is the breakeven point at a price of £4 a unit which is 7,500 units or £30,000 in costs and revenues.

$$\frac{\text{Required contribution to break even}}{\text{Contribution per unit}} \quad = \quad \frac{£15,000}{£2 \text{ a unit}} \quad = \quad 7,500 \text{ units.}$$

The margin of safety is 10,000 units – 7,500 units = 2,500 units or 25% of expected sales.

Since a price of £4 a unit gives a higher expected profit and a wider margin of safety, this price will probably be preferred even though the breakeven point is higher than at a sales price of £4.40 a unit.

Exercise 3

In the above example, what would have been the breakeven point at a price of £3.50 a unit?

Example: variations in fixed and variable costs

Streamline Ltd budgets to sell 5,000 units of its product each year at a price of £4.80 a unit. Until this year, the variable cost of sale per unit had been £2 and fixed costs had been £9,800 a year. With the introduction of new electronic equipment, however, variable costs have now been reduced to £1.20 a unit, although annual fixed costs have risen to £12,000.

Draw a breakeven chart showing the position before and after the introduction of the new equipment, and state the budgeted annual profits and the breakeven points.

Solution

		Before £		After £
Fixed costs		9,800		12,000
Variable costs	5,000 units × £2	10,000	5,000 × £1.20	6,000
Total costs		19,800		18,000
Revenue 5,000 × £4.80		24,000		24,000

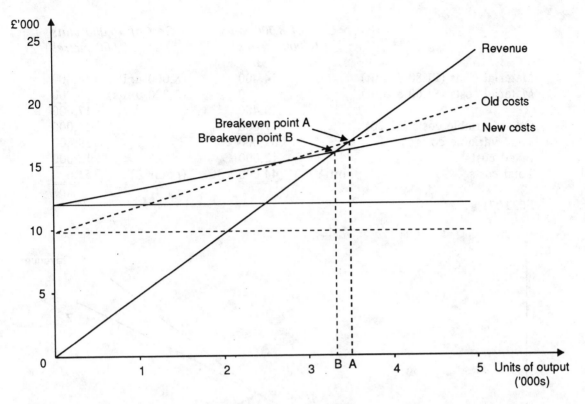

(a) Before the changeover, annual profit was budgeted as £4,200 and the breakeven point (A) was £9,800/£2.80 = 3,500 units or £16,800.

(b) After the changeover, annual profit should be £6,000, and the breakeven point (B) will be £12,000/£3.60 = 3,333.3 units or £16,000.

Example: variations in variable costs

Musketeer Ltd purchases its raw materials from a single supplier, and uses two metres of the material in each unit of its finished product. Variable costs of the finished product, at output below 5,000 units a year are £4.20 a unit, of which £2 is the raw material cost. The supplier offers a discount of 10% on *all* purchases, if Musketeer Ltd buys at least 10,000 metres each year, and a *further* discount of 10 pence per metre on the *additional* purchases only above 16,000 metres a year. The selling price of the finished product is £6 a unit and fixed costs are £12,000 a year.

Draw a breakeven chart.

Solution

		Cost of 5,000 units (10,000 metres) No discount £		Cost of 5,000 units (10,000 metres) 10% discount £
Material costs	(× £2)	10,000	(× £1.80)	9,000
Other variable cost	(× £2.20)	11,000	(× £2.20)	11,000
Total variable costs		21,000		20,000
Fixed costs		12,000		12,000
Total costs	(point W)	33,000	(point X)	32,000

	Cost of 8,000 units (16,000 metres) £		Cost of 10,000 units (20,000 metres) £
Material costs (£1.80 a unit)	14,400	(8,000 units)	14,400
Material costs (£1.60 a unit)	0	(2,000 units)	3,200
	14,400		17,600
Other variable costs (£2.20)	17,600		22,000
Total variable costs	32,000		39,600
Fixed costs	12,000		12,000
Total costs (point Y)	44,000	(point Z)	51,600

F03T071

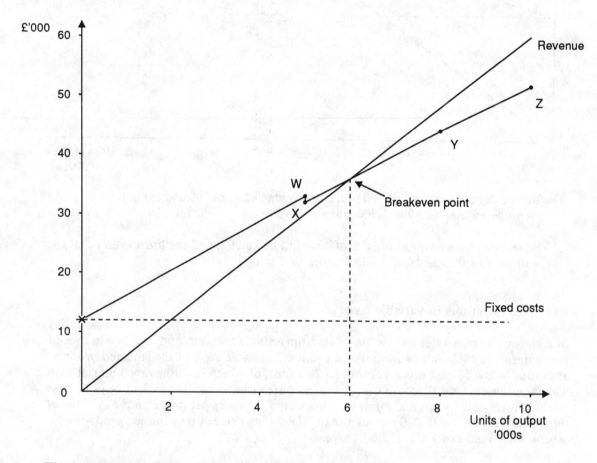

£'000

The breakeven point is 6,000 units (£36,000 of costs and revenues).

Exercise 4

If, in the above example, the cost per metre of materials above 16,000 metres had been £2.90 (because of shortages) but all other costs remained the same, where would the next breakeven point have been?

The P/V chart

The P/V (profit-volume) chart is a variation on the breakeven chart which provides a simple illustration of the relationship between profit and sales, and of the margin of safety.

A P/V chart is constructed as follows.

(a) The horizontal axis represents either sales volume in units, or sales value.

(b) The vertical axis represents profit, extending above and below the horizontal axis with a zero point at the intersection of the two axes, and the negative section below the horizontal axis representing losses. At zero production, the firm incurs a loss equal to the fixed costs.

(c) The profit-volume line is a straight line drawn with its starting point (at zero production) at the point on the vertical axis representing the level of fixed cost, and with a gradient of contribution per unit. The profit line will cut the horizontal axis at the breakeven point of sales volume. Any point on the profit line above the horizontal axis represents the profit (measured on the vertical axis) for that particular level of sales.

Example: P/V charts

Cabbage Patch Ltd makes and sells a single product which has a variable cost of sale of £5. Fixed costs are £15,000 a year. The company's management estimates that at a price of £8 a unit, annual sales would be 7,000 units.

Construct a P/V chart.

Solution

At sales of 7,000 units, total contribution will be 7,000 × £ (8 - 5) = £21,000, and total profit will be £6,000.

P/V chart

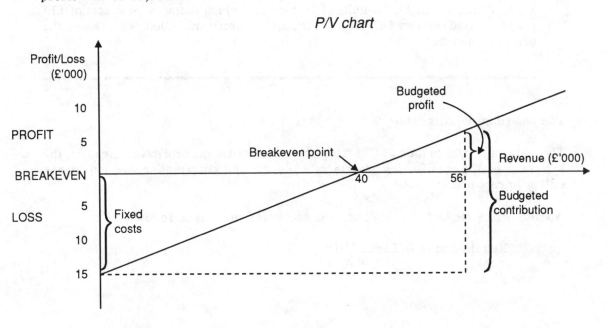

BPP Publishing

3 Breakeven arithmetic

Target profits

A company may wish to achieve a certain profit during a period. To achieve this profit, contribution must cover fixed costs plus the required profit.

Example: a required profit

Riding Ltd makes and sells a single product, for which variable costs are as follows.

	£
Materials	10
Labour	14
	24

The selling price is £30 a unit, and fixed costs are £68,000 a year. The company wishes to make a profit of £16,000 a year. What sales are required to achieve this profit?

Solution

Required contribution	= Fixed costs + Profit
	= £68,000 + £16,000 = £84,000

$$\frac{\text{Required contribution}}{\text{Contribution per unit}} = \frac{£84,000}{£(30 - 24)}$$

$$= 14,000 \text{ units} = £420,000 \text{ in revenue.}$$

Exercise 5

B Ltd wishes to sell 14,000 units of its product, which has a variable cost of £15 per unit. Fixed costs are £47,000 and the required profit is £23,000. What should the price per unit be?

The contribution/sales ratio

The contribution/sales ratio or C/S ratio (sometimes called the profit/volume ratio, the P/V ratio or the contribution margin ratio) is the unit contribution divided by the selling price per unit.

An alternative method of calculating the breakeven point is as follows.

$$\text{Required sales} = \frac{\text{Fixed costs}}{\text{C/S ratio}}$$

The resulting breakeven point will be expressed in terms of sales revenue at the breakeven point.

Example: the C/S ratio

Newsflash Ltd makes and sells a magazine for which the variable costs are £2.40 a copy.

The price is £3.00 per magazine and annual fixed costs are £9,000. The company wishes to make an annual profit of £12,000.

Using the C/S ratio in your workings, calculate:

(a) the sales value and sales quantity at breakeven point;
(b) the sales quantity required to meet the target of £12,000 profit.

Solution

$$\text{C/S ratio} = \frac{\text{contribution per unit}}{\text{unit price}}$$

$$= \frac{£3.00 - £2.40}{£3.00} = 0.2$$

(a)
$$\text{Sales value required to break even} = \frac{\text{Fixed costs}}{\text{C/S ratio}}$$

$$= \frac{£9,000}{0.2} = £45,000$$

$$\text{Sales quantity required} = £45,000/£3.00 = 15,000 \text{ copies}$$

(b)
$$\text{Required contribution} = \text{fixed costs} + \text{profit}$$

$$= £9,000 + £12,000$$

$$= £21,000$$

$$\text{Sales value required} = \frac{\text{required contribution}}{\text{C/S ratio}}$$

$$= \frac{£21,000}{0.2} = £105,000$$

$$\text{Sales quantity required} = £105,000/£3.00 = 35,000 \text{ copies}$$

BPP Publishing

Exercise 6

Mal de Mer Ltd makes and sells a product which has a variable cost of £30, and which sells for £40 a unit. Budgeted fixed costs are £70,000 and budgeted sales are 8,000 units.

What is the C/S ratio and what is the breakeven point?

The limitations of breakeven analysis

Breakeven analysis should be used carefully. The major limitations are as follows.

(a) Each analysis can cover only one product or a single mix (that is fixed proportions) of a group of products. This restricts its usefulness.

(b) It is assumed that fixed costs are the same in total and variable costs are the same per unit at all levels of output. This assumption is a great simplification. However, it may be at least approximately true over the likely range of levels of output (the *relevant range*).

(c) It is assumed that selling prices will be constant at all levels of activity. This may not be true, especially at high volumes of output, where the price may have to be reduced to win extra sales.

(d) Uncertainty in the estimates of costs is often ignored in breakeven analysis.

Chapter roundup

(a) Marginal costing analyses costs into fixed costs and a marginal (variable) cost per unit. The contribution per unit is the selling price minus the marginal cost, and a business breaks even (it makes neither a profit nor a loss) when total contribution equals fixed costs. The margin of safety is the difference between budgeted sales volume and breakeven sales volume.

(b) Breakeven charts may be drawn either with a slab for fixed costs and a wedge for variable costs on top, or with a wedge for variable costs and a slab for fixed costs on top. In both cases, the breakeven point is indicated by the intersection of the sales line and the total costs line.

(c) Changes in selling prices and costs can be reflected by re-drawing relevant lines on breakeven charts, so that the new breakeven points may be identified.

(d) A P/V chart has a single line for profit or loss, which crosses the horizontal axis at the breakeven point.

(e) Breakeven analysis can be extended to find the required sales to achieve a given profit, by adding that profit to fixed costs.

(f) The contribution/sales ratio can be used to compute the required sales to break even.

(g) Breakeven analysis makes several assumptions which may not apply in practice.

Quick quiz

1   What is contribution?

2   At the breakeven point, will total contribution equal fixed costs?

3   Sketch a breakeven chart.

4   Sketch a P/V chart.

5   What is the contribution/sales ratio?

Solutions to exercises

1   Fixed costs = contribution at breakeven point = $38,000 \times £(15 - 11) = £152,000$.

2   The vertical gap between the sales line and the total costs line shows the profit or loss.

3   $£15,000/£1.50 = 10,000$ units.

4   At 8,000 units (16,000 metres) we have total revenue of £48,000 and total costs of £44,000, giving a profit of £4,000.

Above 8,000 units, we would have a contribution per unit of £6 - £(2.20 + 2 × 2.90) = -£2. This negative contribution would reduce the profit to zero after £4,000/£2 = 2,000 further units, so there would be a breakeven point at 10,000 units and a loss above that level. With this price structure, the company should limit production to 8,000 units in order to maximise profits.

5   Required contribution=   =   Fixed costs plus profit
                               =   £47,000 + £23,000
                               =   £70,000
    Required sales   =   14,000 units

		£
Required contribution per unit sold = £70,000 ÷ 14,000 =		5
Variable cost per unit		15
Required price per unit		20

6   C/S ratio = £(40 – 30)/£40 =0.25

$$\text{Breakeven point (sales)} = \frac{\text{Fixed costs (required contribution)}}{\text{C/S ratio}} = \frac{£70,000}{0.25} = £280,000$$

$$= \text{7,000 units}$$

14 NETWORK ANALYSIS

Signpost

A large project, such as building a bridge, will comprise many activities, which must be done in the right order. Network analysis is a way of mapping out the activities in a project, and showing their interrelationships: we will see how to draw a type of network diagram called an activity on arrow diagram.

Timing is often crucial in large projects. We will see how to find the critical path, which is a sequence of those activities which, were any of them to run late, would mean that the whole project was delayed. We will also see how to find the earliest time each activity might be able to start (an earliest event time) and the latest time by which it must be finished (a latest event time). We can then work out by how much an activity might be allowed to overrun (its float). Activities may take more or less time than anticipated, and so we will look at PERT, a method of dealing with such uncertainties. Finally we will look at Gantt charts, which can be used to estimate the amount of resources required for a project.

Your objectives

After completing this chapter you should:

(a) understand the use of networks;

(b) be able to draw activity on arrow diagrams;

(c) be able to identify critical paths;

(d) be able to compute earliest and latest event times;

(e) be able to compute the float of activities;

(f) be able to apply PERT to deal with uncertain activity durations;

(g) be able to use a Gantt chart to estimate the amount of resources required for a project.

---

1 Presenting projects as networks

Network analysis is a technique for planning and controlling large projects, such as construction work, research and development projects or the computerisation of business systems. Network analysis helps managers to plan when to start various tasks, to allocate resources so that the tasks can be carried out within schedule, to monitor actual progress and to find out when control action is needed to prevent a delay in completion of the

---

project. The events and activities making up the whole project are represented in the form of a diagram or chart. Network analysis is sometimes called Critical Path Analysis (CPA) or Critical Path Method (CPM).

Drawing a network diagram: the activity on arrow presentation

Here is an example of a network for building the Channel Tunnel, with the whole project simplified to just three activities.

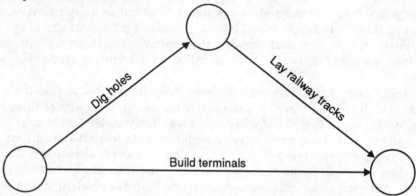

The holes must be dug before the tracks can be laid, which is why laying the tracks follows on from digging the holes in the diagram. However, building the terminals in France and England can be done at the same time as the other two activities, which is why building the terminals runs across the page alongside those other activities in the diagram.

This form of network diagram is an activity on arrow diagram, which means that each activity within a project is represented on the diagram by an arrowed line. An alternative form of diagram is activity on node, but we shall use the activity on arrow presentation because it is easier to follow.

A project is analysed into its separate activities and the sequence of activities is presented in a network diagram. The flow of activities in the diagram is from left to right.

An *activity* within a network is represented by an arrowed line, running between one *event* and another event. An event is simply the start and/or completion of an activity, which is represented on the network diagram by a circle (called a *node*).

Let us suppose that in a certain project there are two activities A and B, and activity B cannot be started until activity A is completed. Activity A might be building the walls of a house, and activity B might be putting the roof on. This would be represented as follows.

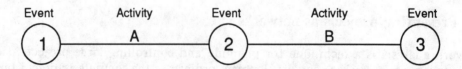

The rule is that an activity cannot start until all activities leading into the event at its start have been completed.

Events are usually numbered, just to identify them. In this example, event 1 is the start of Activity A, event 3 is the completion of Activity B, and event 2 is both the completion of A and the start of B.

Let us now suppose that another project includes three activities, C, D and E. Neither activity D nor E can start until C is completed, but D and E could be done simultaneously if required. This would be represented as follows.

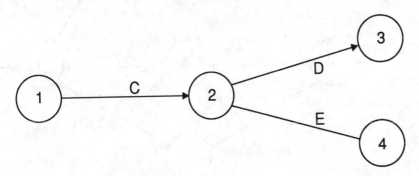

In this diagram, event 2 represents the point when C is completed and also the point when D and E can start, so the diagram clearly shows that D and E must follow C.

A third possibility is that an activity cannot start until two or more activities have been completed. If H cannot start until F and G are both complete, then we would represent the situation like this.

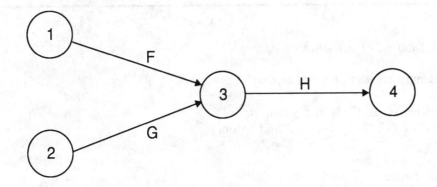

Example: network diagrams

Draw the network for the following project to build a factory.

Activity	Preceding activity
A: lay foundations	-
B: build walls	A
C: lay drains	A
D: instal electricity cables	A
E: fit window frames	B
F: fit door frames	B
G: fit windows	E
H: fit doors	F
I: plaster inside walls	G,H
J: lay floor	C
K: fit power outlets	D
L: instal machines	I, J, K

Solution

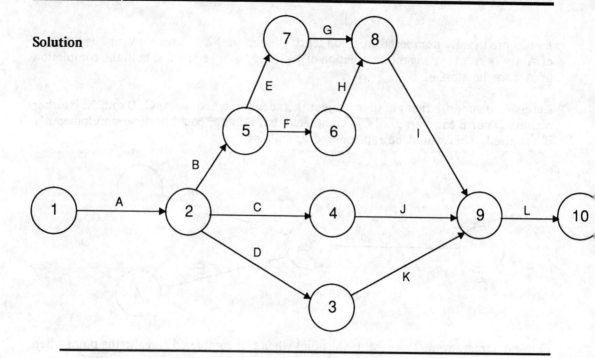

Exercise 1

In the above network, could activities E and H be carried on simultaneously?

The identification of activities

Activities may be identified as either:

(a)   activities A, B, C, D and so on; or
(b)   activities 1-2, 2-5, 2-4, 2-3 and so on.

Dummy activities

It is a convention in network analysis that two activities are not drawn between the same events. The convention makes diagrams clearer.

To avoid having two activities running between the same events, we use a *dummy activity*, which is represented by a broken arrowed line. A dummy activity takes no time and no resources to complete.

For example, suppose that the sequence of activities in a project to instal a computer system is as follows.

Activity	Preceding Activity
A: instal computer	-
B: write programs	A
C: hire trained staff	A
D: test system	B, C

In theory, we could draw the network as follows.

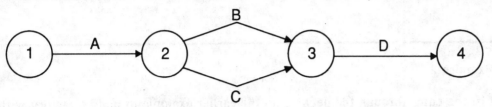

By convention, this would be incorrect. Two separate activities must not start and end with the same events. The correct representation is shown below.

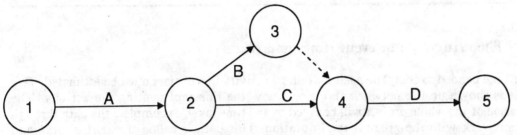

Sometimes it is necessary to use a dummy activity not just to comply with the convention, but to preserve the basic logic of the network.

Consider the following example of a project to instal a new office telephone system.

Activity	Preceding activity
A: buy equipment	-
B: allocate extension numbers	-
C: install switchboard	A
D: install wiring	B,C
E: print office directory	B

The project is finished when both D and E are complete.

The problem arises because D can only start when both B and C have been finished, whereas E is only required to follow B. The only way to draw the network is to use a dummy activity.

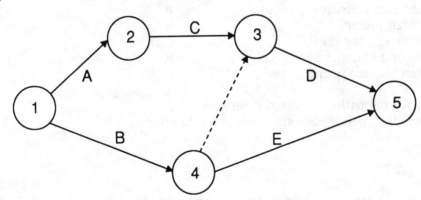

Paths through the network

Any network can be analysed into a number of different paths or routes. A path is simply a sequence of activities from the start to the end of the network. In the example above, there are just three paths.

(a) A C D;
(b) B Dummy D;
(c) B E.

BPP Publishing

Exercise 2

List the paths through the network in the earlier example to build a factory with activities A - L.

2   The critical path, event times and floats

The time needed to complete each individual activity in a project must be estimated. This time is shown on the network above or below the line representing the activity. The duration of the whole project will be fixed by the time taken to complete the path through the network with the greatest total duration. This path is called the *critical path* and activities on it are known as *critical activities*. A network can have more than one critical path, if several paths tie for the greatest duration.

Activities on the critical path must be started and completed on time, otherwise the total project time will be extended. The method of finding the critical path is illustrated in the example below.

Example: the critical path

The following activities comprise a project to renovate a block of flats.

Activity		Preceding activity	Duration (weeks)
A:	replace windows in lounges	–	5
B:	rewire	–	4
C:	replaster walls of lounges	A	2
D:	fit lights in lounges	B	1
E:	decorate bedrooms	B	5
F:	install plumbing	B	5
G:	decorate lounges	C,D	4
H:	decorate kitchens	F	3
I:	decorate bathrooms	F	2

(a)   What are the paths through the network?
(b)   What is the critical path and what is its duration?

Solution

The first step in the solution is to draw the network diagram, with the time for each activity shown.

A network should have just one start node and one completion node, and in the diagram below, this is achieved by introducing a dummy activity after activity I. Dummy activities always have zero duration.

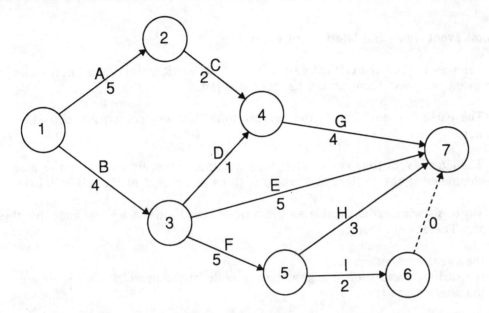

We could list the paths through the network and their durations as follows.

Path			Duration (weeks)	
A	C	G	(5 + 2 + 4)	11
B	D	G	(4 + 1 + 4)	9
B	E		(4 + 5)	9
B	F	H	(4 + 5 + 3)	12
B	F	I Dummy	(4 + 5 + 2 + 0)	11

The critical path is the longest path, BFH, with a duration of 12 weeks. This is the minimum time needed to complete the project. Note that a network may have more than one critical path, if two or more paths have equal highest durations.

Exercise 3

The following activities comprise a project to agree a price for some land to be bought for development.

Activity	Preceded by	Duration Days
P: get survey done	–	4
Q: draw up plans	–	7
R: estimate cost of building work	Q	2
S: get tenders for site preparation work	P	9
T: negotiate price	R, S	3

Within how many days could the whole project be completed?

Listing paths through the network in this way is easy for small networks, but it becomes tedious for bigger and more complex networks.

BPP Publishing

Earliest event times and latest event times

Another way to find the critical path is to include earliest times and latest times for each event, showing them on the network diagram.

(a) The earliest event time is the earliest time that any subsequent activities can start.

(b) The latest event time is the latest time by which all preceding activities must be completed if the project as a whole is to be completed in the minimum time.

One way of showing earliest and latest event times is to divide each event node into three sections. These will record:

(a) the event number;
(b) the earliest event time. For the starting node in the network, this is time 0;
(c) the latest event time.

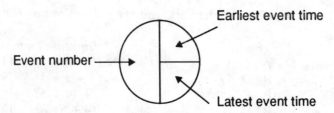

Earliest event times

The next step is to calculate the earliest event times. Always start at event 1 with its earliest starting time of 0. We will continue the previous example to show how times are calculated.

Work from left to right through the diagram calculating the earliest time that the next activity following the event can start. For example, the earliest event time at event 2 is the earliest time activity C can start. This is week $0 + 5 = 5$. Similarly, the earliest event time at event 3 is the earliest time D, E and F can start, which is week $0 + 4 = 4$, and the earliest time at event 5 is the earliest time activities H and I can start, which is $4 + 5 =$ week 9.

A slight problem occurs where more than one activity ends at the same node. For example, event 4 is the completion node for activities C and D. Activity G cannot start until both C and D are complete, therefore the earliest event time at event 4 is the higher of:

(a) earliest event time, event 2 + duration of C $= 5 + 2 = 7$ weeks;
(b) earliest event time, event 3 + duration of D $= 4 + 1 = 5$ weeks.

The earliest event time at event 4 is 7 weeks.

Similarly, the earliest event time at event 7 is the highest of:

Earliest event time, event 3 + duration of E $= 4 + 5 = 9$
Earliest event time, event 4 + duration of G $= 7 + 4 = 11$
Earliest event time, event 5 + duration of H $= 9 + 3 = 12$
Earliest event time, event 6 + duration of dummy activity $= 11 + 0 = 11$

The highest value is 12 weeks. This also means that the minimum completion time for the entire project is 12 weeks.

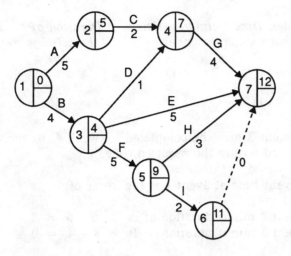

Exercise 4

If activity C had taken four weeks, which earliest event times would have been affected, and what would they have changed to?

Latest event times

The next step is to calculate the latest event times. These are the latest times at which each event can occur if the project as a whole is to be completed in the shortest possible time, 12 weeks. The latest event time at the final event must be the same as the earliest event time, which in this example is 12 weeks.

Work from right to left through the diagram calculating the latest time at which each activity can start, if it is to be completed by the latest event time of the event at its end. The latest event time for:

(a) event 4 is 12 – 4 = week 8;
(b) event 6 is 12 – 0 = week 12;
(c) event 2 is 8 – 2   = week 6.

Event 5 might cause difficulties as two activities, H and I lead back to it.

(a) Activity H must be completed by week 12, and so must start at week 9.
(b) Activity I must also be completed by week 12, and so must start at week 10.

The latest event time at node 5 is the earlier of week 9 or week 10, that is, week 9. All activities leading up to node 5, which in this case is just F, must be completed by week 9 so that both H and I can be completed by week 12.

Notes

The latest event time at event 3 is calculated in the same way. It is the earliest time which enables all subsequent activities to be completed within the required time. Thus, at event 3, we have the following.

Subsequent event	Latest time of that event (a)	Intermediate activity	Duration of the activity (b)	Required event time at event 3 (a) − (b)
4	8	D	1	7
5	9	F	5	4
7	12	E	5	7

All activities before event 3 must be completed by week 4, to enable all subsequent activities to be completed within the required time.

Similarly, the latest event time at event 1 is the lower of:

Latest event time, event 2 minus duration of A = 6 - 5 = 1
Latest event time, event 3 minus duration of B = 4 - 4 = 0

The latest event time at event 1 is therefore 0. It must always be 0. If your calculations give any other value, you have made an error.

The final network diagram is now as follows. The critical path has been indicated by a double line.

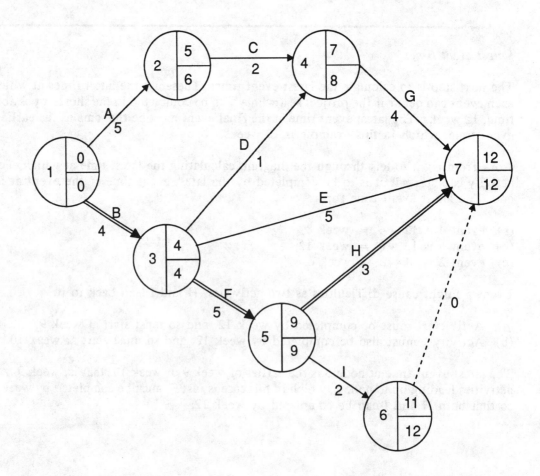

Finding the critical path

Critical activities are those activities which must be started on time, otherwise the total project time will be increased. It follows that each event on the critical path must have the same earliest and latest times. The critical path for the above network is therefore B F H (events 1,3,5,7). An event with the same earliest and latest times is called a *critical event*.

Exercise 5

The following activities comprise a project to make a film.

Activity		Preceded by	Duration Weeks
J:	negotiate distribution	–	6
K:	arrange publicity	J	5
L:	write screenplay	–	3
M:	hire cast and crew	L	5
N:	shoot and edit	M, Q	4
P:	design sets	L	2
Q:	build sets	P	1

What are the earliest and latest event times of the event at the end of activity P?

You may find that an activity connects two events each of which has the same earliest and latest event times, but that the activity itself is not critical.

For example, in the following extract from the above example to renovate a block of flats events 3 and 7 are on the critical path.

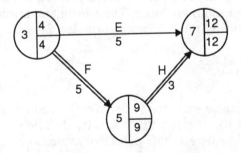

Activity E, however, is not critical: the critical path goes through event 5. If you are in doubt as to whether an activity is on the critical path you should check to see whether it has any float (see below). All critical activities have zero float.

Float

Activities which are not on the critical path are non-critical, and they can, within limits:

(a) start late; and/or
(b) take longer than the time specified,

without holding up the completion of the project as a whole.

The float for any activity is the amount of time by which its duration could be extended up to the point where it would become critical. This is the same as the amount of time by which its duration could be extended without affecting the total project time.

The effect on the time available for preceding and subsequent activities is ignored. The total float for an activity is therefore equal to its latest finishing time minus its earliest starting time minus its duration.

For example, look at activity C in the above example to renovate a block of flats. This must be completed by week 8 if the total project time is not to be extended. It cannot be started until week 5 at the earliest, but as it only takes two weeks there is one spare week available. The float for activity C is (8 - 5 - 2) = 1 week.

Exercise 6

What are the floats for activities D and G in the above example?

---

3   Uncertain activity durations

Network problems may be complicated by uncertainty in the durations of individual activities. For example, building works can easily be delayed by bad weather.

PERT (Project Evaluation and Review Technique) is a form of network analysis which takes account of this uncertainty. For each activity in the project, optimistic, most likely and pessimistic estimates of durations are made. These estimates are converted into a mean duration and a variance, using the following formulae.

(a) Mean μ $= \dfrac{a + 4m + b}{6}$

where a = optimistic estimate of activity duration
m = most likely estimate of activity duration
b = pessimistic estimate of activity duration

(b) Variance $\sigma^2 = \dfrac{1}{36} (b-a)^2$

The standard deviation, σ, is $\dfrac{1}{6}(b-a)$.

Once the mean duration and the standard deviation of durations have been calculated for each activity, we can:

(a) find the critical path using the mean activity durations;
(b) estimate the standard deviation of the expected total project time.

Variations in activity times are usually assumed to be normally distributed. This is a big assumption: it makes the mathematics easy, but in many cases it may be false, so the results of PERT must be treated with caution.

Example: PERT

A project consists of four activities.

Activity	Preceding activity	Optimistic (a) Days	Most likely (m) Days	Pessimistic (b) Days
A	-	5	10	15
B	A	16	18	26
C	-	15	20	31
D	-	8	18	28

Analyse the project using PERT.

Solution

The mean duration for each activity is calculated by the formula $\frac{a + 4m + b}{6}$

Activity	a + 4m + b	Divided by 6 Days
A	5 + 40 + 15 = 60	10
B	16 + 72 + 26 = 114	19
C	15 + 80 + 31 = 126	21
D	8 + 72 + 28 = 108	18

The standard deviation of durations for each activity is calculated by the formula

$\frac{b - a}{6}$

Activity	b - a	Divided by 6 Days
A	15 - 5 = 10	1.67
B	26 - 16 = 10	1.67
C	31 - 15 = 16	2.67
D	28 - 8 = 20	3.33

The network can be drawn using the mean durations.

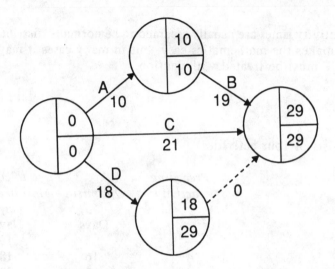

If we now wish to calculate the probability that the total project time will exceed, say, 31 days, the procedure is as follows.

(a) We add the *variances* of the uncertain activities in a path. We can do this provided the activity durations are independent.

Variance of activity A's time = 1.67^2	2.78
Variance of activity B's time = 1.67^2	2.78
Combined variance of path AB	5.56

The standard deviation of the durations of path AB is $\sqrt{5.56} = 2.36$ days.

(b) (i) The probability that the duration of AB will remain within 31 days is the probability that it will be not more than $(31 - 29)/2.36 = 0.85$ standard deviations above the mean.

From normal distribution tables, this is $0.5 + 0.3023 = 0.8023$.

(ii) The probability that the duration of C will be within 31 days is the probability that it will be not more than $(31 - 21)/2.67 = 3.75$ standard deviations above the mean, which is very nearly 1.

(iii) The probability that the duration of D will be within 31 days is the probability that it will be not more than $(31 - 18)/3.33 = 3.9$ standard deviations above the mean, which is very nearly 1.

(c) The probability of exceeding 31 days is therefore the same as the probability that path AB will take more than this time, which is $1 - 0.8023 = 0.1977$.

Exercise 7

A path through a network comprises four activities, with the following estimated durations.

Activity	Duration in days		
	Optimistic (a)	*Most likely (m)*	*Pessimistic (b)*
A	3	7	11
B	2	5	10
C	4	4	4
D	5	6	11

All the activity durations are independent of each other. Applying the PERT formulae, what is the probability that the duration of the path will exceed 25 days?

4 Gantt charts

Gantt charts can be used to estimate the amount of resources required for a project. A Gantt chart is a line diagram, with lines representing both time and activities. Where activities are in a continuous 'chain', with one activity able to follow immediately after the other, these can be drawn as a continuous line on the chart. Consider this example.

Example: Gantt charts

Flotto Limited is about to undertake a project about which the following data is available.

Activity	*Must be preceded by activity*	*Duration*	*Men required for the job*
		Days	
A	–	3	6
B	–	5	3
C	B	2	4
D	A	1	4
E	A	6	5
F	D	3	6
G	C,E	3	3

There is a labour force of nine men available, and each man is paid a fixed wage regardless of whether or not he is actively working on any day. Every man is capable of working on any of the seven activities. If extra labour is required during any day, men can be hired on a daily basis at the rate of £120 per day. If the project is to finish in the minimum time what extra payments must be made for hired labour?

Solution

Draw the network to establish the duration of the project and the critical path. Then draw a Gantt chart, using the critical path as a basis, assuming that jobs start at the earliest possible time. Float times on chains of activities should be shown by a dotted line.

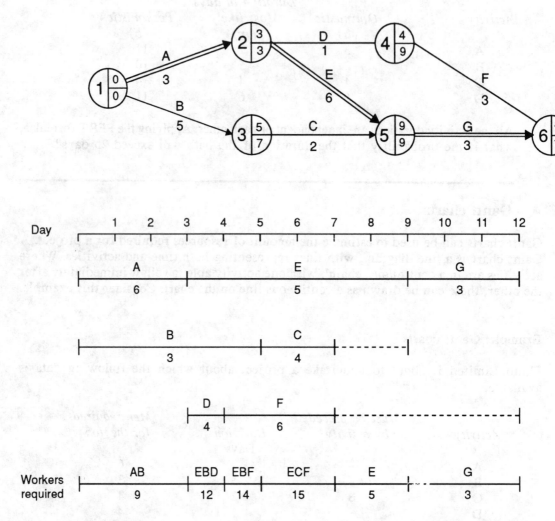

It can be seen that if all activities start at their earliest times, as many as 15 men will be required on any one day (days 6-7) whereas on other days there would be idle capacity (days 8-12). The problem can be reduced, or removed, by using up float time on non-critical activities. Suppose we deferred the start of activities D and F until the latest possible day. This would be the end of day 8/start of day 9 - leaving four days to complete the activities by the end of day 12.

The Gantt chart would be redrawn as follows.

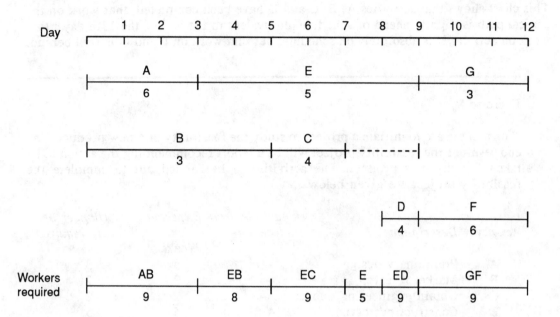

The project can be completed in the minimum time without hiring any additional labour.

Gantt charts used for control

Gantt charts can also be used very conveniently to show the progress of a project. Consider the following chart which shows progress on a project at day 10.

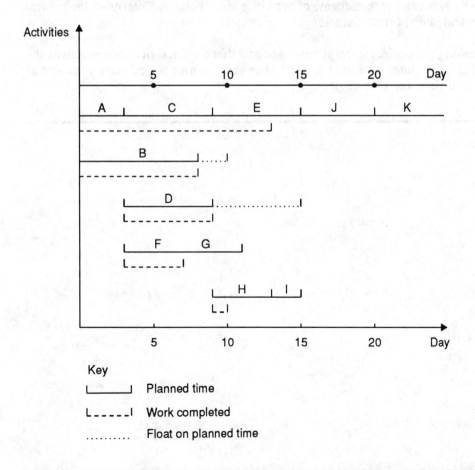

Key

L____J Planned time

L-----I Work completed

.... Float on planned time

This chart shows that activities A, B, C and D have been completed; that work on the critical path is slightly ahead of schedule (equivalent to the end of the 13th day); that work on activity H is absolutely on schedule, but that work on F and G is well behind.

Exercise 8

Thurnon plc are to initiate a project to study the feasibility of a new product. The end result of the feasibility project will be a report recommending the action to be taken for the new product. The activities to be carried out to complete the feasibility project are given below.

Activity	Description	Immediate predecessors	Expected time Weeks	Number of staff required
A	Preliminary design	–	5	3
B	Market research	–	3	2
C	Obtain engineering quotes	A	2	2
D	Construct prototype	A	5	5
E	Prepare marketing material	A	3	3
F	Costing	C	2	2
G	Product testing	D	4	5
H	Pilot survey	B, E	6	4
I	Pricing estimates	H	2	1
J	Final report	F, G, I	6	2

(a) Draw a network for the scheme of activities set out above. Determine the critical path and the shortest duration of the project.

(b) Assuming the project starts at time zero and that each activity commences at the earliest start date, construct a chart showing the number of staff required at any one time for this project.

Chapter roundup

(a) A network represents a project by breaking it down into activities and showing their interdependence.

(b) Activities are represented by arrows, which are drawn between nodes which represent events. Dummy activities may be needed. Any sequence of activities from the start to the end of a network is a path through the network.

(c) The path with the greatest duration is the critical path. Any delay on this path will delay the project as a whole.

(d) The earliest event time for an event is the earliest time that activities starting at that event can start. The latest event time is the latest time by which all activities leading into that event must be completed if the whole project is to be completed in the minimum time.

(e) For events on the critical path, the earliest and latest event times are the same. Activities on the critical path have zero float: an activity's float is the latest event time of the event at its end minus the earliest event time of the event at its start minus its duration.

(f) If activity durations are uncertain, the PERT formulae can be used to estimate mean durations and variances of durations. The variances of the durations of activities on the critical path can then be added, and the probability that the duration of the critical path will exceed any given value can be computed.

(g) Gantt charts can be used to estimate the amount of resources required for a project.

Quick quiz

1   When is a dummy activity necessary in a network?

2   What is the critical path?

3   What is an activity's float?

4   What are the formulae used in PERT to estimate the mean and the standard deviation of an activity's duration?

5   Where we have a chain of activities with uncertain durations, can we add the standard deviations of their durations?

Solutions to exercises

1   Yes, E and H could be carried on simultaneously. Indeed, that might be the most sensible thing to do. If E took five days and F only took one day, H could be started while E was still in progress.

2   There are four paths, as follows.

     ABEGIL
     ABFHIL
     ACJL
     ADKL

3

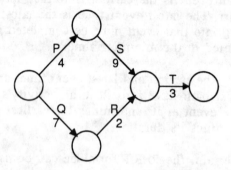

     The paths are PST (4 + 9 + 3 = 16 days) and QRT (7 + 2 + 3 = 12 days). The minimum overall duration is 16 days. The critical path is PST.

4   The only earliest event times affected would be those for event 4 (revised to week 9) and for event 7 (revised to week 13).

5

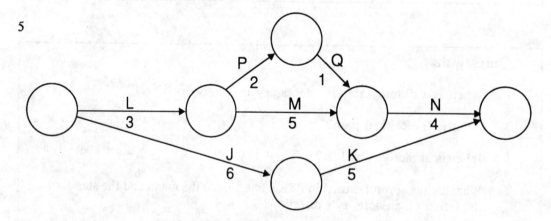

     The critical path is LMN, with a duration of 12 weeks. The earliest event time for the event at the end of activity P is 3 + 2 = 5 weeks. The latest event time is 12 - 4 - 1 = 7 weeks.

6   Float for activity D = 8 - 4 - 1 = 3 weeks.
     Float for activity G = 12 - 7 - 4 = 1 week.

7

Activity	Mean duration Days	Variance
A	7.000	1.778
B	5.333	1.778
C	4.000	0.000
D	6.667	1.000
	23.000	4.556

The probability that the duration of the path will exceed 30 days is the probability that the duration will be more than $(25-23)/\sqrt{4.556} = 0.94$ standard deviations above the mean.

From normal distribution tables, this probability is $0.5 - 0.3264 = 0.1736$.

8   (a)

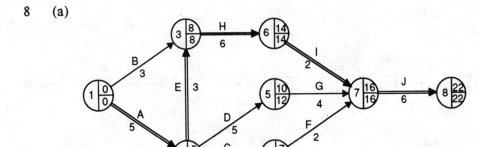

The critical path is AEHIJ, and the minimum total duration is 22 weeks.

(b)   To construct a Gantt chart we need to list all possible paths through the network.

AEHIJ
ADGJ
ACFJ
BHIJ

Then using the critical path as the basis, we can construct the Gantt chart as follows.

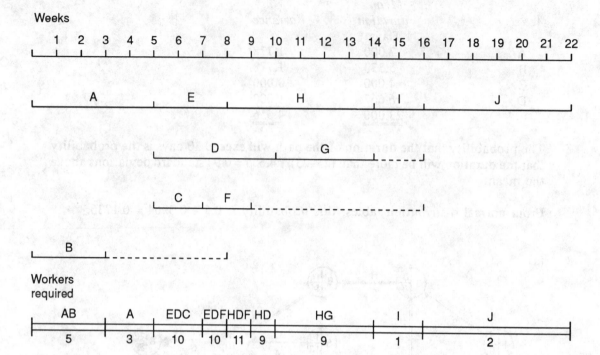

15 COMPOUND INTEREST AND DISCOUNTING

1 Financial mathematics

Financial mathematics deals with problems of investing money, or capital. If a company (or an individual investor) puts some capital into an investment, a *financial return* will be expected.

(a) If Arthur puts £1,000 into an account with a building society, he will expect a return in the form of *interest*, which will be added to the original investment in his account.

(b) If Newbegin Ltd invests £10,000 in an item of equipment, the company will expect to make a profit out of the item over its working life.

Investors may wish to know:

(a) how much return will be obtained by investing money now for a given period, say five years;

(b) how much return will be obtained in (say) five years time by investing some money every year for five years.

Time is an important element in investment decisions. The longer an investment continues, the greater will be the return required by the investor. For example, if a bank lends £20,000 to a company, it would expect bigger interest payments in total if the loan lasted for two years than if it lasted for only one year.

This time factor in investment decisions is not solely to do with inflation, and the declining value of money over time. The required total return would increase the longer an investment lasted even if inflation did not exist. The effect of inflation is simply to *increase* the size of the return required by the investor over *any* period of time.

2 Compound interest

Interest is normally calculated by means of compounding.

If a sum of money, the principal, is invested at a fixed rate of interest such that the interest is added to the principal and no withdrawals are made, then the amount invested will grow by an increasing number of pounds in each successive time period, because interest earned in earlier periods will itself earn interest in later periods.

Suppose, for example, that £2,000 is invested in a building society account to earn 10% interest.

(a) After one year, the original principal plus interest will amount to £2,200.

	£
Original investment	2,000
Interest in the first year (10%)	200
Total investment at the end of one year	2,200

(b) After two years the total investment will be £2,420.

	£
Investment at end of one year	2,200
Interest in the second year (10%)	220
Total investment at the end of two years	2,420

The second year interest of £220 represents 10% of the original investment, and 10% of the interest earned in the first year.

(c) Similarly, after three years, the total investment will be £2,662.

	£
Investment at the end of two years	2,420
Interest in the third year (10%)	242
Total investment at the end of three years	2,662

The basic formula for compound interest is $S_n = P(1 + r)^n$

where
P = the original sum invested
r = the interest rate, expressed as a proportion (so 5% = 0.05)
n = the number of periods
S_n = the sum invested after n periods.

In the previous example, £2,000 invested at 10% per annum for three years would increase in value to

$£2,000 \times 1.10^3$
$= £2,000 \times 1.331$
$= £2,662.$

The interest earned over three years is £662.

Exercise 1

What would be the total value of £5,000 invested now:

(a) after three years, if the interest rate is 20% per annum;
(b) after four years, if the interest rate is 15% per annum;
(c) after three years, if the interest rate is 6% per annum?

BPP Publishing

Additions, withdrawals and changes in the interest rate

An investor may put extra money into or take money out of an investment, or the interest rate may change. Thus suppose that £3,000 is invested at 8%. After two years, a further £1,000 is added. Three years after that, £2,000 is withdrawn. A year after the withdrawal, the rate falls to 6%. We can find the balance five years after the fall in the rate as follows.

$$
\begin{array}{llll}
£3,000 & \times\ 1.08^2 & =\ £3,499.20 & \text{(years 1 and 2)} \\
£3,499.20 + £1,000 & & =\ £4,499.20 & \\
£4,499.20 & \times\ 1.08^3 & =\ £5,667.70 & \text{(years 3, 4 and 5)} \\
£5,667.70 - £2,000 & & =\ £3,667.70 & \\
£3,667.70 & \times\ 1.08 & =\ £3,961.12 & \text{(year 6)} \\
£3,961.12 & \times\ 1.06^5 & =\ £5,300.87 & \text{(years 7 to 11)}
\end{array}
$$

The final balance is £5,300.87

Exercise 2

(a) If £8,000 is invested now, to earn 10% interest for three years and 8% thereafter, what would be the size of the total investment at the end of five years?

(b) An investor puts £10,000 into an investment for ten years. The annual rate of interest earned is 15% for the first four years, 12% for the next four years and 9% for the final two years. How much will the investment be worth at the end of ten years?

The frequency of compounding

In the previous examples, interest has been calculated annually, but this need not be the case. Interest may be compounded daily, weekly, monthly or quarterly.

The *effective annual rate of interest*, when interest is compounded at shorter intervals, may be calculated as follows.

$$
\text{Effective Annual Rate} = [(1 + r)^{\frac{12}{n}} - 1] \ \text{ or } \ [(1 + r)^{\frac{365}{x}} - 1]
$$

where   r is the rate of interest for each time period
             n is the number of months in the time period
             x is the number of days in the time period.

When you see the annual percentage rate (APR) quoted in an advertisement for credit, it is basically the effective annual rate, but adjusted to allow for any charges made in addition to interest.

Example: the effective annual rate of interest

Calculate the effective annual rate of interest of:

(a) $1\frac{1}{2}\%$ per month, compound;
(b) $4\frac{1}{2}\%$ per quarter, compound;
(c) 9% per half year, compound.

Solution

(a) $1.015^{12} - 1 = 0.1956 = 19.56\%$
(b) $1.045^{4} - 1 = 0.1925 = 19.25\%$
(c) $1.09^{2} - 1 = 0.1881 = 18.81\%$

Nominal rates of interest

Quite commonly, the annual rate of interest quoted to investors is a nominal rate of interest, and not an effective rate of interest. We can, however, work out the effective rate.

Example: nominal and effective rates of interest

A building society may offer investors 10% per annum interest payable half-yearly. If the 10% is a nominal rate of interest, the building society would in fact pay 5% every six months, compounded so that the effective annual rate of interest would be

$$1.05^{2} - 1 = 0.1025 = 10.25\%$$

Similarly, if a bank offers depositors a nominal 12% per annum, with interest payable quarterly, the effective rate of interest would be 3% compound every three months, which is

$$1.03^{4} - 1 = 0.1255 = 12.55\% \text{ per annum.}$$

Exercise 3

Calculate the effective annual rate of interest of:

(a) 15% (nominal annual rate) compounded quarterly;
(b) 24% (nominal annual rate) compounded monthly.

Regular investments

An investor may decide to add to his investment from time to time, and you may want to calculate the final value (or *terminal value*) of an investment to which equal annual amounts will be added. An example might be an individual or a company making annual payments into a pension fund: we may wish to know the value of the fund after 20 years.

Example: regular investments

A person invests £400 now, and a further £400 each year for three more years. How much would the total investment be worth after four years, if interest is earned at the rate of 10% per annum?

Solution

In problems such as this, we call now 'Year 0', the time 1 year from now 'Year 1' and so on.

		£
(Year 0) The first year's investment will grow to £400 × 1.10^4	=	585.64
(Year 1) The second year's investment will grow to £400 × 1.10^3	=	532.40
(Year 2) The third year's investment will grow to £400 × 1.10^2	=	484.00
(Year 3) The fourth year's investment will grow to £400 × 1.10	=	440.00
		2,042.04

The solution is $400 \times 1.1 + 400 \times 1.1^2 + 400 \times 1.1^3 + 400 \times 1.1^4$ (with the values placed in reverse order, for convenience). This is a *geometric progression*, that is a series in which each term is the previous term multiplied by some fixed amount (the *common ratio*).

The formula for the sum of such a progression is

$$S_n = \frac{a(1 - x^n)}{(1 - x)}$$

where S_n is the sum of n terms
a is the initial expression in the series
x is the common ratio, in this case $1 + r = 1.1$
n is the number of items in the series

$$S_4 = \frac{400 \times 1.1 \times (1 - 1.1^4)}{1 - 1.1} = \frac{440 \times (-0.4641)}{-0.1} = £2,042.04$$

Example: investments at the ends of years

If, in the previous example, the investments had been made at the end of each of the first, second, third and fourth years, so that the last £400 invested had no time to earn interest, the value of the fund after four years would have been

$$400 + 400 \times 1.1 + 400 \times 1.1^2 + 400 \times 1.1^3$$

$$= \frac{400 \times (1 - 1.1^4)}{1 - 1.1} = £1,856.40$$

If our investor made investments at the ends of years, but also put in a £2,500 lump sum one year from now, the value of the fund after four years would be

$$£1,856.40 + £2,500 \times 1.1^3$$
$$= \quad £1,856.40 + £3,327.50 = £5,183.90$$

That is, we can compound parts of investments separately, and add up the results.

Exercise 4

£500 is invested in a fund earning 9% interest each year for ten years. Investments are made at the start of each year. What is the value of the fund at the end of the tenth year?

---

3 The concept of discounting

Discounting is the reverse of compounding. Its major application in business is in the evaluation of capital expenditure projects, such as the purchase of new machines, to decide whether they offer a satisfactory return to the investor. This use of discounting is known as discounted cash flow, or DCF.

The basic principles of compounding and discounting

The basic principle of *compounding* is that if we invest £P now for n years at r% interest per annum, we should obtain $£P (1 + r)^n$ in n years time.

Thus if we invest £10,000 now for four years at 10% interest per annum, we will have a total investment worth $£10,000 \times 1.10^4 = £14,641$ at the end of four years (that is, at year 4 if it is now year 0).

The basic principle of *discounting* is that if we wish to have £S in n years' time, we need to invest a certain sum *now* (year 0) at an interest rate of r% in order to obtain the required sum of money in the future. For example, if we wish to have £14,641 in four years time, how much money would we need to invest now at 10% interest per annum?

Let P be the amount of money invested now.
$$£14,641 = \quad P \times 1.10^4$$
$$P = \quad £14,641 \times \frac{1}{1.10^4} = £10,000.$$

Present values

£10,000 now, with the capability of earning a return of 10% per annum, is the equivalent in value of £14,641 after four years. We can therefore say that £10,000 is the *present value* of £14,641 at year 4, at an interest rate of 10%.

The formula for discounting

The discounting formula is

$$P = S_n \times \frac{1}{(1 + r)^n}$$

where
- S_n is the sum to be received after n time periods
- P is the present value of that sum
- r is the rate of return, expressed as a proportion
- n is the number of time periods (usually years).

The rate r is sometimes called a *cost of capital*.

Example: discounting

(a) Calculate the present value of £60,000 at year 6, if a return of 15% per annum is obtainable.

(b) Calculate the present value of £100,000 at year 5, if a return of 6% per annum is obtainable.

Solution

(a) $PV = £60,000 \times 1/1.15^6 = £25,940$

(b) $PV = £100,000 \times 1/1.06^5 = £74,726$

Exercise 5

What is the present value at 7% interest of £16,000 at year 12?

Capital expenditure appraisal

Discounted cash flow techniques can be used to evaluate capital expenditure projects. Discounting is applied to the estimated future cash flows (receipts and expenditures) from a project in order to decide whether the project is expected to earn a satisfactory rate of return.

The two methods of using DCF techniques are:

(a) the net present value (NPV) method;
(b) the internal rate of return (IRR) method.

4 The net present value (NPV) method

We will start with an example. Spender Fortune Ltd is considering whether to spend £5,000 on an item of equipment. The cash inflows cash from the project would be £3,000 in the first year and £4,000 in the second year.

The company will not invest in any project unless it offers a return in excess of 15% per annum.

Is the investment worthwhile?

Solution

In this example, an outlay of £5,000 now promises a return of £3,000 *during* the first year and £4,000 *during* the second year. It is a convention in DCF, however, that cash flows spread over a year are assumed to occur *at the end of the year*.

An NPV statement can be drawn up as follows.

Year	Cash flow £	Discount factor 15%	Present value £
0	(5,000)	1.0000	(5,000.00)
1	3,000	1/1.15	2,608.70
2	4,000	$1/1.15^2$	3,024.57
		Net present value	+633.27

The project has a positive net present value, so it is acceptable.

The net present value (NPV) method works out the present values of all items of income and expenditure related to an investment at a given rate of return, and then works out a net total. If it is positive, the investment is considered to be acceptable. If it is negative, the investment is considered to be unacceptable. That is, we are not just looking for a cash profit. We are looking for a cash profit after adjusting all cash inflows and outflows to their present day equivalents.

Exercise 6

A company is wondering whether to spend £18,000 on an item of equipment, in order to obtain cash profits as follows.

Year	£
1	6,000
2	8,000
3	5,000
4	1,000

If the company requires a return of 10% per annum, is the project worthwhile? Use the NPV method.

BPP Publishing

Discount tables

Ready reckoner tables (called discount tables) show the value of $\dfrac{1}{(1 + r)^n}$ for different values of r and n. Tables are given at the start of this text.

Example: discount tables

Flower Potts Ltd is considering whether to make an investment costing £28,000 which would earn £8,000 cash per annum for five years. The company expects to make a return of at least 11% per annum. Is the project worthwhile viable? Use a table of present value factors.

Year	Cash flow	Discount factor	Present value
	£	11%	£
0	(28,000)	1.00	(28,000)
1	8,000	0.90	7,200
2	8,000	0.81	6,480
3	8,000	0.73	5,840
4	8,000	0.66	5,280
5	8,000	0.59	4,720
		NPV +	1,520

The NPV is positive, therefore the project is viable because it earns more than 11% per annum.

5   Annuities

An annuity is a constant sum of money each year for a given number of years.

In the example at the end of Section 4, there was a constant annual cash flow of £8,000 for five years, years 1 to 5.

The arithmetic in the solution could have been simplified, as follows.

	$8,000 \times 0.90$	
plus	$8,000 \times 0.81$	
plus	$8,000 \times 0.73$	
plus	$8,000 \times 0.66$	
plus	$8,000 \times 0.59$	£
equals	$8,000 \times 3.69$	= 29,520
Less PV of costs		28,000
NPV		1,520

Annuity tables

To calculate the present value of a constant annual cash flow, or annuity, we can multiply the annual cash flows by the sum of the discount factors for the relevant years. These total factors are known as *cumulative present value factors* or *annuity factors*. There are tables for annuity factors, which are also shown at the start of this text. (For example, the cumulative present value factor of £1 per annum for five years at 11% per annum is in the column for 11% and the year 5 row, and is 3.70. The figure we found above was 3.69, and the difference of 0.01 is due to rounding differences building up in our computation.)

Example: annuities

(a) The present value of £1,000 earned each year from years 1 to 10 when the required return on investment is 11% per annum is £1,000 × 5.89 = £5,890.

(b) The presente value (PV) of £100 earned each year from years 3 to 6 when the required return is 5% per annum is found as follows.

PV of £1 per annum for years 1 to 6 at 5%	5.08
Less PV of £1 per annum for years 1 to 2 at 5%	1.86
PV of £1 per annum for years 3 to 6 at 5%	3.22

£100 × 3.22 = £322

(c) Hannah U Witty Ltd is considering a project which would cost £14,000 now and earn £3,000 per annum in years 1 to 4 and £2,000 per annum in years 5 to 10. The cost of capital is 12%. Is the project worthwhile?

PV of £1 per annum at 12%, years 1 to 10	5.65
Less PV of £1 per annum at 12%, years 1 to 4	3.04
PV of £1 per annum at 12%, years 5 to 10	2.61

Years	*Cash flow* £	*Discount factor* 12%	*Present value* £
0	(14,000)	1.00	(14,000)
1 – 4	3,000	3.04	9,120
5 – 10	2,000	2.61	5,220
		Net present value	+340

The project has a positive NPV and is therefore worthwhile.

The formula for the present value of an annuity

You may need to use a formula to calculate the present value of an annuity. The present value of an annuity of £a starting a year from now with an interest rate of r, is as follows.

$$PV = \frac{a}{1 + r} + \frac{a}{(1 + r)^2} + \frac{a}{(1 + r)^3} + ... + \frac{a}{(1 + r)^n}$$

This equals

$$\frac{a\left[1 - \left(\frac{1}{1 + r} \right)^n \right]}{r}$$

BPP Publishing

Example: the annuity formula

What is the present value of £4,000 per annum for years 1 to 4, at a discount rate of 10% per annum?

Solution

$$PV = \frac{£4,000 \times (1 - (\frac{1}{1.10})^4)}{0.1}$$

$$= \frac{£4,000 \times (1 - 0.6830)}{0.1} = £12,680$$

This can be checked from the annuity tables: the PV for years 1 to 4 is £4,000 × 3.17 = £12,680.

Exercise 7

What is the present value of £6,000 per annum for four years, years 1 to 4, at a discount rate of 7% per annum? Use the formula and not tables.

Calculating a required annuity

$$\text{If } P = \frac{a(1 - (\frac{1}{1+r})^n)}{r}$$

$$\text{then } a = \frac{Pr}{[1 - (\frac{1}{1+r})^n]}$$

This enables us to calculate the annuity required to yield a given rate of return (r) on a given investment (P).

Example: loan repayments

A building society grants a £30,000 mortgage at 7% per annum. The borrower is to repay the loan in ten annual instalments. How much must he pay each year?

Solution

$$a = \frac{30,000 \times 0.07}{1 - 1/1.07^{10}}$$

$$= \quad \frac{2,100}{1 - 0.5083}$$

$$= \quad \frac{2,100}{0.4917} = \text{£4,271 per annum}$$

The use of annuity tables to calculate a required annuity

Just as the formula can be used to calculate an annuity, so too can the tables. Since the present value of an annuity is PV = a × annuity factor from the tables, we have

$$a \quad = \quad \frac{\text{PV}}{\text{annuity factor}}$$

In the previous example, the annual repayment on the mortgage would be

$$\frac{\text{£30,000}}{\text{PV factor of £1 per annum at 7\% for 10 years}}$$

$$= \quad \frac{\text{£30,000}}{7.02}$$

$$= \quad \text{£4,274 (a rounding error of £3 arises)}$$

Perpetuities

A *perpetuity* is an annuity which lasts for ever, instead of stopping after n years.

The present value of a perpetuity is PV = a/r where r is the cost of capital as a proportion.

Example: a perpetuity

Evermore Ltd is considering a project which would cost £50,000 now and yield £9,000 per annum every year in perpetuity, starting a year from now. The cost of capital is 15%. Is the project worthwhile?

Solution

Year	Cash flow £	Discount factor 15%	Present value £
0	(50,000)	1.0	(50,000)
1 onwards	9,000	1/0.15	60,000
		NPV	10,000

The project is worthwhile because it has a positive net present value when discounted at 15%.

The timing of cash flows

Note that both annuity tables and our formulae assume that the first payment or receipt is a year from now. Always check when the first payment falls.

For example, if there are five equal payments starting now, and the interest rate is 8%, we should use a factor of 1 (for today's payment) + 3.31 (for the other four payments) = 4.31.

Exercise 8

A loan of £250,000 is repayable in 15 equal annual instalments, starting a year from now. The interest rate is 8%. Find the annual repayment, without using annuity tables.

---

6 The internal rate of return (IRR) method

The internal rate of return (IRR) method of evaluating investments is an alternative to the NPV method.

The NPV method of discounted cash flow determines whether an investment earns a positive or a negative NPV when discounted at a given rate of interest. If the NPV is zero (that is, the present values of costs and benefits are equal) the return from the project would be exactly the rate used for discounting.

The IRR method of discounted cash flow is to determine the rate of interest (the internal rate of return) at which the NPV is 0. The internal rate of return is therefore the rate of return on an investment.

Example: the IRR method over two years

If £1,000 is invested today and generates £700 in the first year and £600 in the second year the internal rate of return can be calculated as follows.

PV of cost = PV of benefits

$$1,000 = \frac{700}{1 + r} + \frac{600}{(1 + r)^2}$$

Multiply both sides by $(1 + r)^2$

$$1,000 (1 + r)^2 \quad = \quad 700(1 + r) + 600$$

$$1,000 + 2,000r + 1,000r^2 \quad = \quad 700 + 700r + 600$$

$$1,000r^2 + 1,300r - 300 \quad = \quad 0$$

$$10r^2 + 13r - 3 \quad = \quad 0$$

$$r \quad = \quad \frac{-13 \pm \sqrt{[169 - (4 \times 10 \times (-3))]}}{20}$$

$$= \quad \frac{-13 - 17}{20} \quad \text{or} \quad \frac{-13 + 17}{20}$$

$$= \quad -1.5 \quad \text{or} \quad +0.2$$

$$= \quad -150\% \quad \text{or} \quad 20\%$$

Since high negative returns are not a practical proposition, IRR = 20%

The IRR method will indicate that a project is worthwhile if the IRR exceeds the minimum acceptable rate of return. Thus if the company expects a minimum return of, say, 15%, a project is worthwhile if its IRR is more than 15%.

Exercise 9

An investment of £2,000 today will yield £320 in one year's time and £2,320 in two years' time. What is the IRR?

The example and the exercise so far used to illustrate the IRR method have been for two year projects. The arithmetic is more complicated for investments and cash flows extending over a longer period of time. A technique known as the interpolation method can be used to calculate an approximate IRR.

Example: interpolation

A project costing £800 in year 0 is expected to earn £400 in year 1, £300 in year 2 and £200 in year 3. What is the internal rate of return?

Quantitative methods

Notes

Solution

The IRR is calculated by first of all finding the NPV at each of two interest rates. Ideally, one interest rate should give a small positive NPV and the other a small negative NPV. The IRR would then be somewhere between these two interest rates: above the rate where the NPV is positive, but below the rate where the NPV is negative.

A very rough guideline for estimating at what interest rate the NPV might be close to zero, is to take

$$\frac{2}{3} \times \left(\frac{profit}{cost\ of\ the\ project}\right)$$

In our example, the total profit over three years is £(400 + 300 + 200 - 800) = £100

$$\frac{2}{3} \times \frac{100}{800} = 0.08 \text{ approx.}$$

A starting point is to try 8%.

(a) Try 8%

Year	Cash flow £	Discount factor 8%	Present value £
0	(800)	1.00	(800)
1	400	0.93	372
2	300	0.86	258
3	200	0.79	158
		NPV	(14)

The NPV is negative, therefore the project fails to earn 8% and the IRR must be less than 8%.

(b) Try 6%

Year	Cash flow £	Discount factor 6%	Present value £
0	(800)	1.00	(800)
1	400	0.94	376
2	300	0.89	267
3	200	0.84	168
		NPV	11

The NPV is positive, therefore the project earns more than 6% and less than 8%.

The IRR is now calculated by *interpolation*. The result will not be exact, but it will be a close approximation.

The IRR, where the NPV is zero, can be calculated as:

$$a\% + \left[\frac{A}{A - B} \times (b - a)\right]\% \text{ where}$$

a is one interest rate
b is the other interest rate
A is the NPV at rate a
B is the NPV at rate b

$$\text{IRR} = 6\% + [\frac{11}{(11 - (-14))} \times (8 - 6)]\%$$

$$= 6 + 0.88\%$$

$$= 6.88\% \text{ (approx)}$$

To give you an idea of how good the approximation is, the exact IRR (to two decimal places) is 6.93%.

Note that the formula will still work if A and B are both positive, or both negative, and even if a and b are a long way from the true IRR, but the results will be less accurate.

Exercise 10

An investment has an NPV of £4,000 at 9% and an NPV of £1,000 at 12%. What is the approximate IRR?

Chapter roundup

(a) Investors expect to earn a return over time. Interest bearing investments usually pay compound interest, under which interest retained within the investment earns interest itself.

(b) The basic compound interest formula is $S_n = P(1 + r)^n$. If there are additions or withdrawals, or if the interest rate rises or falls, the value of the investment up to the change should be worked out, and then the growth from the change onwards can be found.

(c) Rates for periods of less than a year, and nominal annual rates, can be converted into effective annual rates.

(d) If regular investments are made, the final value of the investment can be found using the geometric progression formula.

(e) The present value of a given amount n years into the future is what would have to be invested now (at a rate of interest r) in order to yield that future amount. The future amount is discounted to its present value by multiplying by $1/(1 + r)^n$.

(f) The net present value (NPV) of a series of cash flows is the net sum of the present values of all the cash inflows and outflows. An investment may be considered to be worthwhile if its NPV is positive. Discount tables help us to compute NPVs quickly.

(g) The present value of an annuity may be found with a formula or with annuity tables. Either the formula or the tables may be used in reverse to compute loan repayments. The present value of a perpetuity is annual amount/r.

(h) The internal rate of return (IRR) of an investment is the interest rate at which its NPV is zero. If cash flows stretch beyond year 2, it may be estimated using interpolation.

Quick quiz

1   If a sum P is invested earning a compound annual interest rate of r, how much will the investor have after n years?

2   How should withdrawals of money be dealt with in compound interest calculations?

3   How should changes in the rate of interest be dealt with in compound interest calculations?

4   What is meant by an effective annual rate of interest?

5   What is the meaning of the term 'present value'?

6   What is the present value of a sum of money S_n in n years time, given an interest rate of r?

7   What are the two usual methods of capital expenditure appraisal using DCF techniques?

8   What is the formula for the present value of an annuity?

9   How would you determine the internal rate of return of a series of cash flows using interpolation?

Solutions to exercises

1   (a)   £5,000 × 1.20^3 = £8,640
    (b)   £5,000 × 1.15^4 = £8,745.03
    (c)   £5,000 × 1.06^3 = £5,955.08

2   (a)   £8,000 × 1.10^3 × 1.08^2 = £12,419.83
    (b)   £10,000 × 1.15^4 × 1.12^4 × 1.09^2 = £32,697.64

3   (a)   15% per annum (nominal rate) is 3.75% per quarter. The effective annual rate of interest is

$$1.0375^4 - 1 = 0.1587 = 15.87\%$$

    (b)   24% per annum (nominal rate) is 2% per month. The effective annual rate of interest is

$$1.02^{12} - 1 = 0.2682 = 26.82\%$$

4   The value is £500 × 1.09 + £500 × 1.09^2 + ... +500 × 1.09^{10}

$$= \frac{£500 \times 1.09 \times (1 - 1.09^{10})}{1 - 1.09} = £8,280$$

BPP Publishing

5   £16,000 × 1/1.07^{12} = £7,104.

6
Year	Cash flow £	Discount factor 10%	Present value £
0	(18,000)	1.0000	(18,000.00)
1	6,000	1/1.1^1	5,454.54
2	8,000	1/1.1^2	6,611.57
3	5,000	1/1.1^3	3,756.57
4	1,000	1/1.1^4	683.01
		Net present value	(1,494.31)

The NPV is negative, which means that the project is not worthwhile.

7    $PV = \dfrac{£6,000 \times (1 - (\frac{1}{1.07})^4)}{0.07} = £20,323$

8   Annual repayment $= \dfrac{£250,000 \times 0.08}{1 - 1/1.08^{15}} = £29,207$

9    $2,000 = \dfrac{320}{1+r} + \dfrac{2,320}{(1+r)^2}$

$2,000(1+r)^2 - 320(1+r) - 2,320 = 0$

$2,000r^2 + 3,680r - 640 = 0$

$r = \dfrac{-3,680 \pm \sqrt{[3,680^2 - 4 \times 2,000 \times (-640)]}}{2 \times 2,000}$

$= +0.16$ or -2

We can ignore the negative value. The IRR is 16%.

10    $9\% + [\dfrac{4}{4-1} \times (12 - 9)]\% = 13\%$

BPP Publishing

BPP Publishing

ORDER FORM

To order your BUSINESS BASICS books, ring our credit card hotline on 0181-740 6808.
Alternatively, send this page to our Freepost address or fax it to us on 0181-740 1184.

To: BPP Publishing Ltd, FREEPOST, London, W12 8BR   **Tel: 0181-740 6808**
                                                           Fax: 0181-740 1184

Forenames (Mr / Mrs): _____

Surname: _____

Address: _____

Post code: _____ Date of exam (month/year): _____

Please send the following books:

	Price	Quantity	Total
Accounting	£9.95	......	......
Human Resource Management	£9.95	......	......
Law	£9.95	......	......
Organisational behaviour	£9.95	......	......
Economics	£9.95	......	......
Information Technology	£9.95	......	......
Marketing	£9.95	......	......
Quantitative Methods	£9.95	......	......

Please include postage:

UK: £2.50 for first plus £1.00 for each extra	......	......
Europe (inc ROI): £5.00 for first plus £4.00 for each extra	......	......
Rest of the World: £7.50 for first plus £5.00 for each extra	......	......

Total _____

I enclose a cheque for £ _____ **or charge to Access/Visa**

Card number ☐☐☐☐ ☐☐☐☐ ☐☐☐☐ ☐☐☐☐

Expiry date _____ Signature _____

REVIEW FORM

Name:

College:

We would be grateful to receive any comments you may have on this book. You may like to use the headings below as guidelines. Tear out this page and send it to our Freepost address: **BPP Publishing Ltd, FREEPOST, London W12 8BR**

Topic coverage

Objectives, exercises, chapter roundups and quizzes

Student-friendliness

Errors (please specify and give a page number)

Other

BPP Publishing